Latin America: A geographical commentary

LATIN AMERICA

A GEOGRAPHICAL COMMENTARY

by
IRMGARD POHL
JOSEF ZEPP
and
KEMPTON E. WEBB *(editor)*

Associate Professor of Geography and
Associate Director of the Institute of Latin
American Studies, Columbia University

A Dutton  *Paperback*

NEW YORK
E. P. DUTTON
1967

Preface

In recent years Latin America has increasingly become an unsettled and an unsettling part of the world. Some of its economic, social, and political problems can be traced to the upheavals which accompany a rapid transition from a pre-industrial to an industrial society. Other problems stem from the struggle for men's minds between totalitarian and democratic political systems. The outcome of this struggle in Latin America is not at all predictable. This region is unsettling to many people, but mainly to those who have traditionally regarded it as one of the lesser culture realms, and thus an area not meriting much attention, scholarly or otherwise. The current stream of writings about Latin America reflects the great need for knowledge of that area, a need which has outstripped the rate at which the public can be educated.

This book is meant to be an introduction to Latin America from a geographer's point of view rather than a comprehensive portrayal of minute areas and all of their pertinent facts. Because facts and numbers constantly change and, moreover, are difficult to remember, emphasis here is on presenting a background against which facts become meaningful. Thus we stress materials which might appear somewhat peripheral to the mainstream of geography, but which really lie at the core of regional characterization and clarify the cultural and physical processes which have shaped particular landscapes. We dwell upon the pre-Conquest and the Conquest as critical periods in the formative processes of Latin American culture, not only in terms of Indian influences and Spanish and Portuguese colonial institutions, but also in terms of the tremendous impact of the Conquest in the form of domesticated plants and animals, tools, and ideas. The writings of historians, anthropologists, and economists have been tapped as well as those of geographers.

The inclusion of vignettes quoted from the writings of perceptive travelers, as well as a liberal use of photographs, is intended to give the reader a stronger flavor of actual scenes and landscapes.

In a very real sense, this book is the product of both sides of the Atlantic Ocean. The original authors used German sources almost exclusively, while I have edited from a background of North American training and experience in Latin America. The book, therefore, has more materials on the physical geography of Latin America than is found in most North American texts; also, it reflects a cultural-determinist outlook that is more characteristically French or American than German or British.

Why, finally, is it particularly important and even crucial to study the geography of Latin America? In addition to the intellectual and philo-sophical justifications for studying any phenomenon or part of human experience, there are plainly practical reasons. To cite one example, area knowledge is the foundation block of any regional development plan or of aid to underdeveloped countries in general. Surprisingly enough, this fact is not widely understood. In northeast Brazil, while doing a field study in 1963-64, I witnessed the frustrations as well as the successes attending a massive regional development effort involving cooperation between Brazilians and Americans. It was expected that some of the frustrations would be unavoidable; others, however, might have been avoided had there been a deeper understanding of the area itself by the technicians and especially by the administrators. All too often, program administrators have the very best intentions but are simply amateurs in the realm of substantive area knowledge and inter-pretation. Unfortunately, the amateur point of view is occasionally embodied in key decisions involving vast sums of money and even the larger dimensions of high expectations, both of which might be more wisely channelled into other more realistic and professionally conceived programs.

Area study is a field to which the geographer brings unique concepts and talents. In today's world of increasing awareness of the complexity of area problems and problem areas, the geographer must make his contribution to the understanding and interpretation of the earth's surface.

KEMPTON E. WEBB

Columbia University
New York

Contents

Plates

Maps and Diagrams

Acknowledgements

In this edition for English readers, the following authors and publishers have kindly permitted the inclusion of a number of extracts from books which did not appear in the German edition.

Ernest Benn Ltd (Pierre Denis, *The Argentine Republic*).

Faber and Faber Ltd (Maurice Collis, *Cortes and Montezuma*; Mona Macmillan, *The Land of Look Behind*).

Harcourt, Brace and World, Inc. (S. G. Inman, *Latin America: Its Place in World Life*; C. H. Haring, *The Spanish Empire in America*, Copyright 1947 by Oxford University Press).

William Heinemann Ltd (Antoine de St-Exupéry, *Wind, Sand and Stars*, translated by Lewis Galantière).

Alfred A. Knopf, Inc. (H. Herring, *A History of Latin America*).

Oxford University Press Ltd (E. Lieuwen, *Venezuela*, published under the auspices of the Royal Institute of Internal Affairs).

Thames and Hudson Ltd (C. Arthaud and F. Hébert-Stevens, *The Andes: Roof of America*).

Original German works, from which extracts are quoted, are listed separately on page 289. To these and other sources of copyright material, both literary extracts and photographs, the publisher's thanks are due.

PART ONE

SOUTH AMERICA

CHAPTER ONE

South America: Introduction

Discovery and Exploration

It was in 1498, in the course of his third voyage, that Christopher Columbus discovered South America. His previous voyages had taken him as far as the islands of the Caribbean, where in 1492 he made his first landfall on what is now Watling Island. On his third voyage he reached Trinidad and the mouth of the Orinoco. He was soon followed by other Spaniards, who explored the same region and penetrated as far down the coast of the new continent as the present site of Pernambuco. Then, in the year 1500, a Portuguese captain, Cabral, set out from Portugal for the Cape of Good Hope on the newly discovered route to India. The north-east trade winds, however, carried him westwards from the Cape Verde Islands and he landed on the coast of Brazil between the present cities of Salvador and Rio de Janeiro. Arriving thus by accident in the New World, he promptly claimed the whole coast for Portugal. Cabral believed that he had discovered a new continent, and called it Santa Cruz. It was only later that it was given the name of Brazil. (It was named after a dyewood discovered there.)

An expedition hurriedly organised by the Portuguese after Cabral's discovery reached the new continent in the vicinity of Cabo São Roque (5° S), and followed the coast southwards. There followed other expeditions whose task was to search for a sea passage to the west. In the course of these explorations Juan Dias de Solis discovered the Rio de la Plata in 1515-16, but found to his disappointment that even here there was no way through to the Pacific. The southern tip of the continent was reached in 1519, by Ferdinand Magellan—who was in the service of Spain—during his circumnavigation of the globe. Magellan's voyage revealed the existence of a sea route into the Pacific,

3

a route which had been sought for in vain by explorers from Columbus onwards and, more intensively, since Balboa had crossed the Isthmus of Panama in 1513 (see Fig. 1).

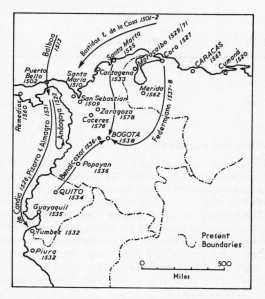

Fig. 1. South America: Spanish penetration into the north-west, showing settlements with their date of foundation.

In the years that followed, numerous other expeditions contributed to the knowledge of the continent's shape, and by the 1560's its general outline had been established, apart from Tierra del Fuego which was only finally recognised as an island in 1616.

The effective exploration of the continent followed, but in this undertaking the Atlantic coast was not the centre of interest. Vague reports from Balboa had reached Europe that there existed a wealthy civilisation south of Panama. The first overland attempt to find this was made in 1524 by the Spaniard, Francisco Pizarro, whose name has gone down in history as the most successful, but also the most cruel, of all the Spanish conquistadors. By 1535 he had destroyed the Empire of the Incas in Peru, advancing from the coast to the high plateaux of the Andes, and wresting from the inhabitants great quantities of gold and silver. And just as Mexico was the springboard for further Spanish advances into North America, so Peru became the base for South American exploration, with the initial efforts directed towards Chile and the interior of Colombia.

Later explorers completed the work by pushing on into the extreme south, and so it came about that the whole of Central and South America—with the exception of the Portuguese holdings in Brazil and the southern part of what is now Chile—came into the possession of Spain, and so remained for 300 years (see Plate 1). The newer maritime powers—the Netherlands, England and France—which only came on the scene much later, occupied a few remnants of unconquered territory such as the Guianas and the Falkland Islands and took over certain Spanish possessions in the Caribbean area.

Yet it is important to realise that the European discoverers of South America were not at first looking for new lands with a view to permanent colonial settlements. To them, the new continent was primarily a most inconvenient obstacle on the route to the East Indies, since the traditional eastward route to the Spice Islands had been blocked to Europeans by the spread of Islam. While the Conquistadors sought openings for trade with the Indians they encountered, they were not particularly concerned with finding empty lands for future settlers. On the contrary, the Spanish generally sought areas of dense Indian settlement in order to exploit native labour and wealth.

Penetration and exploration in many cases went hand in hand. The geography of South America today still bears the mark stamped upon it by the Treaty of Tordesillas in 1494 (as a glance at any language map will show). By this treaty Pope Alexander VI pronounced the demarcation line between the Spanish and Portuguese realms in America to lie 370 leagues (or about 1250 miles) west of the Cape Verde Islands, placing the boundary through Central Brazil.

Expansion out from the various points of penetration did not take place at the same rate in every case. Because of the great distance between the Iberian Peninsula and the new continent, it was necessary to establish points of entry on the American side, where newcomers could be equipped for their ventures inland. The opening up of the Spanish colonial empire was based on expansion from Mexico and Peru which became the centres of Spanish influence.

From Mexico, Spain conquered Central America and large areas of what is now the southern and western parts of the U.S.A. From Peru, Spanish rule was extended in all directions, as shown in Fig. 2. To the south along the coast lay the territory of the Araucanian Indians, and there, in present-day Chile, the Spaniards were able to establish themselves only as far south as the Bió-Bió River (at the mouth of which now stands the city of Concepción). South-eastwards, penetration beyond the Andes was less significant, and the early attempts to establish settlements in the La Plata region met with little success. Expansion came to a halt in the region of what is now Paraguay, but before Buenos Aires was founded—for the second time—in 1580 when the Spaniards

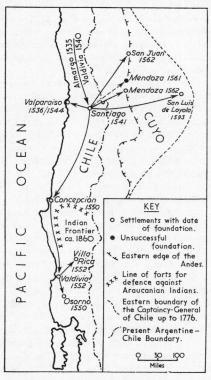

Fig. 2. South America: Spanish penetration into Chile, showing settlements with their date of foundation, and the zone of conflict with the Araucanian Indians.

determined to stop the southward expansion of Portuguese influence. Throughout these southern and eastern territories, the Spaniards found themselves involved in continuous warfare with the Indians, who by that time had learned to ride horses which had escaped from the early Spanish corrals and had rapidly multiplied in an environment with no natural enemies.

Spain's colonial empire stretched over an immense expanse from California almost to the Straits of Magellan. This huge empire the Spanish rulers regarded as their personal property, and after they had dealt with the enormous claims of Columbus (who had demanded, among other things, a tenth of all income derived from the new lands) they settled down to enjoy a revenue of fantastic proportions. Legally one-fifth (the royal 'quinto') of all the gold and silver produced in Spanish America belonged to the Spanish Crown. All trade with 'the Indies' was channelled through the Spanish port of Seville; needless to say, this unique privilege (only later shared by the port of Cadiz) brought immense wealth and expansion to Seville, but for the nation and its economic development as a whole it was distinctly unhealthy, causing inflation and an excessive import of manufactured goods from Northern Europe. Even more disastrous for Spain was the Spanish tendency to treat America mainly as a source of gold or as a place to get rich quickly. Both of these policies were made possible by the pitiless exploitation of the native labour supply. No thought was given to the possibility of a soundly planned development of the vast natural resources of the continent. In order to 'civilise' the native population as quickly as possible and to convert them to Christianity, the Spaniards placed the Indians under the protection and supervision of individual Europeans. Work assignments were enforced with such zeal that the natives, reduced to slavery, broke down under the labour demanded of them in the mines and on the plantations. With their resistance lowered, vast numbers of Indians died of new diseases and from physical and psychological strain. However, thanks to the protests of a Dominican priest, Las Casas, who had himself been a planter and slave-owner until he could bear the misery of the natives no longer, Negroes from the Guinea Coast were brought in as slaves from 1516 onwards. They supplemented the Indians, and thus it was that in 1530 slavery could be abolished, at least in theory, among the Indians. Las Casas, however, returned later to attack the system, declaring that enslaving Negroes was just as immoral as enslaving Indians.

In all this it must not be forgotten that, whatever the abuses of the system, many Spanish missionaries, and particularly the Jesuits, did act as a restraining influence, and for Indian tribes which remained beyond Spanish control in the interior, most notably in Paraguay, they organised effective and humane settlements.

The Conquistadors' interests lay essentially in the acquisition of goods which would bring immediate returns. They failed to realise that the greater riches of the continent were not so much its gold as the immense range of products which could be grown or gathered from its largely unoccupied forests and grasslands. To the eye of the colonist the most attractive parts of the empire were already densely populated, and were characterised by a highly developed civilisation, some kind of political organisation and a flourishing economic life. Their interest lay in exploiting this situation.

Historically speaking, European colonies in the New World in the sixteenth and seventeenth centuries may be divided into two general classes, which have been designated by some economists as farm colonies and exploitation colonies . . . The 'farm colonies' were generally established in regions that produced the same commodities as were produced in Europe, i.e. they were situated in the temperate zone. They possessed no special advantage in the way of producing exports for which there was a large European demand, whether by agriculture or by mining. Many of them were, therefore, founded by settlers who were anxious chiefly to find a refuge from the political and social discontents in the home country. These settlers came out not primarily to produce or acquire wealth; exportable products were a secondary objective. They were content with the satisfaction of moderate wants. Such colonies were most of those established by the English in North America, and to some extent those created by the Spaniards in Chile and Buenos Aires, and by the Portuguese in southern Brazil.

The 'exploitation colonies', on the other hand, were nearly always situated in the tropics, or in regions rich in mineral wealth; areas, that is to say, which produced commodities not easily obtainable in Europe, or to be had only in small quantities; commodities, moreover, for the production of which the soil and climate, or the geological formation, of these colonies presented peculiar advantages. There the industry of the settlers was turned primarily to the production and export of a few staple articles: sugar, cotton, indigo, gold, and silver; the impulse to colonisation was chiefly economic, the accumulation of wealth. Such were practically all the tropical colonies on the continent, whether Spanish, Portuguese, or English; all the European establishments in the West Indies; and the great mining communities of Peru, Mexico, and New Granada on the Spanish American mainland.

Out of these differing economic conditions there naturally developed different types of society, as expressed in the systems of landholding and in social and political organization. The typical property in the temperate farm colony was the small freehold, developing out of the clearing made in the forest by the more or less isolated pioneer. In the exploitation colony, whose commodities were few in number, and where production became highly specialized and therefore soon established on a capitalistic basis, a start was generally made with a larger unit of land, and the great estate became the prevalent form of land-holding.[1]

On the Portuguese side of the continent, however, a somewhat different pattern developed. For a number of reasons, settlement was limited to a few places along a narrow coastal belt. The first of these concerned the distribution of the Indian population. While there was an advantage in not encountering hostile tribes, there was an equal disadvantage in the absence of any large body of Indians, peaceful or warlike, who could be put to work for private gain. Another factor was the scarcity of readily exploitable resources for which a market could be found in the sixteenth century. Most important, perhaps, the Portuguese during this period were devoting the best part of their energies to an attempt to consolidate and extend their hold on their empire in the East. It was not until the end of the sixteenth century, when the Dutch drove them out of their East Indian Empire and when several other European nations were showing an increasing interest in the east coast of South America, that the Portuguese made serious attempts to develop Brazil. The earliest settlement was around Bahia, which grew up as the terminus of the route from southern Europe, and as an occasional way-station on the sailing route from Europe to South Africa and India (see Fig. 3).

In this Portuguese territory the method of colonisation used was for the Crown to grant holdings to members of the aristocracy, who were then responsible—at their own expense—for developing them. On these lands they grew tobacco and the equally valuable sugar cane, under conditions of monoculture and using as labourers first the Indians and later African slaves, but the extent of colonisation was very limited.

Considering all these facts it is important not to overestimate the number of Europeans involved in the opening up of South America. Most authorities estimate that during the first two centuries of European colonisation less than 200,000 people were involved, even including those who came as adventurers looking for gold or silver. But development was controlled by relatively few families which were granted vast estates by the Crown and possessed wide privileges. In the Spanish

1 Haring, C. H., *The Spanish Empire in America*, New York, 1963, pp. 27-8.

Empire this meant the establishment of a feudal system under which the great latifundia were carved out of the Indians' lands.

The agriculture of these New World lands underwent a tremendous change as a result of the introduction of domesticated plants and animals from Europe, a change whose effects remain to the present day. Before the coming of the Europeans, maize (or Indian corn) was

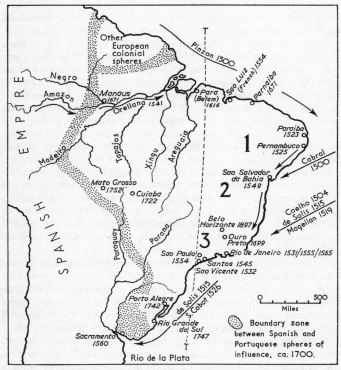

Fig. 3. South America: Portuguese penetration and settlement in Brazil. The numbers 1, 2, 3, indicate the successive areas to which the main colonising efforts were directed. The line T–T marks approximately the division established by the Treaty of Tordesillas between the Spanish and Portuguese spheres of influence; the rapid progress made by Portugal, despite preoccupations in the Far East, is seen by comparing the position of this line with that of the frontier zone of 1700.

the staple crop of the population, together with such other food crops as beans, fruits, squashes, manioc, potatoes and other root and seed crops of lesser importance, although these were unevenly distributed over the Western Hemisphere. Crops like wheat, barley, sugar-cane, coffee and many garden fruits and vegetables, all of which have now become commonplace in the New World, came in only with the European conquest. With regard to domesticated animals, there were really only the dog, guinea pig, Muscovy duck, llama and turkey before the Europeans introduced the horse, cow, pig, sheep, goat, chicken and mule. But in the same way the agriculture of the Old World profited by the introduction of American products, of which maize and the potato are outstanding examples.

In comparison with the territories acquired by Spain and Portugal, the penetrations of the Dutch and other Europeans into South America were on a very modest scale. The Dutch were temporarily successful in establishing a colony in Pernambuco in 1630 in an area which was formerly part of the Portuguese Empire. It was not until 1654 that the Portuguese Brazilians were able to recover their lost territory. In the south, too, where there was rivalry with the Spanish, the frontiers of the Portuguese sphere of influence fluctuated. Although the Portuguese were able to extend their control as far as the Rio de la Plata by the beginning of the eighteenth century, they were later forced to withdraw with the formation of the buffer state of Uruguay.

As time went by, and the economic value of the South American colonies became more apparent, so the fate of the individual colonies became more problematic and their histories more stormy. Gold strikes in Minas Gerais in Brazil produced a fresh rush of prospectors, and in due course, after fierce struggles for power, these adventurers succeeded in making themselves temporarily independent of the State. There were recurrent revolutions, most of them not so much political as economic and social in origin; there were often clashes between labourers and land-owners, while great discontent existed because of the mercantilist policies of both Portugal and Spain, which favoured the mother country and inhibited local development of industry and trade in the New World. The Catholic Church itself, after taking the part of the Indians, quarrelled bitterly with the royal administration. The most serious case of this conflict of policy resulted in the expulsion of the Jesuits in 1767 from the New World.

But whatever their internal troubles, the greatest threats to the continued existence of the Spanish and Portuguese colonial empires came from outside in the form of the concepts of freedom and independence

—from the wars in Europe (the French Revolution in particular) and the American War of Independence (1776-83) which had so profound an effect on men's minds everywhere. The South American Creoles[1] benefited in particular from the pressure exerted by Napoleon on Spain. A series of outbreaks occurred in the years after 1810, leading up to the decisive struggle in 1824 for the heart of the Spanish Empire in Peru.

In the struggle for independence the leading fighters were Simón Bolívar of Venezuela and, in the south, José de San Martin. In the first flush of independence, politicians and soldiers in the states which are now Venezuela, Colombia (formerly known as New Granada), Ecuador, Peru and Bolivia, all united to elect Bolívar as president of the great 'Colombian Republic' which he believed he had created. But the unwieldy republic rapidly disintegrated into the present separate states, between which boundary disputes still occur. The further development of each of these states will be traced in the later sections of this book.

In the meantime, further exploration was taking place, some of it by foreigners. The Spaniards had already made use of German miners and engineers in the mines of the Andes, and from the end of the eighteenth century onwards they permitted the entry of scientists. Thaddeus Haenke, a doctor and a botanist with very wide interests, travelled throughout western South America for twenty-six years, formulating problems and suggesting solutions in a thoroughly up-to-date manner. Unfortunately his early death occurred before his materials could be assembled in any final form. Of the other great names of later South American exploration, perhaps three deserve special mention: Charles-Marie de La Condamine (the leader of a remarkable French expedition which surveyed in the Andes during the years 1737-44 and returned via the Amazon); Alexander von Humboldt (who travelled in South America and Mexico between 1799 and 1804); and Charles Darwin (who spent some months in 1833-4 in South America during his famous voyage on the *Beagle*, during which he formulated some of his basic notions concerning the theory of evolution).

The Physical Background

STRUCTURE, LANDFORMS AND REGIONS

The long, tapering continent of South America is thought, on the basis of the similarity of rock structures and land forms with those of Africa

[1] Persons of European parents and culture born in the New World.

and Australasia, to have once formed part of the great southern continent of Gondwanaland in remote geological time.

South America's coastline is less indented than that of any other continent except Africa. Those embayments which exist are few and far between—the Gulf of Darien and the Gulf of Venezuela (together with Lake Maracaibo) in the north, the estuaries of the Amazon and the Rio de la Plata in the east, and the Gulf of Guayaquil in the west. The only section of the coastline which forms an exception to this general character is in southern Chile, which possesses a fjord coast and offshore archipelago.

From east to west across South America, there are three main structural zones. The eastern zone includes the Brazilian and Guiana Highlands, two geologically related blocks of old age, whose surfaces, stepped and dissected, form great plateaux. The foundation of these blocks, as is the case with the Laurentian Shield in Canada and the Baltic Platform, is a mass of highly metamorphosed rocks of great geological age. In these two areas younger strata play an unimportant part, except that they conceal a great wealth of mineral resources; resources as yet only imperfectly known and surveyed.

The present upper surface of this arch of ancient rocks is a combination of a very old erosion surface and highly resistant cap rock formations such as the extensive quartzite areas in the Brazilian Highlands. On top of the older crystalline rocks are wide areas of younger sedimentary covering, often in the form of sandstones which are red, grey, or greenish in appearance. The sedimentary cap formations, together with the existence of widespread successive erosion surfaces, have given the highland surface its step-like character.

The great earth movements of the Tertiary period—the same movements which gave us the Cordilleran mountains in the west—produced in the central zone of the continent an immense depression which became filled with sedimentary materials, and which still retains its character as a vast lowland, an interior corridor connecting and including the two dominant drainage systems of the continent, the Amazon and the Paraguay-Paraná basins. Seldom does its surface rise to more than 600 feet above sea-level. It seems probable that folding and faulting are still going on beneath its surface, or at least have done so until very recently. Borings made in 1950 at Marajó Island, at the mouth of the Amazon, gave a thickness of 7200 feet for the sedimentary cover, and Hilgard O'R. Sternberg has estimated that in the Amazon Basin the cover probably attains, in certain places, a thickness of 8000 feet. This seems to conform to the suggestion

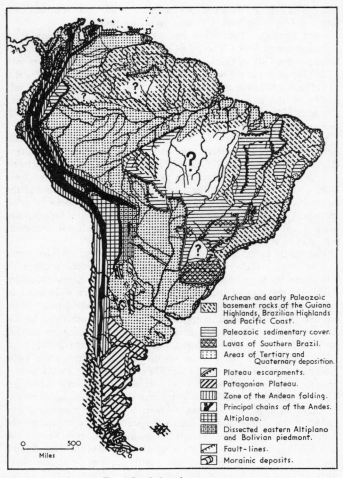

Archean and early Paleozoic
basement rocks of the Guiana
Highlands, Brazilian Highlands
and Pacific Coast.

Paleozoic sedimentary cover.

Lavas of Southern Brazil.

Areas of Tertiary and
Quaternary deposition.

Plateau escarpments.

Patagonian Plateau.

Zone of the Andean folding.

Principal chains of the Andes.

Altiplano.

Dissected eastern Altiplano
and Bolivian piedmont.

Fault-lines.

Morainic deposits.

0   500
Miles

Fig. 4. South America: structure.

that the main lines of the drainage pattern in the region round Manaus (which run NW-SE and SW-NE) are related to lines of weakness in the earth's crust, between which the central Amazon Valley has sunk under the weight of sediments covering it. A somewhat similar occurrence has evidently shaped the Lower Mississippi Valley in North America.

How far-reaching were the effects of the Tertiary earth movements is best seen at the eastern edge of the Andes, where sections of the Archean basement complex of the continent have both been involved in the general mountain-building uplift, and also have been forced up to form isolated wedge-shaped blocks rising above the central lowland to the east of the Cordillera. These 'foreign bodies' in the lowland zone often rise abruptly from its level surface; they include the hills of the Pampas and the Chaco, and the highlands of northern Patagonia.

But the most dramatic results of these earth movements are to be found in the third, or western, zone. On at least two occasions—in the late Palaeozoic era and in the Tertiary—mountains have been thrust up out of the sedimentary accumulations of a geosyncline. Between the mountains and the Pacific are to be found small remnant areas of the same old crystalline rocks which formerly made up the Archean base. In Colombia, Ecuador, and Chile they form the western edge of the continent, cutting off the Central Valley of Chile from the Pacific by forming the coastal hills. Farther south they terminate in the islands of the Chilean archipelago.

The Andes themselves form, in effect, a semicircle between Trinidad in the north and the southern borders of Peru. They then swing abruptly southwards, and continue with this orientation until they reach Tierra del Fuego. The shape of the Andes, especially in their central portion, is not that of sharp serrated ridges but rather of a broad block of the earth's crust which has been uplifted *in toto*. The top surface, in areas yet untouched by the headward eroding streams on the eastern flank, bears the aspects of a gently rolling late mature land surface which is surmounted here and there by snow-capped prominences. The broadest and, in general, the highest part of the Andes lies at the 'corner' in southern Peru and northern Chile, where flanking ranges enclose the high central Andean basins. In the manner of mountain ranges of comparable height elsewhere, the Andes owe their present form to the interaction of several natural forces: faulting and folding; uplift and depression; snow and ice; frost action and erosion by water and wind. It is obvious that tectonic activity has by no means ceased in this region, both from the presence of intrusive volcanic materials of recent age and also from the frequent earthquakes and the continuing activity of some of the many volcanoes which are concentrated in certain parts of the Cordillera.

While in general the eastern coasts of South America slope gently to the ocean floor, this is by no means the case on the west coast. The coast of Argentina is actually bordered by a continental shelf which stretches out to, and includes, the Falkland Islands. The west coast ocean bottom, on the other hand, plunges abruptly to great depths. This is especially true off-shore from Northern Chile and Peru, where the Atacama Trough is known to plunge to a depth of almost 25,000 feet below sea-level within 60 miles of the coast.

CLIMATE, VEGETATION AND WILD LIFE

The interaction of landforms, climate and vegetation cover has produced in South America a number of more or less well-defined natural regions. This interaction is illustrated by Fig. 6, which shows the relationship of rainfall and vegetation to the natural landscape, and it will at once be evident that the continent contains areas in which tropical, sub-tropical, and mid-latitude conditions respectively are dominant.

In climatic terms South America offers a wide diversity of habitats. Much of the continent is under the influence of the north-easterly and south-easterly trade winds blowing off the Atlantic, while the Amazon Basin, lying in the region of convectional precipitation along the Inter-Tropical Front, has a very heavy rainfall. Even outside this equatorial belt, rain forest vegetation in its varied aspects flourishes in many coastal areas on the east, north-east and north-west sides of the continent. In human terms, however, this widespread combination of heat and moisture poses serious problems; it produces a climate which, because of the very slight changes of temperature and the slow evaporation of perspiration which it permits, is considered unhealthy by some unacclimatised people from higher latitudes.

The magnitude of the cultural imprint upon these so-called 'unhealthy' lands however, is seen in places such as the Panama Canal Zone where technological victories over disease and pests combined with realistic house design and wardrobe habits produce an environment which is both comfortable and healthy. The chief problem is whether most of the tropical forest areas have sufficient economic or strategic importance to justify the great amounts of capital necessary to establish and maintain man in such an environment, as has been done in the Panama Canal Zone for a very limited number of people.

In South America, as in western North America, the Cordillera forms a very pronounced climatic division. It is responsible for the fact that regions of high precipitation and of desert are found in close proximity, with the dry areas forming a belt of varying width which crosses the Andes diagonally from western Peru to eastern Patagonia. Particularly noteworthy in this connection is the effect of the cold 'Peru

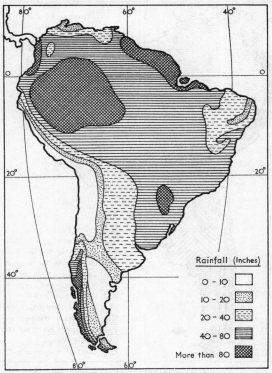

Fig. 5. South America: annual average rainfall.

(Humboldt) Current' along the Pacific Coast. It is this current, whose waters may reduce air temperatures at coastal stations by 10-15° F below the temperatures found a few miles inland, which is one of the primary factors in producing the Atacama Desert in Chile.

Taking into account both these striking variations in amount of rainfall from place to place, and also the range of temperature conditions, we may say that South America has a broad sequence of tropical, sub-tropical, mid-latitude, and cold montane climates. In passing from one to another of these climates, the traveller observes that the vegetation exhibits every possible transitional form.

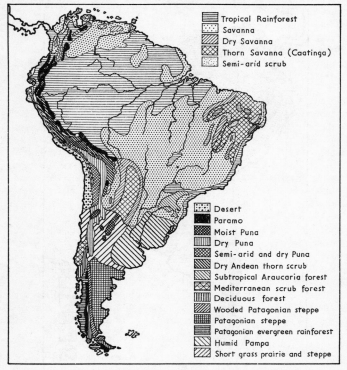

Fig. 6. South America: natural vegetation.

The rain-forests of the Amazon are flanked on their poleward sides by savannas. These vary in character from place to place, and indeed go by a variety of names. They are particularly widespread on the plateaux of the eastern uplands. On the southern edge of the savannas lies the sub-tropical vegetation belt, of which the coniferous Araucaria forest may be mentioned as representative. The open, parklike landscape of the Gran Chaco then forms the transition zone to the wide, treeless grass plains of the Pampas. Farther south, in southern Argentina, the grasslands are replaced by a thin cover of dry forest, which gives way in some areas to thorn scrub, while along the eastern foot of the Andes is a strip of true desert, with numerous salt pans.

On the west side of the Andes, the plant cover varies according to the presence of warm ocean currents, which are productive of rainfall, or cold currents, which tend to hinder it. In the north—as far south as the Gulf of Guayaquil—it consists chiefly of tropical rain-forest, but farther south, where the coast is increasingly under the influence of the Peru Current, it passes through a series of transitional types, ending as plantless desert in the Atacama. Farther south again, in central Chile, the vegetation may be described either as bushy steppe or evergreen scrub forest; it is a transitional type somewhat reminiscent of the *maquis* of the Mediterranean, and in this region a good deal of land is under cultivation. Finally, this bush vegetation gives way to the luxuriant mid-latitude rain-forests of southern Chile. In the higher parts of the Andes the vegetation is generally of two types—on the moister slopes and plateaux, the *paramo*, or grassland with a mixture of heath and laurel included in the cover, and in the semi-arid areas the *puna*, or short grass bushy steppe.

Carl Troll's work in the Andes has demonstrated how very localised factors can affect the nature of the plant cover. It seems clear, therefore, that we can no longer be satisfied with a simple classification of the plant cover into a few categories based on plant type or distribution, although that may be possible in areas of lower relief elsewhere. Studies carried out in this area and in Africa show that one of the most significant controls of the vegetation type is the duration of the dry season in any given locality. Thus we find the following rough correlation:

Number of Humid Months	Vegetation Belts	Number of Dry Months
12-9½	Rain-forest and transitional forest	0-2½
9½-7	Humid savanna	2½-5
7-4½	Dry savanna or tropical scrub forest	5-7½
4½-2	Savanna with thorn bushes	7½-10
2-1	Semi-desert	10-11
1-0	Desert	11-12

With this in mind, and using the results of Troll's work to refine the usually accepted vegetation classification for this area, we can summarise the results in tabular form (see opposite page).

Recent investigations, notably those of Wilhelmy, make it difficult to avoid the conclusion that the climate of the continent is becoming progressively drier. In consequence, the vegetation cover is gradually changing its character, and this quite apart from the effects of man's activities. Wilhelmy has drawn attention to the shrinkage of certain lakes in western Patagonia which are post-glacial in origin, a phenomenon associated with the retreat of the region's glaciers. He has noted, also, indications of drying out in various swamp areas in parts of the savannas which are regions of perennial flooding. It can be said with some certainty that the main features of the present changing plant cover are inherited from a more humid past. Among the features of that earlier vegetation cover were the great primeval forests of the Orinoco and Amazon Basins, while in the basin of the Paraná there was a huge lake.

The wildlife of South America is both varied and peculiar to the continent; varied, because of the great range of habitats offered by a land that contains both equatorial forests and snow-clad mountains; peculiar, because in all probability South America, like Australia, was separated in a very early phase from the other continents. Thus it possesses a fauna which is second only to Australia's in antiquity. One feature of this in both continents is the presence of animals with few teeth, such as the armadillo, the sloth and the ant-eater. All the beasts of prey of the Old World are replaced here by animals of the same families but smaller or weaker; the lion by the puma, the tiger by the jaguar. The rhinoceros, the elephant and the hippopotamus are not found here; only the tapir serves as a poor substitute. On the other hand, South America's fauna is rich in brightly coloured birds and insects; in amphibians and reptiles; in tortoises and apes. Locusts are always a danger to be reckoned with, swarming out of the hot moist areas of the Chaco at certain seasons, and wreaking devastation on neighbouring regions.

An Introduction to the Human Geography of South America

POPULATION

In mid-1962 the population of South America was estimated at 145 millions. This represents an average density of some twenty-one persons

CLIMATE AND VEGETATION IN THE TROPICAL SECTION OF THE ANDES

Number of Humid Months	Tierra Caliente (Warm Zone)	Tierra Templada (Temperate Zone)	Tierra Fria (Cool Zone)	Tierra Helada (Frost Zone)
12 / 11 / 10	Evergreen lowland rain-forest, and semi-deciduous transitional forest	Upland forest	Mountain mist-zone or moss forest	Paramo (grassland) with heath and shrubs
9 / 8	Humid savanna (mixed woodland and grassland)	Humid middle-altitude vegetation (mixed woodland and grassland)	Humid mountain bush vegetation	Humid Puna (shrubs and grasses)
7 / 6 / 5	Dry savanna (mixed woodland and grassland)	Dry middle-altitude vegetation (mixed woodland and grassland)	Dry mountain bush vegetation	Dry Puna (brush and shrub)
4 / 3 / 2	Savanna with thorn bush vegetation	Middle-altitude thorn shrub and scrub forest	Mountain thorn bush vegetation	Dry Puna with thorn bush
1	Semi-desert	Middle-altitude semi-desert	Mountain	Puna
0	Desert	Middle-altitude desert	Desert	Desert

per square mile, and thus in contrast to other parts of the world South America is still relatively thinly populated. Unfortunately, reliable statistics regarding the composition of the population are as hard to come by as precise figures for the area of the continent's states and provinces. However, the relative sizes of the figures obtainable are likely at least to be fairly accurate, and from them we may obtain some impression of this heterogeneous population.

Long before the arrival of the Europeans there was a sharp contrast between the naked jungle tribes, nomadic or semi-nomadic in their manner of life, and the peoples of the mountain west who had already evolved a complex culture which provided not only adequate shelter and food supplies in that high altitude setting, but also the economic and political means whereby neighbouring groups could be subjugated. The level which their culture reached is apparent from the remaining traces of their construction work (see Plate 20). Thus in the northern and central Andes there lived civilised peoples; in the surrounding immensity of the continent were peoples with only rudimentary characteristics of a civilised way of life. These marked differences in cultural levels are apparent in parts of South America up to the present day.

Steward and Faron, in their book *The Native Peoples of South America*, estimate that at the beginning of the sixteenth century there must have been just over 10 million inhabitants in South America: some 2 million in the tropical east; about 2 million outside the tropical region; and about 6 million in the Andean lands. This native population proved indispensable to the plans of the European conquerors for the development—or, more accurately, the exploitation —of the continent. We have already considered the difficulties which the newcomers encountered, and some of the ways in which they attempted to overcome them. Undoubtedly the great labour potential, which the Spaniards found in the population of the Andean lands, served to establish their hegemony much more rapidly than would otherwise have been the case. Because the Spaniards required vast numbers of workers for the mining of precious metals and for other tasks, they were naturally attracted to the areas with dense agglomerations of Indians.

In many cases Indian town-settlements became the centres from which the Spanish influence spread. This influence, however, did not actually penetrate deeply into Indian life; it extended merely as a thin veneer over a small section of the population, the bulk of whom continued to live with their Indian concepts and Indian habits essentially unaffected. In the former Portuguese sphere of eastern South America circumstances were rather different, but there, too, we find this phenomenon of a series of different cultural levels existing side by side in quite restricted areas.

It is outside the scope of this book even to list by name all the tribes that may be met with between Venezuela and Tierra del Fuego, with their manifold racial, cultural and economic differences. The many groups include the economically organised and interrelated communities of the Andean highlands on the one hand and the water nomads of Tierra del Fuego on the other, and in between these extremes is a range of cultures which includes primitive hunters and gatherers as well as rudimentary cultivators. South America possesses representatives of every possible level of cultural development from the highest to the lowest, all living within their own patterns of life, and many of them still not integrated into the life of the nations of which they ostensibly form a part.

In South America the boundaries of political, racial and cultural groups seldom coincide. There is a mixing process at work in both the biological and social spheres, which began at certain places along the coasts and progressed inland, and which has brought together the brown, white and black races, and their cultures. Today, within the individual states, there are considerable differences among the population, but the most marked of these is not so much between races as between the 'haves' and 'have-nots', in the modern sense of rising living standards and purchasing power. A correlation, however, generally exists in some countries such as Peru and Brazil, between socio-economic status and race. Mixed parentage as such has a decreasing importance today; indeed, it is perhaps the very fact that so large a part of the population is the product of the intermingling of European and indigenous South American strains which is responsible for the emergence of what one writer has called the spiritual substance of the new South America.

There are two common factors which constitute the core of this basic South Americanism: an Iberian culture and the Roman Catholic Church. For in most of the South American countries, in recent years as in the remoter past, the dominant element in the immigrant stream has come from lands of Romance culture. In every country except Brazil, Spanish is the official language, but this Spanish, like the Portuguese spoken in Brazil, has developed many peculiarities which now distinguish it from the parent language. Distance from the country of the mother tongue is in part responsible for this development; so, too, is the influx of new arrivals from other countries of Romance or Germanic language associations. Today there is probably more difference between Latin American Spanish or Portuguese and the mother tongue than there is between English spoken in Great Britain and English spoken in the United States. The significance of religion in the life of its people is discussed separately for each country.

To try to compare the size and distribution of the populations of individual South American states can produce some very misleading conclusions. The impression created, for example, by the political map is quite false. Over tens, and indeed hundreds, of thousands of square miles, no effective sovereignty—effective in terms of governmental techniques of today—is exercised. This is in general the case with areas where the population is very sparse. Right up until the present day, the centre of gravity of practically every nation's power lies close to the coast. With increasing distance from the coast, or with mounting problems of accessibility, the effective control exercised by the state decreases so markedly as to be meaningless—at least when considered in terms of administrators and governmental authority on the spot. The increasing significance of the capital city in relation to the total population of almost every country is illustrated in Fig. 7. Only Quito, of the ten cases given, is exceptional in this respect, and even there the capital's share of the country's population had grown to 8% by 1960.

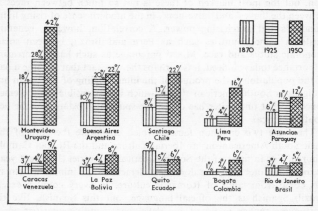

Fig. 7. Capital cities of South America: the bar graphs indicate the percentage of the total population of each country that was resident in the capital city in 1870, 1925 and 1950.

In those parts of the continent where Europeans had settled, the preservation and spread of western Christian cultural values finally became firmly established when, at length, the influx of adventurers and treasure-seekers was supplemented, a century ago, by the immigration of genuine settlers who were intent upon making their permanent homes in South America.

Important as the role of the recent immigrant has been in the settlement of South America, however, that role has in no way compared with the part played by migrants into North America during the same period. Writing in 1942, S. G. Inman commented on the reasons for this state of affairs:

> There are four chief difficulties in the way of immigration in Latin America. One is the system of great landed estates prevalent in most of these countries—in some cases one can travel for days within the limits of a single estate. The absentee landlords, with an income sufficient to keep them in luxury in the cities, have little incentive for intensive development of their lands. Too often the immigrant is able to find a place only as a day labourer, or at best can become, precariously, a renter. This is no doubt a principal reason why more than two million of the immigrants who came to Argentina during the last seventy years have returned to their homes. . . .
>
> Another detriment to immigration has been the recurrence in most of the Latin American countries, of revolutions, which result in the destruction of social life and progress, especially in less densely populated areas. A third is the lack of educational facilities in many new territories; for Latin America has given little attention to rural education. Mexico is now leading in this direction, but at her present rate of development it will take years to make any deep impression on the mass of her population.
>
> A fourth factor in discouraging the immigrant is the lack in most of these countries of good titles to land holdings. This condition arises from the importation of the old Spanish law into the New World. Often the legal processes for acquiring permanent titles are not clear, and the right of eminent domain has remained more largely in the consciousness of the people than it has in older, more accurately surveyed areas of the world. It may happen that a man develops a tract of land only to find after years of litigation that his title is not good.[1]

ECONOMIC CONDITIONS AND COMMUNICATIONS

In South America, the contrast between adjacent landscapes of forest and cultivated fields is always striking. Just as the map of population distribution reveals a pattern of a few dense concentrations in small

1 Inman, S. G., *Latin America: Its Place in World Life*, New York, 1942, pp. 52-3.

isolated areas where the centres of economic power lie, so also the map of land use and resource use follows the same discontinuous, immature pattern.

South America possesses an immense area of land suitable for agricultural and livestock farming. It possesses, too, a wide range of mineral resources, among which the only serious omission is, perhaps, coal, of which so far only small deposits have been discovered—in Brazil, Chile and the north-western Andes. The lack of coal is, however, of decreasing significance as oil and natural gas can now replace it for most uses. The continent's huge hydro-electric potential has been tapped only in a few places. (Most of the sites with the greatest hydro-potential are located too far from consuming centres to be economically feasible until the technology of long-distance transmission has been further improved.) Oil production plays an important role in the continent's economy, especially in Venezuela and Colombia which export oil; but in several other countries (Argentina, Chile, etc.) sufficient is produced to meet most domestic requirements and elsewhere small-scale production is accompanied by active exploration for further supplies. The old mining belt of the Andes continues to yield a variety of ores, as do those other long-prospected regions, the Brazilian and Guiana Highlands. Several countries have already been able to create the beginnings of their own heavy industry—Brazil, Argentina, Chile and Venezuela (see Fig. 40). At the same time, the bulk of their mineral output, now as always, goes for export. In this sphere of mineral production the U.S.A. is not only the principal buyer of the Latin American exports, but is itself deeply involved financially in the industry. There can be little doubt that future changes in the technology of the mining industry will bring with them far-reaching changes in the economic positions both of the producing countries and also of the countries in Europe and North America which import their mineral products.

The industrial centres of the continent in general lie within relatively short distances from the coast, while the principal mining regions are often outside the settled areas and bear little relation to the general distribution of population or cultivation. For the rest of the continent the intensity and pattern of land use vary greatly from area to area, whether we are considering the banana plantations of the north coast, the vineyards of Chile, the extensive cereal growing of the south-east or the hunting and collecting of the tropical rain forest tribes.

Closely bound up with the continent's economic development and land use is the evolution of communications. Except on the two great natural waterways—the Amazon and the Paraguay-Paraná system

—river traffic is restricted, or is for the present impossible, because of waterfalls and rapids. The old-fashioned methods of travel, such as native bearers and pack animals, are of importance only in a few remaining areas. As the basis of land transport, the motor vehicle has established itself, often as a means of filling in the gaps left by the very incomplete railway network. Lately, however, the motor truck has superseded the railway even in areas where railways operate. Actually the term 'network' can only be applied in a few South American countries, and the pattern of the railway system, as revealed on the map, was, until the recent development of road transport, a remarkably accurate indicator of the stage of economic development reached. In South America today it is true, just as it was four centuries ago, that communications precede settlement, and indeed make settlement possible, whereas in the Old World the reverse has generally been the case; the need for transport has led to its development.

An extension of the communication system which holds the prospect of future importance is the Inter-American Highway. Its main course follows the Andes (with numerous branches in Colombia and Venezuela), and then divides into several sections which link the main stem to Chile, Argentina, Uruguay and Brazil.

This brief survey must not be concluded without some reference to the changing form of South America's economy. This process of change began with the First World War, and was accelerated by the Second, and is a process of harnessing the continent's own great potential to the needs of its people. One of the main objectives of every South American nation is to break away from its old role in world affairs as exporter of raw materials and importer of finished goods. It must be added, however, that to achieve this goal in the short time hoped for, these states need, but can by no means assure themselves of, some important prerequisites—the capital, know-how and educated labour needed for development, coupled with political and monetary stability. The common motives which foster a wider expansion of industry (and not merely industries manufacturing consumer goods) are, first, the often-demonstrated sensitivity of the primary producing economy in times of crisis—in depression or war; second, the development of an ever-growing number of synthetic replacements for South America's traditional export products; and third, perhaps, the rise of other competitors—producing-areas in similar climatic zones which, coming only recently on the scene, have challenged old monopolies.

It seems clear that the basic problem of these South American states is to balance their desire for a greater degree of self-sufficiency against their need for the greatest possible volume of exports. The obstacles that may hinder them from striking such a balance are massive: poor communications; a widely scattered population, the bulk of which lives in circumstances that give it little means to produce, or power to purchase; and, equally threatening in its persistence, the spiralling inflation which occurs as a result of structural bottle-necks in the economy and government expenditure unmatched by tax collection.

With the expansion of the continent's industries—which almost invariably takes place in the areas already thickly settled—the contrast between the condition of the urban and the rural populations, already pronounced, becomes sharper still (see Plate 2), and the contrast between rich and poor likewise increases. The rise of industry is not accompanied by any evidence of the agricultural development which is so urgently and equally necessary. In the present phase of development it is interesting, however, to note that (in contrast to former conditions) State enterprises are coming to replace private enterprise in the new industrial countries, a trend which has possibly been strengthened by a fear that otherwise South America's industry might fall under the control of foreign capital, and also by the propensity of private domestic savings to be invested abroad in Europe and North America rather than at home.

CHAPTER TWO

Brazil

Brazil: General

The immense area known as the United States of Brazil is not a 'country' or a 'state' in the European sense of those terms. It embraces almost half the continent and almost half its total population. In terms of area it is virtually the same size as Europe, but it lies almost wholly in the tropics. Only two South American states (Chile and Ecuador) have no common frontier with Brazil. In the north it stretches across the equator; in the south it extends across the Tropic of Capricorn (which runs close to Rio de Janeiro); in the west its borders reach the Andes between latitude 7° and 9° S. Of 14,400 miles of frontiers, 4570 miles represent coastline, which in the north-east is flat and unindented. Farther south, as far as Salvador, coral reefs fringe the shore. To the south again is a cliff coastline, which is better suited for shipping, and which possesses sheltered harbours such as Rio de Janeiro and Vitória. Finally, in the extreme south, the coastline is made up of sand-bars backed by lagoons—a coastline owing its present form to the northward movement of alluvial material deposited by the Rio de la Plata.

The largest of these lagoons is the Lagôa dos Patos (Lagoon of the Ducks), some 200 miles long. At its outlet lies the small port of Rio Grande and at its inland limit lies the important regional centre and port of Pôrto Alegre.

The territory of Brazil comprises areas which, in terms of structure, landforms, climate and vegetation, are markedly different from each other, and in recent years a fivefold division of the country into regions has commonly been recognised—not only by geographers, but semi-officially by the Brazilian government also (see Fig. 11, page 45). However, we shall first consider Brazil as a whole.

STRUCTURE

There are two main structural provinces, which have in common nothing but their great size. They are the lowlands of the north and north-west—the Amazon Basin—and the highlands of the east and south-east, with the former occupying rather more than half the extent of the latter. Almost a half of the total area of Brazil lies below 650 feet, and only some 4% above the 3000-foot contour. In general, the higher parts of the Brazilian Highland slope inland towards the centre of the continent. Most of the drainage runs in that direction also, apart from the few rivers which cut steeply down through the rim of the Highland towards the coast.

This Brazilian Highland dips beneath the Tertiary sediments of the Amazon Basin on a broad front, to re-emerge farther north as the Guiana Highland. Both these uplands display the same characteristics: a crystalline core, overlaid with volcanic materials and remnants of the Mesozoic cover which often have a stepped or terrace-like appearance, and which have in some cases been folded by more recent earth movements. The stepped appearance is due partly to sedimentary formations of varying resistance and partly to a series of retreating erosional surfaces. It is only near the coast in the south-east, in the region of most pronounced faulting and folding, that the upland really takes on the character of a mountain mass. In neither of the upland areas, the Brazilian and the Guianan, does the height of the mountains exceed 10,000 feet; indeed, there are only a dozen peaks rising above 7000 feet. The five highest are:

Name	Height	Location by States
Pico da Bandeira	9462 ft.	Minas Gerais-Espírito Santo
Pico do Cristal	9383 ft.	Minas Gerais
Pico do Monte Roraima	9219 ft.	Amazonas-Venezuela-British Guiana
Pico do Cruzeiro	9177 ft.	Minas Gerais-Espírito Santo
Itatiaia	9145 ft.	Rio de Janeiro-Minas Gerais

A prominent feature of the zone of granite and gneiss within the Highlands are the characteristic sugarloaf hills which are found particularly in Rio de Janeiro and Espírito Santo (see Plates 3 and 4). For the rest, the great inland sweep of the Highland generally takes the form of a rolling tableland lying between 1000 and 3000 feet, cut by incised valleys and broken here and there by the steep edges of sills and plateau steps.

The great lowland of Amazonia presents a marked contrast to the Brazilian Highland. Its area is some 1,750,000 square miles, and it is sometimes known simply as the *selva* (or tropical rain forest). This region of downfold was submerged beneath the sea as recently as the Tertiary period. The Tertiary deposits, which are many thousands of feet thick, have been dissected by the rivers, and often left to form steep terrace edges along their banks. Consequently, the flood plains of the rivers are limited in extent to a mere 1 to 2 % of the total drainage area. The great Tertiary geosyncline became the catchment area of the Amazon system, which drains no less than 2,053,000 square miles and forms a perfect dendritic pattern within the Basin. It is in this basin of the Amazon that the densest and most fully developed tropical rain forest in the world is to be found, with here and there in it a patch of grassy savanna like an island among the forest trees. This vegetation cover is described in more detail in a later section.

CLIMATE

With the exception of the upland areas in the three southern states of Paraná, Santa Catarina and Rio Grande do Sul, the whole of Brazil has a tropical climate, with a mean annual temperature of more than 68° F and a small annual range. The highest temperatures occur, not in Amazonia, but in the interior of the north-east, and in the south-east; here temperatures of 100° F and over are sometimes recorded. In general, the diurnal and annual temperature ranges increase away from the coast and the Amazon Basin, where they are at a minimum, up to the mountains of the interior. It is in the Amazonian lowland that the daily means show the least variation—at Manaus, for example, the daily mean is in the region of 80° F throughout the year. In view of these temperature conditions, it is variation in the amount and seasonal distribution of the rainfall which distinguishes the different climatic régimes.

The *selva* region of the Amazon Basin has a climate characterised by high temperatures the year round and rain at all seasons. The amount of rainfall increases from east to west. Temperatures of less than 68° F or more than 85° F are uncommon. The eastern part of the basin has two seasons of pronounced rainfall, while in the region around Pará the season of maximum precipitation is clearly defined and occurs between December and May. A characteristic feature of the rain forest climate are the almost daily thunderstorms which break with elemental

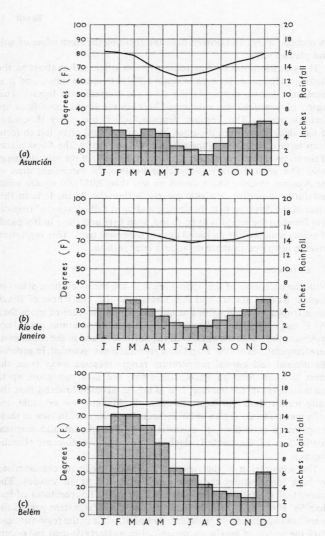

Fig. 8. Brazil and Paraguay: temperature and rainfall diagrams for one inland (*a*) Asunción (25° S), and two coastal stations—(*b*) Rio de Janeiro (23° S), and (*c*) Belém (1° S).

fury in the early afternoon. Everywhere in Brazil, indeed, the summer rains frequently fall during thunderstorms which follow an hour or two after the sun has passed its zenith. Precipitation is particularly heavy in the coastlands of the south-east, owing to the abrupt rise of the mountains that line the coast. A large part of the interior has a climate that combines a dry season with a small annual range of temperature. These variations in rainfall régime are responsible, in turn, for the wide variety of natural vegetation types which Brazil possesses, and which are indicated by Fig. 6.

DRAINAGE

Like almost everything else about Brazil, the drainage system is on an immense scale. Parts of the continent's two greatest river systems lie within its borders. The principal watershed runs across the Planalto de Mato Grosso, and then through the state of Goiás to its border opposite Salvador. It then follows the border north-eastwards. South of this watershed, the principal rivers—disregarding the short streams that flow directly to the Atlantic—are the São Francisco and the Paraná. For the first 800-900 miles of its course the São Francisco is a river of the high plateaux, over which it runs northward on the Planalto roughly parallel with the coast. Then it turns east and drops to the coastal plain by way of the falls near Paulo Afonso. It is navigable from its mouth to Paulo Afonso Falls, and from just above the falls to Pírapora, a section about 800 miles long called the Middle São Francisco River. The river played a significant role as a route during the opening up of the interior. The Paraná, on the other hand, represents a main axis of movement in southern Brazil, with its multitude of tributaries and its neighbour the Paraguay. In the still youthful upper courses of the Paraná and its tributaries, there are numerous waterfalls not yet eliminated by erosion. Among them are the Iguaçú Falls, which rank among the largest in the world.

A Visit to the Iguaçú Falls

The Iguaçú (from the Indian, meaning Great Water) is a relatively short, but strongly-flowing tributary of the Rio Paraná. Its mouth lies at the point where Brazil, Argentina and Paraguay meet. It rises quite near the sea, some 60 miles north of the German settlement of Blumenau, and then follows the gentle slope of the upland's surface towards the west. All the rivers of the plateau have waterfalls at the point where they cut down through the edge of the upland, including the Paraná itself, with its well-known Guaira Falls 200 miles above its junction with the Iguaçú. Little wonder, then, that this region has earned the name of Land of Waterfalls.

The most impressive and most beautiful of these falls—perhaps, indeed, the most impressive in all the world—are those of the Iguaçú. They are located 15 miles above its junction with the Paraná, and are enveloped in a world of such tropical splendour that words can hardly do justice to its beauty.

It takes the steamer on the Paraná three days to reach the mouth of the Iguaçú from Posadas, the capital of the Argentinian province of Misiones. The trip up the mile-wide river is fascinating; there are countless crocodiles sunning themselves on the banks, monkeys and parrots of a dozen kinds in the trees, and giant goldfish swimming round the boat. Settlements are few and far between. The nearer we get to the mouth of the Iguaçú, the higher and steeper become the banks of the Paraná, and the greater becomes our wonderment at this tropical paradise.

On the Brazilian, or northern bank of the Iguaçú, there is a 25-foot roadway cleared through the maze of the forest giants; it runs upstream and is passable for cars. Despite its width, the road merely seems to plunge the traveller ever deeper into the gloom and silence of the forest, for the trees and creepers have swiftly grown to form an arch over the road in their struggle up towards the light. If the road were not constantly kept clear and maintained, it would quickly be overwhelmed again by the vegetation.

Long before he reaches the falls, the traveller can hear in the distance a roar which swells to thunder as he draws nearer. Soon, he is standing, as one writer has expressed it, 'before one of the grandest of all nature's displays. . . . It is not, as it is with the Zambesi, the falls alone that captivate the eye; it is the whole overwhelming spectacle of tropical nature, a fairy-tale world in which the visitor seems to have lost himself.' Even before the falls themselves come into view, the approach to them through the forest is hung with splendours and is quite outstandingly beautiful. Then come the falls: on the Brazilian side of the river, the water plunges in a single horseshoe fall into the thunderous depths below, while on the Argentinian side the river breaks into a hundred separate falls, and drops over a series of black volcanic sills along a front which is more than a mile in width. The whole great spectacle—plunging water, towering cliffs, rocky steps and the dark walls of the gorge into which the Iguaçú drops—all this is enveloped in luxuriant forest growth, while over all rise white clouds of spray, flung up by the foaming torrent (von Hesse-Wartegg).

The Paraná, which, like the Paraguay River, serves for long distances as an international boundary, also serves as a route linking Brazil with Uruguay, Paraguay and Argentina. By contrast, the rivers of the north-east of Brazil have little significance as avenues of communication, for most of them flow only seasonally, and others have torrent courses or flow too swiftly for navigation.

It is in the Amazon Basin that we find the greatest river system in the world, fed from the Brazilian Upland by such immense tributaries as the Tapajós, Xingú and Tocantins. The Amazon is the mightiest and, it appears from the most recent statistics, the longest river in any continent. It begins its course as the Rio Maranhão, 18,000 feet up in the Andes, pours as a great torrent northwards parallel with the trend of the Andes, and then cuts through the easternmost ridges of the mountains in a series of wild gorges. By the time it reaches the eastern edge of the Andes, it has already fallen over 7000 feet to only 500 feet above sea-level. From here its waters, sluggish now, wind their way eastwards. At Iquitos in Peru, in its upper course some miles from its mouth, it is already 2000 yards wide. In spite of the minute gradient on its lower course—an inch or two per mile—its rate of flow is between 2 and 3 feet per second, owing to the tremendous thrust of the water pouring down behind. For most of its course, the river has a depth of between 100 and 150 feet. At the point where it is joined by the Rio Negro, the undivided river has attained a breadth of 3 miles. From this point onwards, the river is navigable for large ocean-going vessels; ships of under 3000 tons can reach further up, to Iquitos. On this lower course, the river splits into innumerable channels, separated by islands. On either bank occur lagoons, linked with the main stream at their extremities.

At certain points, where the Amazon is joined by its major tributaries, the river broadens to the dimensions of a lake, and ships moving in the centre of the channel lose sight of both banks. On the side channels of the river grows the giant water lily (*Victoria regia*), the loveliest of all water plants. Its huge round leaves, with their turned-up rims, may measure 10 feet in diameter, while the flowers attain sizes up to 18 inches. The great funnel-shaped mouth of the river, which lies right on the equator, is cluttered with islands. The estuary is some 60 miles wide (or, if we include that of the Tocantins and the Rio Pará, over 150 miles wide).

Tributaries. Since rainfall is exceptionally heavy over the eastern Andes and their slopes, the Amazon is joined from here by a number of powerful tributaries, such as the Ucayali, the Purús and the Madeira. The last of these is itself over 1800 miles long, or nearly the same length as the whole course of the Volga; it is the largest of all the Amazon's tributaries. It rises on the Bolivian Highlands and its flow is almost as great as that of the Amazon itself. From the Brazilian Upland, as we have already seen, the Amazon receives the Tapajós, Xingú and Tocantins.

The region between these three rivers is, even at the present day, far less known than darkest Africa.

The left bank tributaries are not so powerful as those on the right bank. The principal streams are the Japurá and the Rio Negro, or Black River. (This is so called because of its dark waters. Such 'black rivers' are found in the northern Amazon Basin, and owe their colour to the dissolution by water of the humus cover of certain silicated areas. 'White water streams' are found in some chalk areas but also reflect great amounts of sediment held in suspension. The black rivers are in general malarial vicinities; the white river areas, in spite of attracting some types of mosquito, are generally much healthier.) The Rio Negro is connected, by way of the Casiquiare, with the Orinoco River; there is no true watershed. The Casiquiare thus provides the best-known example of the phenomenon of a bifurcating stream, feeding both the Orinoco and Amazon rivers.

Almost all the important tributaries of the Amazon are interrupted by falls or rapids at the point where they enter the lowland region, and in some cases these are very numerous. With its 200 or more major tributaries, the Amazon has the greatest volume of flow of any of the world's rivers. In comparison with the Mississippi, which has a catchment area of some 1·4 million square miles, the Amazon's is no less than 2·7 million square miles in extent. (The area of the whole European land mass is 3·7 million square miles.) The Mississippi System has a navigable length of 20,000 miles; the Amazon of 31,000 miles (more than twice as much as that of all the river systems of Europe), and of this total four-fifths lie within the borders of Brazil. The Amazon carries more water to the sea than all the rivers of Europe put together—between 40,000 and 100,000 cubic metres per second, according to season. This huge outflow carries fresh water out to sea for more than 250 miles.

The greatest known depth of the Amazon is found above its junction with the Tapajós (see Fig. 9), at Óbidos; it is some 250 feet, and the river bed is thus well below sea-level. The very heavy rainfall in the western section of the Amazon Basin and the eastern Andes is responsible, however, for flood levels that rise 30–50 feet above the low season level. They spread the river over its flood plain, and sometimes the high water lasts from February to June, with nothing but the tops of the palm trees showing above the expanse of waters. Indeed, these floods would be far greater in volume and effect, were it not for the fact that the north-bank and south-bank tributaries have completely different régimes. These constant changes of level are a hindrance to navigation; specifically, they are one more hindrance to add to the effects of shifting sandbanks, underwater vegetation, a navigation channel which is perpetually changing its course and, last but not least, the dangerous Amazon bore, known locally as the *pororoca*.

The *pororoca* usually occurs at the time of the spring tides. It is a great, banked-up flood of a wave, caused by the pressure of the water pouring in with the tide into the channel of the Amazon estuary. Rising like a wall, 12, 15 or even 30 feet high, the roaring mass of sea water

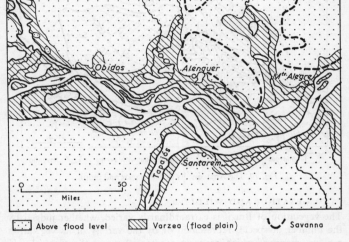

Fig. 9. The Amazon: the river at its confluence with the Tapajós.

hurtles against the outflowing land water and pours over it, rolling and mixing the two water masses. Upstream it rushes with astonishing speed, sometimes above the fresh water but, in the deepest parts of the river, flowing below it. The river banks are swamped and devastated by the tidal wave. Such bores are, of course, well known—though on a far smaller scale—on other rivers with funnel-shaped estuaries such as the Seine, the Severn and the Ganges. The Amazon bore makes its effects felt for over 500 miles inland from the sea. It is dangerous to shipping and obliges ships passing the mouth of the river at spring tides to use the quieter side channels instead of the main stream. Partly on this account, and partly because the main channel silts up more seriously, the usual entrance to the river for ships is by the Rio Pará and then south of Marajó Island (see Fig. 10).

Thus the great Amazon System forms the only practicable surface means of entry into the still largely unsettled heart of the forested interior.

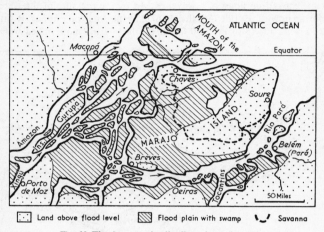

Fig. 10. The Amazon: its distributaries and mouth.

VEGETATION AND WILDLIFE

The vegetation of Brazil is extraordinarily varied, whether judged by the number of species represented or by the variety of its vegetation regions, many of which cover vast areas. Between the tropical rain forest and the driest steppes, which are not even capable of supporting range cattle, there is a wide variety of intermediate vegetation types.

The tropical rain-forest. This vegetation region occupies an immense area in Amazônia, and for variety of species and luxuriance outdoes even the forests of the Congo Basin. It is broken only occasionally by open grasslands (the *campos*) while on the other hand it extends in the form of *galeria* forests[1] along the river courses into neighbouring

1 *Galeria* means a corridor or colonnade. The reference is to the fact that the trees lining the water courses form an arch over the stream. Thus these tree tunnels extend from the forest proper into the adjacent grasslands and savannas (*campos cerrados*).

vegetation regions. The Amazon itself is generally lined with a strip of flood plain 15–20 miles wide, on whose swampy floor a uniform type of seasonally flooded woodland is found. On the middle and upper Amazon this consists mainly of palm trees, of which there are scores of varieties, rising to 150 feet or more above the plain. Their tops form a kind of canopy beneath which grow smaller trees and coarse grasses. The annual floods, lasting often for many months, prohibit the growth of many of the ferns, creepers, and deciduous trees found elsewhere in the forest. River silt, plastered on the trunks of the palm trees, serves as a guide to each year's flood levels. Farther downstream, however, deciduous trees make their appearance, notably the great *Ceiba pentandra*.

The area of the Amazon Valley which is regularly flooded is known as the *várzea*. Downstream from Manaus, the forest along the river edge of the flood plain is backed by more open grasslands, where *Eichornia*, wild rice and giant water lilies are found. Outside the flood season, these areas dry out and can then be used for grazing livestock.

The true tropical rain-forest begins beyond and above the flood plain, on what is known as *terra firme*. Here is found the full splendour, variety and immensity of tropical vegetation—giant trees, grasses the height of a man, ferns with fronds 15 feet long and 6 feet broad, and everywhere flowers in a dreamlike kaleidoscope of colours. The *terra firme* is never flooded, however, and therefore never receives the annual deposits of fertile silt which favour the *várzea* (flood plain) areas.

This true rain-forest covers almost the whole of the great Amazonian Lowland; virtually unbroken in its extent, it is also virtually impassable, save along its sun-drenched margins where breaks occur in the forest, thanks to the endless variety of undergrowth, ferns, lianas and epiphytes that form the forest's lowest layer. To this forest, the name *selva* is generally applied (though Humboldt suggested *hylea*, and this name is also sometimes used); here, as one writer has said, 'is the most extensive and most varied stretch of tropical rain-forest on earth . . . man is lost to sight by contrast with a nature that here unfolds its most lavish, indeed prodigal, variety'.

It was this feature of the rain-forest landscape which evidently impressed Kingsley in Humboldt's account of his South American journeys, and which finds expression in the following passage from Kingsley's *Westward Ho!*

The Banks of the Meta

They paddled onward hour after hour, sheltering themselves as best they could under the shadow of the southern bank, while on their right hand the full sun-glare lay upon the enormous wall of mimosas, figs, and laurels, which formed the northern forest, broken by the slender shafts of bamboo tufts, and decked with a thousand gaudy parasites; bank upon bank of gorgeous bloom piled upward to the sky, till where its outline cut the blue, flowers and leaves, too lofty to be distinguished by the eye, formed a broken rainbow of all hues quivering in the ascending streams of azure mist, until they seemed to melt and mingle with the very heavens.

And as the sun rose higher and higher, a great stillness fell upon the forest. The jaguars and monkeys had hidden themselves in the darkest depths of the woods; the birds' notes died out one by one; the very butterflies ceased their flitting over the tree-tops, and slept with outspread wings upon the glossy leaves, indistinguishable from the flowers around them. . . . a stillness in which, as Humboldt says, 'If beyond the silence we listen for the faintest undertones, we detect a stifled, continuous hum of insects, which crowd the air close to the earth; a confused, swarming murmur which hangs round every bush, in the cracked bark of trees, in the soil undermined by lizards, millipedes, and bees; a voice proclaiming to us that all Nature breathes, that under a thousand different forms life swarms in the gaping and dusty earth, as much as in the bosom of the waters, and the air which breathes around.

A special word may be said about the epiphytes, the most characteristic part of this tropical forest growth. These plants, of which there are innumerable varieties, are either parasites or semi-parasites living on other plants, particularly trees. These they use either as supports or as a base from which to grow even higher, in their struggle to reach the light. The true parasites suck nourishment out of the host tree and eventually strangle it by cutting off the sap. The semi-parasites satisfy their water requirements by collecting rain water; their lack of soil is made good by a kind of substitute humus which collects in the crevices of the bark on their host tree. The semi-parasites do not, therefore, draw upon the food resources of their host. Beneath the quick-growing, leafy epiphytes and the myriad creepers, the trunks and heads of the forest trees are often completely lost to sight. One of the characteristic sounds of the rain-forest is the crack of branches, breaking under the weight of enveloping vegetation. Often this upper storey of the forest goes on flourishing, long after the tree trunks on which it originally depended have rotted away, rather like a piece of wire netting after the supports have gone. Some of the multitudes of creepers and lianas are as thick as a man's leg, and so thickly are they interlaced among the tree tops that the trees cannot, in fact, fall down when they die. The term epiphyte, when used of the tropics, includes among other plants, numerous aroids (*Araceæ*), a variety of ferns and many orchids, beautifully coloured and scented. (Orchids are the most expensive of all commercial flowers. In America, there are special orchid 'hunters', who spend their lives in a search for new varieties for cultivation. Some 6000 varieties are known so far.) Many of these plants send out long roots or suckers in search of nourishment down to the ground or across to neighbouring trees. Others hang like great beards from branches, and others again twist their suckers, ivy-like, around their host and strangle it.

This tropical rain-forest, the most luxuriant vegetation type of all in South America, extends over the Atlantic coast slopes of the Brazilian Highland also. Its immeasurable wealth of forest products is only now coming to be appreciated in full: the attractive, dark-striped wood of the jacarandá; the Brazilian cedars; and Pernambuco wood. As with timber, so with spices and medicinal products; the forest yields vanilla, castor oil and quinine. The value of the cacao and rubber trees, on the other hand, has long been recognised, and for the various products of the palm trees a wide range of uses has been found.

Rubber can be obtained from the milky sap of a number of tropical plants of quite different families. These plants are found over the whole region between Mexico in the north and northern Argentina on the south. Here the rubber-yielding plants—most of them are actually trees—find an environment to suit their every requirement, with moist soils and warm, humid air. They are nearly always found scattered and standing singly in the forest, often almost hidden amid the vegetation, and in excessively unhealthy districts. It is, therefore, understandable that wild Brazilian rubber has not been able to compete with the plantation product of South-East Asia.

The development of plantations in Brazil has been prevented by difficulties of transport and by labour scarcity and plant diseases.

The *Hevea brasiliensis*—the main rubber-producing plant—is a fairly large tree, with a smooth whitish trunk, which is found throughout the rain-forest of Brazil but particularly in the south-western parts of the Amazon Basin. In the rubber operations, the tree is usually cut or slit, or less often felled. A tree will yield 5 to 10 lb of rubber the first few times it is tapped; later on, this will rise to 20 to 40 lb. Ring-like incisions are made in the bark and the white latex drips into cups to be later coagulated. A rubber tapper who is fortunate in locating the rubber trees in the forest may hope to collect between 2500 and 3000 lb of rubber during a harvest season. Since, however, everything depends on locating the trees, his total may only be half as much.

A modified version of the tapping technique is merely to make a few cuts in the bark with an axe or hatchet, out of which the rubber seeps and can be collected in cups. As the cuts quickly heal, the tree rapidly recovers from this treatment. The rubber so collected is poured out either in a hole dug in the ground, or simply on a clean patch of earth, where it congeals and hardens in a few days into sheets or blocks. It can also be coagulated on a stick by smoke.

In the early days of the rubber trade, before 1900, virtually all the production came from wild rubber trees, and up to about 1913 Brazil was the world's leading rubber producer. But from that date onward the new plantations in South-East Asia and Africa, with their high yields and much greater output, increasingly came to eclipse Brazil as producers.

The degree to which South-East Asia has established itself as the world's leading rubber-producing area is well enough known, though the efforts of Brazil to preserve for itself at least a fraction of the lost world market have received less attention. It is, however, the growth of a home market for the product which has recently reinvigorated Brazil's rubber industry in Amazônia. How this revived natural rubber industry will compete in the future with the synthetic products developed over the last thirty years—which are for many purposes superior to natural rubber—must remain a matter for speculation.

In many ways the rain-forests which cover the coastlands of Brazil, in a belt of varying width, from Rio Grande do Norte to northern Rio Grande do Sul, resemble the forest areas we have been considering. They contain many fine, and indeed famous, hardwoods such as rose-wood. Unlike the Amazon forests, however, large parts of them have felt the effects of man's hand, either by being used for logging operations or through clearance for cropland and pastures. In these areas the second growth forest, where it exists, is noticeably less flourishing than the virgin forest. Tropical rain-forest is also to be found in the Paraguay Basin and on the middle Paraná.

A coastal vegetation belt with a special grouping of tropical plant forms, is usually identified by the Brazilians as among the country's vegetation regions. Various formations belong to it, adapted to the environment of the coastlands. Among these may be mentioned the mangrove swamps, which occupy the inter-tidal zone here in the tropics. Tree growth is of various types, all supported on a maze of stilt-like roots which are exposed at low tide. Some of these tree forms have fruits that float; others have their fruits sprouting directly from the tree. When the fruit is ripe, the seed breaks out of the shell, falls into the mud and grows there very rapidly to form a new plant. Other special forms of the coastal vegetation belt include the tall, slender coconut palms, and a woody growth that is found on the sand-bars and spits which have been thrown up along the coast of Rio de Janeiro State.

The remaining vegetational forms of Brazil are the result of varying lengths of wet seasons, and soils. On the plateau lands of southern Brazil (in the states of Paraná, Santa Catarina and Rio Grande do Sul) grow immense forests of the so-called Paraná pine, a member of the Araucaria family. In some parts of Maranhão and Mato Grosso, on the other hand, conditions favour the growth of the Babaçu palm, which yields a valuable oil.

On the wide open expanses of the interior, the plant cover is extremely varied and almost defies classification. Research has shown that quite small differences from place to place of edaphic conditions—soil, aspect, drainage—may produce markedly different vegetation forms within the same climatic region. There are, for example, the *campos limpos*, which are true grasslands as distinct from the *campos cerrados*, which are formed of dense grassland with low trees and shrubs. The term *cerrado* is used to denote a savanna-type vegetation with dry forest 30–40 feet high. A particular vegetation type of these drier lands is the *caatinga* of the north-east, the *sertão*. This region of semi-desert has a vegetation cover made up of sparse thorn forest with cactus and other water-storing plants; the forest is largely leafless in the dry season. *Sertão* in this sense means a particular place—the dry interior of north-east Brazil; in a more general usage *sertão* means the sparsely inhabited backlands of the interior of Brazil. It is the equivalent of the Australian 'outback'.

The Brazilian government has made considerable efforts to introduce reforestation programmes wherever there was a need for them, especially in the south. Apart from these programmes, and following the example of the U.S.A., the government has set up a number of national parks, with the object of conserving areas of special or typical character in their natural condition. There are at present three such parks, including one in the Organ Mts. near Rio de Janeiro and one at the Iguaçú Falls.

Wild Life. The wild life of Brazil is immensely varied, and is especially rich in insects, birds and fishes. On the other hand, the Amazon's habit of annual flood eliminates some species that might otherwise be found, and the numbers of animals are not very great. Besides an unrivalled variety of beautifully coloured butterflies, there are also many poisonous, or at least irritating, insects such as malarial mosquitoes, which are the plague of the swamp areas, and ants, sand fleas and the poisonous giant spiders. Tortoises, turtles[1] and crocodiles abound, not to speak of lizards up to 3 feet in length, and chameleons. There are more than 200 kinds of poisonous snakes, including the highly dangerous rattlesnake, which is found in southern Brazil. Among the largest snakes are the non-poisonous boa constrictor (up to 18 feet in length) and the anaconda, which may reach 37 feet. The latter lives mainly in the rivers and feeds on fish and crocodiles. In this connection, the Butantan Snake Institute near São Paulo is world famous; snakes are bred there for the specific purpose of extracting their poison and using it to develop anti-snakebite serums. People who are bitten by snakes do not always die of the bite; often the limb which has been bitten simply withers or becomes paralysed, or again it may swell up as with elephantiasis. Many rural homes keep snakebite remedies constantly available.

Among the many varieties of birds, most of which are fantastically colourful in their plumage, mention may be made of parrots, woodpeckers, toucans, herons and hummingbirds. The forests abound with monkeys and especially howling monkeys. These use their tails as a fifth hand, and at night hold forth in concerts of the most bloodcurdling sounds; one starts and then the rest come in with a roar in chorus. Smaller and less powerful than their cousins in the Old World are the South American jaguar, relative of the Indian tiger, the dangerous puma, and the tapir which is a pachyderm. Finally, there are animals here which remind us of the fauna of Australia, such as toothless armadillos and ant-eaters and sloths. Their presence strongly suggests that, at some time in the remote past, a connection existed between the two continents.

The Regions of Brazil

For political and administrative purposes, Brazil is divided into 22 states, 4 territories and a federal district. This sub-division, however, bears little relation to the country's physical geography, and an attempt has been made to define a series of 'natural zones' which will represent, at least from an economic point of view, a more useful basis for subdividing this immense area. These are the five regions of Brazil (Fig. 11).

1 In the Amazon Basin as many as 250 million turtle eggs used to be collected each year in order to produce 'turtle butter' which is very rich in natural oil, and is an important article of trade. It has been necessary to control production by law, as otherwise the turtles were threatened with extermination.

None of these regions exactly corresponds either to a single state or to a group of states. For statistical purposes, each state is counted as belonging to the region in which the bulk of its territory lies. Among these states, Amazonas is the largest—it has an area of 610,000 square miles—while the smallest is Sergipe, with only 8100 square miles.

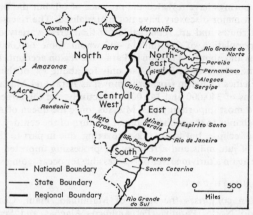

Fig. 11. Brazil: administrative regions.

THE NORTH

The North embraces the states of Amazonas, Acre and Pará, and the territories of Rondônia (formerly called Guaporé), Roraima and Amapá. It lies on both sides of the equator, with the greater part of it south of the line. It can be sub-divided in more detail into three parts: the southern slopes of the Guiana Highland, the basin proper of the Amazon, and the northern slopes of the Brazilian Highland. The whole region has a climate which is warm and humid, and it is sparsely populated throughout with an average density of 1·3 persons per square mile. Economic development within the region is at present limited to the exploitation of wild rubber, various kinds of tropical hardwood, cacao, jute, medicinal plants and palm oil products. On the whole, the economy has not yet passed the exploitive stage. In a few places covered with savanna vegetation—namely, in the territory of Roraima and on Marajó Island (Fig. 10)—it is possible to raise livestock.

In addition, efforts have been made to cultivate the rubber plant *Hevea brasiliensis* as a plantation crop, but it has been necessary first to find a method of overcoming leaf diseases and provide an adequate labour supply. In Amapá, not far from the mouth of the Amazon, there are huge deposits of manganese bedded in gneisses; they have been worked since 1956. Furthermore, near Nova Olinda, close to Manaus, borings have revealed the presence of oil, but the Brazilians' hopes of a major discovery have not materialised. The rivers serve as transport routes and are remarkable for their great variety of fishes. With a population of 2·3 million—of whom some 640,000 live in Amazonas and about 1·4 million in Pará—the region accounts for some 42% of the total area of Brazil, but only for about 3% of the population. The cities of Belém (formerly known as Pará) and Manaus, with populations of 340,000 and 142,000 respectively, are the largest settlements and most important ports. Manaus, once the queen of Amazonian cities thanks to the rubber boom at the turn of the century, suffered a period of eclipse, but today it is recovering, due in part to the establishment of jute mills and a refinery for processing imported oil. It is now once again a thriving river port accessible for ocean-going shipping.

THE NORTH-EAST

This region comprises the states of Maranhão, Piauí, Ceará, Rio Grande do Norte, Paraíba, Pernambuco, Alagôas and Sergipe; it occupies 11·2% of the total area of Brazil, but contains 24% of the population. The density of population, however, declines from east to west across the region, from between 25 and 50 per square mile in the east, to as low as 2, and generally to 10, per square mile in the west.

This region is commonly sub-divided into four parts; the coastlands, the traditional *agreste*, the *sertão*, and the zone of plateaux and crystalline uplands. The coastlands (the *zona da mata* or forest zone) possess a tropical forest climate. Inland from a coast thickly fringed with coconut palms is the area of the sugar-cane plantations which, in the past, enabled this region to play a particularly influential role in inter-state politics and rivalries. Inland again, beyond the edge of the uplands and *agreste*, begins the wide belt of the *sertão*. Here the dry season lasts for eight months of the year—in periods of drought it may last up to 20 or 32 months—and the vegetation is of the *caatinga* or thorn forest type. In this area ranching is possible, but all too often the rains fail altogether, and the stock dies off in the ensuing drought. The period 1951–2 was such an occasion, when the available water supplies were barely sufficient even for the population without their livestock. In recent years the situation has been a little improved by the construction of dams and reservoirs, and cotton growing is making some headway. The prolonged droughts of the area coupled with the structure of rural society, most notably the land tenure system, make it the poorest port of Brazil with much of the population on the borderline of starvation. The area is characterised by outward migration to other parts of the country and by serious and justified social unrest. The plateau lands, on the other hand, are a water surplus area, and here the palm tree is characteristic; Babaçu palms in Maranhão, and Carnaúba palms (a source of wax) in Piauí and Ceará. Recife (930,000)—formerly known as Pernambuco—Fortaleza (420,000) and Campina Grande (160,000) are the largest cities and the economic centres of the region.

THE EAST

This region comprises the states of Bahia, Minas Gerais, Espírito Santo and Rio de Janeiro; it covers 14% of the surface area of Brazil and contains 36% of the population. Among the regions of the nation, it competes for economic supremacy with the South.

Between the coast ranges (the Serra do Mar) and the sea lies a narrow coastal strip which has a warm, humid rain-forest climate and conditions ideally suited to the cultivation of tropical plantation crops. North of the Rio Dôce, particularly in southern Bahia, cacao predominates; south of the river, sugar-cane. Banana, citrus and other fruit plantations are widespread.

Inland from the coastal strip is a second section of the region, in marked contrast to the first. This is the deeply dissected eastern slope of the Brazilian Highlands, and the section includes also the mountain ranges that line this eastern edge of the upland, with peaks rising above 8000 feet in places. This is characteristically the zone of the rain-forest; it was also originally the focus of Brazil's coffee production. As coffee-growing has migrated westwards across the state of São Paulo and into northern Paraná, it has been replaced in the East by pastoral farming—especially the dairy products industry—and by manufacturing.

Inland again, the climate becomes drier, and the forest is semi-deciduous. These are the plateau lands of eastern Brazil—the *chapadas* —cut here and there by the stepped edges of the plateau levels and by mountain ranges rising above the general surface. West and south of the chapadas lie the drier lands of the *campo cerrado*; northwards the vegetation merges into *caatinga*. This is a region of livestock raising. Special mention should also be made of the Serra do Espinhaço, which runs from south to north across Minas Gerais and into the state of Bahia (see Plate 8), and which for part of its length is known as the 'diamond plateau'. It contains Brazil's richest deposits of gem stones and ores, including the famous Itabira iron deposits. In the Reconcavo area in the environs of Salvador, Bahia, there is an expanding production of petroleum.

This eastern region is the source of almost 60% of Brazil's agricultural production, and from the standpoint of communications is better integrated than any other. Rio de Janeiro has some 3,800,000 inhabitants, and, together with São Paulo, is Brazil's principal centre for industry, commerce and the tourist trade. Salvador (formerly known as Bahia) is a city of 665,000 inhabitants, and Belo Horizonte, the capital and commercial centre in Minas Gerais, has some 800,000.

THE SOUTH

This region includes the states of São Paulo, Paraná, Santa Catarina and Rio Grande do Sul. With only 10% of the total area of the country, it contains 33% of the population. In the course of the last hundred years, this region has undergone a particularly rapid development, a fact accounted for, in large part, by the immigration of Europeans into the area. Today it is economically the most important region in Brazil. Rio Grande do Sul is the country's largest producer of wool and, together with Santa Catarina, the most important source of coal (although the quantity and quality of it are limited), while the industries of São Paulo are expanding with such astonishing rapidity that the area has become one of the major industrial regions of Latin America. Even so, it is the production of farm crops—cereals (including rice), cotton, coffee, tobacco, fruit, wines and maté—which dominates most of the south's economy. Alongside this varied output of crops, there are vast stretches of natural grassland which support large numbers of livestock, and extensive belts of *Araucaria* forest, which form the basis for numerous processing industries for the forest products.

This is essentially a region of high plateau. Only in a few areas, notably in the south, is there a coastal plain (with lagoons); for the most part, the coastal mountains rise directly from the sea up to 3000 feet, where they level off into a series of stepped plateaux which dip slightly to the west and form the broad Planaltos. These latter are formed partly on Paleozoic shales and sandstones, and partly on a cover of volcanic materials (diabase). Only the southern section of the region is lower. Here are to be found the so-called *campinas*, a large part of which is natural grassland where the Brazilian gauchos live.

São Paulo, the most bustling of all Brazil's cities, rivals Rio de Janeiro; it has a population of 4,430,000. Its port of Santos (260,000) is also growing, albeit at a slower rate. As the main port-city of the southern region, Pôrto Alegre already has some 700,000 inhabitants.

THE CENTRAL WEST

The last region is the Central West, comprising the states of Goiás and Mato Grosso. Here, the relationship between size and population is much the same as in the North; 22% of the total area of Brazil is occupied by a mere 3% of the population of Brazil. The region can be divided, on a basis of landforms, climate and vegetation, into two distinct zones. The greater part of the area is occupied by high plains, topped here and there by isolated mountain ranges; this is the character of central and northern Goiás and of northern Mato Grosso. They are covered with *cerrados*, or natural grasslands on which there is a stunted tree cover of varying density, and over wide areas they are still virtually uninhabited. The second zone is the *pantanal*, the lowlands of the Paraguay Basin, which are regularly flooded in summer. Here, as in the similar areas along the tributaries of the Paraná and the Amazon, there are dense *galeria* forests along the watercourses. The pasture-lands of the high plains have provided a basis for the modest beginnings of a livestock industry, while in Goiás the cultivation of coffee and wheat is developing and in southern Mato Grosso the exploitation of the quebracho tree for tannin. In Goiás, too, large numbers of prospectors roam the countryside, searching the rivers and stream beds for diamonds. Here is found one of the world's most important deposits of quartz crystals, and also some nickel and mica. Yet vast areas surrounding the upper courses of the Xingú and Tapajós are uninhabited. At the principal falls of the Xingú lies the approximate geographical centre of Brazil. It is in this area that the country's new capital is being built, and when Brasilia is completed according to present plans, the Planalto Central will achieve a fuller significance in the nation's geography. By 1965 Brasilia already had a population of around 200,000 and is in the process of being linked to all other parts of the country by new roads and railways (see Plate 7). Goiania, the capital of Goiás, and Anápolis are the two other cities of any size in the area. Anápolis is a commercial centre serving the agricultural hinterland carved out of the Mato Grosso de Goiás, a fertile forested zone in Goiás state.

To the west of this newly developing area, however, the region remains unintegrated with Brazil. Conditions are shown in the following extracts from an account by the ornithologist and naturalist Helmut Sick who was a member of an expedition which began in 1943 and spent seven years in traversing central Brazil.

Meeting with the Chavante Indians

While we were trekking through the region of the Chavantes, thankful that we were having hardly any contact with this dangerous tribe, the Indian Protection Service of the Brazilian government was carefully planning to make a friendly approach to the Chavantes. After months of trying, the government at last succeeded in getting the Indians to take presents which had been left for them at various advanced outposts. For their part, and according to their notions of barter, the Chavantes left arrows and other weapons in exchange. Later on, direct contact was made with the Indians, who suddenly appeared in considerable numbers, bringing with them more arrows for exchange, and leaving their bows behind in the bushes as a sign of friendly intention. So many Indians appeared, however, that the gifts which the white men had brought were insufficient for them all. The tribesmen promptly took this as a sign of hostility, and the result was that the Brazilians barely escaped with their lives. Since the motto of the Indian Service is 'If necessary, die, but never kill', the government men were anxious to avoid a fight. This meant that the only course left to them was to turn tail and flee, and even in this they were only successful because they happened to be mounted. The infuriated Chavantes followed them for miles, moving with incredible speed through the dry brush and forest of the *cerrado*, and it was only by a fortunate chance that the Indians' arrows failed to inflict serious injury on them; two pack animals were the only casualties. Such an incident must inevitably confirm these savages in their belief that the white men are weak and cowardly, as well as being in the minority—for there are as yet only small groups of white people in the area. However, the Indian Protection Service refused to give up and arranged further contacts, which ultimately led to the establishment of peaceful relations with at least a number of the Chavantes. The members of this tribe are well built physically, slim and strong, but to our eyes repulsive in both appearance and conduct; the epitome of all wild creatures, fear-driven and unpredictable. They wear absolutely no clothes and very few ornaments.[1]

The expedition then pressed on towards the head-waters of the Xingú.

The trails, which run across the *campo cerrado* from the Rio Araguaia, came to an end at the Guapurú. From now on, one adopted the mode of travel which is in general use everywhere in the Amazon Basin, and used

1 Sick, Helmut, *Tucani*, Hamburg and Berlin, 1957.

the rivers as waterways. Even here, on the southernmost margins of the rain forest, the luxuriant vegetation made overland travel difficult, although the forest growth was by no means as tall as farther north, and only lay in belts along the watercourses with open *campo* (grasslands) in between. Moreover, the rivers ran north-westwards, which was the direction toward which the expedition was heading. Boats were built and launched. What were we to call these rivers? Some of them we named ourselves, but later on, when we found out what the Indians called them, we adopted their names in certain cases instead of our own.

The streams wound their way between banks lined with dark forest. Hunting and fishing had never before been so productive. Then, one day, the forests opened out, the shorelines receded, and we found ourselves afloat on a broad river. This must surely be the Rio Culuene, the largest of the eastern affluents of the Xingú. We struck out across the current, and presently found on the left bank an open space which could serve as our next base. It was December 1946.

That strange world of the Xingú had captivated us. In the years since Steinen's visit in the 1880's, little had changed in central Brazil. Here the Indians lived, close to nature, just as they had for countless centuries, unaffected by the march of progress, which could not penetrate this vast remoteness. The first of the indigenous Xingú tribes we met were the Calapalo, one of whose villages was close to our camp. The tribal leaders had sent out scouts in our direction, and we realised that they were anxious to make contact with the expedition. To begin with, admittedly, they were distrustful and uncommunicative, but gradually, with the aid of a cautious, friendly approach and the liberal use of presents, they became more amenable.

The Calapalo are a branch of the Caribs, and they themselves were only too eager to emphasise their kinship. Of course, when we first met them, we understood only a little of their language, and actually they picked up Portuguese more quickly than we learned Indian! These Indian languages, which possess many variants, are of the utmost importance as guides to the ethnological grouping of these indigenous tribes. Around the headwaters of the Xingú there are a dozen such tribes. Several of these evidently belong to the Caraíbas—interestingly enough, the Indians called us white 'Caribs'! These linguistic groups, representatives of which either can, or formerly could, be found in other parts of Brazil, are sub-divided in turn into separate families. The result is to be seen in a marked diversity of cultures, which in turn gives an insight into the changeful, precarious quality of life among these savages. The Calapalo had friendly contact with some ten neighbouring tribal groups, all of them sedentary cultivators like themselves. Apart from these, they also talked of others who were their enemies, in particular of a Caraíba group called the Arumá—presumably the same group which we had imagined to live on the Garapú—

and a Gê tribe called the Suiá. Finally, we heard again of the Chicão, a dangerous, isolated tribe in the western Xingú Basin which is largely unknown to the ethnographer.

The Calapalo numbered about 180. They were of medium height and thickset. So closely did the two sexes resemble each other in physique that from the back view one could often confuse men with women unless their hair was visible. The men cut their hair to form a fringe and a small tonsure of the crown, using for the purpose the teeth of a voracious fish called the *piranha*. The women, on the other hand, trim their hair only across the forehead; for the rest, they let it grow and fall free over their shoulders. Body and facial hair is not very prominent, and they pull it out, even to the eyebrows and eyelashes, with their fingers, which they first rub in ashes. For this operation, the tweezers I carried proved highly popular. The Indians' hair is jet black and thick; in old age it neither turns white nor falls out. . . .

These natives possess no clothes at all. Their skin is a rather light or golden brown, but they treat it with vegetable juices, such as the red-coloured Urucú and the yellow Pequi oil, and it darkens to a sort of tobacco brown under the sun's rays. Only in the very young and in those confined for the ritual of puberty can one recognise the natural tone of skin colour. It is because of their dark skins that one is scarcely conscious of the nakedness of these Indians. . . .[1]

Brazil: Political and Economic Development

HISTORICAL

The single area of South America which Portugal was able to secure for herself aroused little interest in the Europe of that day, because in it—by contrast with the areas of Spanish conquest on the west coast —there seemed to be no resources offering quick returns and immediate riches nor large numbers of Indians to put to work on plantations. It was, first of all, the development of extensive sugar-cane plantations along the coast of North-East Brazil in the sixteenth and seventeenth centuries, and secondly, the discovery of gold in the 1690's and of diamonds a few years later, which first attracted white men in any considerable numbers, and the early arrivals were mostly adventurers rather than settlers. Gradually the immigrants' sphere of operations was extended inland, but a concerted opening-up of the interior never took place. A contributing factor to this lack of overall development was the petty interference of the Lisbon Government in Brazilian affairs, which was evident, for example, in the prohibition of oil, wine

1   Sick, H., op. cit.

or salt production—for fear of competition with home products—and in the rule that Brazilian produce might only be exported in Portuguese ships.

Immigration really began in earnest only after the winter of 1807–8, when the Portuguese Prince Regent (who had fled to Brazil to escape the occupation by Napoleon's forces) opened the Brazilian ports to all comers and declared the country, in 1815, to be an independent kingdom. From this time on, economic development gradually became more widespread. Equality of status between Brazil and Portugal was established in practice after the return of the King to Lisbon in 1821, and Brazil's independence was confirmed by an act of the King's son, Dom Pedro I, with only token resistance from the Portuguese side. Pedro I gave the country a liberal constitution and had himself proclaimed Emperor. It was also he who, in accordance with a common European practice, recruited the first German settlers for Brazil, in order to strengthen his hold on his southern frontiers. Already, on this southern flank, Brazil had lost the area which today is Uruguay. European immigration increased steadily after the 1850's (when the population of Brazil was about 6 million), and although the country was shaken by recurrent political and social disturbances, economic expansion continued. Several hundred thousand Negro slaves were brought in to provide labour as they had been formerly brought to work on the colonial sugar plantations in North-East Brazil, and soon afterwards coffee-growing proved a great source of wealth.

In 1888, while Pedro II was in Europe, his daughter abolished slavery. This led to further unrest, since the economic structure of society had been undermined, and the ruling house had lost the support of the old planter aristocracy. A revolt of the army in 1889 forced the Emperor to abdicate. Under pressure from liberal and republican opinion, a 'United States of Brazil' was established, whose constitution (1891) was modelled largely on that of the U.S.A.

But not even the new constitution could assure Brazil's internal peace. The states had achieved a large degree of independence under the federal system, and this led to constant clashes, particularly since the centre of the country's economic life was moving from Minas Gerais towards the state of São Paulo. Since, at the same time, Brazil's exports were suffering from the competition of new rubber—and coffee—producers overseas, political crises were recurrent.

In 1930, after a military *coup d'état*, Getulio Vargas seized power. In foreign affairs, his chief concern was to strengthen the Pan-American idea as it was expressed in the resolutions of the Montevideo

Conference of 1933, and to promote the interests of the continent as a whole. In keeping with this policy, Brazil declared war on Germany in 1942, and provided troops which fought in Italy. The government also made efforts, with the aid of American technicians, to increase the output of rubber from the Amazon Basin. As is now well known, however, the '*Fordlândia*' and '*Belterra*' rubber plantation schemes on the lower Tapajós foundered through uncontrollable plant diseases and the lack of suitable labour supply.

The end of the Second World War meant also the end of Vargas' dictatorship, but under the new constitution of September 1946 he was elected to the presidency. It was not until the summer of 1954 that suicide brought to an end his remarkable 24-year period of rule.

THE POPULATION: COMPOSITION AND GROWTH

In the 100 years since 1850, the population of Brazil has increased by about 60 millions. More than nine-tenths of this amount is apparently due to natural increase, the remainder to immigration, mainly from Europe. The first effect of this immigration has been to increase the white proportion of the population. On the other hand, the proportion of immigrants in the total population has more recently been restricted by the imposition of quotas governing so-called 'spontaneous' immigration.

The distribution of Brazil's population remains today, as it has always been, very uneven. The bulk of the population is concentrated in a comparatively narrow coastal strip, and it is there that the major cities are found. The proportion of Negroes or part-Negroes in the population is highest in the coastal areas, while inland the Indians tend to predominate.

Since racial conflict and religious intolerance are both rare in Brazil, the exact racial composition of the population is extremely difficult to assess. It seems certain, however, that the whites predominate. The pure-blooded Indians number a few hundred thousands. These indigenous people are found mostly in the innermost recesses of the interior, where they either live in complete isolation and self-sufficiency, or, at most, have recently begun to collect forest produce for barter with traders from the world outside. One of the best known of the Indian tribes are the *Botocudos*, who live in government reservations, but, in spite of government help, are dwindling in numbers. They take their name from the round wooden plug (botoque, or bung) which they formerly wore, by way of ornament, in their lower lip. The *Caribas*, north of the Amazon, are a semi-sedentary tribe which has to some extent been integrated into the economic life of the world outside, by finding employment as labourers and artisans. They were formerly known as a brave, warlike people, who probably originated in central Brazil, and migrated northwards from there, driving less powerful tribes before them. Before the coming of the Spaniards, they dominated much of northern South America.

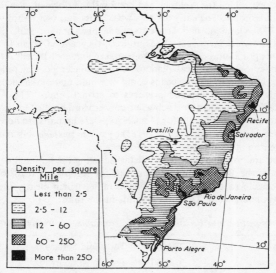

Fig. 12. Brazil: distribution of population and latitudinal extent.

One of the crucial points in the history of Brazil occurred when slavery was abolished. It must be stressed, however, that the crisis was not nearly as serious as that caused by the emancipation of the slaves in the U.S.A. In Brazil, the Negro slaves were often treated as members of the household, and remained voluntarily with their former masters after being freed. The emancipation of some 1,300,000 Negro slaves involved the plantation owners in a loss, on paper, of great sums of money, but the owners' fears that the plantations would also suffer from a sudden crippling shortage of labour proved to be unfounded; in practice, the Negroes had to earn a living and therefore eventually returned to work. As it proved, the planters were then free from the necessity of maintaining their slaves and needed only to pay them for their main seasonal tasks, with the result that the majority of the Negroes obtained little material benefit from their freedom; in sickness and old age, they had to fend for themselves to a much greater extent than during the days of slavery. The output of many plantations actually increased after emancipation, rather than declined.

For the immigrants arriving from central Europe the work on the plantations, which the Negroes had previously performed, was deemed quite undesirable. The early arrivals were Swiss and German; by 1850, some 7000 Germans had arrived seeking new homes, and, like the Swiss (who were farmers by background), they settled down to create effective agricultural colonies in the southern states of Brazil. As far as the labour on the tropical plantations was concerned generally only Asiatics and southern Europeans could or would undertake such work, and this in spite of assisted passages to attract others. The Asiatics and Mediterranean peoples, being less concerned than the Germans and Swiss to create new homes for themselves, were prepared to accept the low rates of pay offered. Then in 1911 the assisted passage was abolished and the rate of immigration at once slackened.

There are no comprehensive statistics covering the national or racial origins of the Brazilian population, but for the period 1820 to 1916, it is possible to compile the following table, which clearly indicates the preponderance of Latin immigrants in the total:

Immigration into Brazil, 1820-1916 (excluding re-immigrants)

Italians	1,370,000	Turks and Syrians	53,000
Portuguese	990,000	French	28,000
Spaniards	480,000	English	22,000
Germans	123,000	Japanese	16,000
Poles and Russians	104,000	Swiss	11,000
Austro-Hungarians	79,000	TOTAL	3·5 millions

In 1930 the Brazilian government instituted a system of quotas in order to restrict the flow of immigrants. The annual quota was calculated for each nation as 2% of the total number of immigrants from that nation who had entered the country between 1883 and 1924. The primary object of this scheme was to limit the numbers of Asiatics entering Brazil. In the event, it had the effect of curbing European immigration too. In the decade 1931–41, Brazil received only 228,000 immigrants, as compared with 840,000 in the previous decade.

Today, as in the past, the principal classes of immigrants sought by Brazil are skilled workmen and farmers, while specialists and technicians can be exempted from the quota restrictions. Among immigrants settling on the land, newcomers from northern and central Europe are rare by contrast with the numbers arriving from southern Europe and other areas, since the northerners not only are less willing to adapt to the tropical conditions, but also are accustomed to higher standards of living than this pioneer farming affords.

The latest available statistics which indicate the distribution of the population by occupation show that, at that date, 2 to 3 million persons were employed in industry, and 9 to 10 million in agriculture. Another official survey in 1948 put the proportions of male workers over ten years old in various occupations at:

Industry	7·6%
Transport	3·2%
Commerce	5·1%
Administration, Education, Law and Military	3·8%

Approximately 95% of the population are Roman Catholics. Church and State have, since 1946, been officially separated. Education is compulsory, but in spite of this only 49·3% of the population over 15 was classified as literate in 1950. To remedy this situation, both the Church and State have unquestionably striven very hard in recent years, and by 1957 there were more than 78,000 schools with a total attendance of over 6·3 million. The curriculum is broad, but the general tone is definitely nationalistic; the government hopes thereby to make. even of those who only remain in the country for a short period, genuine Brazilians. In legal terms, everyone born in Brazil, of whatever parents, is a Brazilian citizen. In practice, however, several generations often elapse before the descendants of the newcomers are really assimilated into the life of the nation. It is probably in view of this fact that a recent regulation has decreed that, in the new pioneer farming areas, at least 30% of the families in each settlement must be Brazilian.

In 1962, there were some 264 daily newspapers published, with a combined circulation of 4,000,900. One is tempted to wonder how many Brazilians never see a newspaper; to wonder, too, what cultural impact is made by the 3232 cinemas (1962 figures) and an active national cinema industry. At all events, in the cities, literary and cultural pursuits are strongly developed among a small proportion of the residents.

As a sample of immigrant experience in Brazil, we may take the case of the Germans. The first immigrants from Germany landed in Pôrto Alegre in 1824, and from the 1850's onwards, the entry of Germans was positively encouraged by the Brazilian government. Almost all of the newcomers settled in the south, where conditions were healthy and more closely resembled climatic conditions in Germany and where the Germans were able to engage in continuous physical labour. In these congenial surroundings, they rapidly increased in numbers, so that Brazil has proved to be the one overseas area where any large number of Germans have retained their language and ways without much modification. This, in turn, was made possible by the fact that the immigrants usually settled in almost purely German communities, where they intermarried and where they considered themselves in some degree distinct from the native-born population.

Before the Second World War the number of persons belonging to such German groups was about half a million. Most of these were in Rio Grande do Sul, Santa Catarina and Paraná (see Fig. 13). The best-known of these German settlements is Blumenau, which was founded in 1850. It developed into a sort of cultural capital of German life throughout the whole region, with its German schools, newspapers, medical services and social centres. Neu-Württemberg occupies a similar position in the interior, in the state of Rio Grande do Sul. The German colonists have, with the passage of time and the expenditure of an immense amount of labour, won from the forest the areas assigned to them. They have laid out plantations, constructed roads and raised their own status until they have become the prosperous owners of fertile lands and great herds and flocks. The raising of hogs has achieved special importance in these areas.

Quite apart from their work as agricultural colonists has been the contribution made by the Germans as well as by other immigrants to scholarship, to commerce and to technology in Brazil. The loyalty of these immigrants to their new homeland has been established over the years. However, the rise of a Brazilian nationalism and the events of the Second World War led to a certain degree of intolerance of the German elements, and to a somewhat changed attitude in official circles. One result was that the teaching of Portuguese in all schools became mandatory.

For several decades the oldest German settlements had neither teachers nor pastors, yet they retained their links with the stream of German culture. Here and there a priest or an old man past the age for active work would begin to teach the children, besides reading and writing, the elements of German culture. A few more decades passed, and there were hundreds of German schools, and even training colleges for German-Brazilian teachers. By the turn of the century, there was a regular flow of immigrant priests and teachers arriving from Germany.

The First World War dealt a serious blow to this development, and the years since then have seen its reversal. There can be little doubt

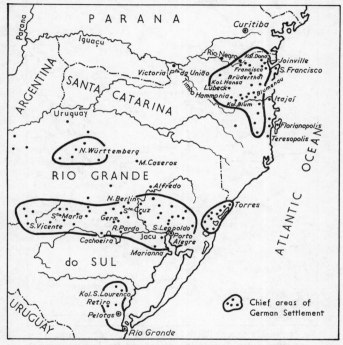

Fig. 13. Southern Brazil: principal regions of German settlement.

that now, with the passage of time, the Germans who have grown up in Brazil are becoming less German and more definitely Brazilian year by year.

THE CITIES OF BRAZIL

The most important cities are to be found near the coast. Rio de Janeiro, capital until April 1960, must rank as one of the most beautiful

cities in the world (see Plate 3). It lies on the narrow strip of coastal plain
tucked among the 'sugar loaf' hills, along a deeply indented shoreline. On
one side lie the mountain slopes with their covering of tropical forest; on
the other lies the sea. The earliest stimulus to the growth of the city

Fig. 14. Brazil: the site of Rio de Janeiro. The major north-south and east-
west arteries, the Avenida Rio Branco and the Avenida Presidente
Vargas, are indicated by dotted lines.

came with the opening up of a road in the early eighteenth century
connecting the gold and diamond mines of Minas Gerais with Rio de
Janeiro, and later, in 1808, with the arrival of the King of Portugal
who, as we have seen, was obliged to flee from Napoleon. By the middle
of the last century it had become the leading commercial city of South
America. This role it has long since lost, even though it possesses a fine

harbour on the sheltered Bay of Guanabara, which is equipped with more than two miles of quays and is accessible to the largest ships afloat. But because Rio has relatively poor connections with its hinterland, São Paulo, with its far better position, has been able to outstrip the capital in the industrial phase of Brazilian development.

Of Rio de Janeiro, Stefan Zweig has written:

> Rio is a unique hymn to the beauty of the earth: a broad, dazzling bay surrounded by sheer-sided cones of rock and curiously shaped mountain spurs pierced by deep lowland passages. The perfect curves and arcs of bays and shorelines create a landscape of quite exceptional splendour. In the midst of an ellipse formed of little hills and plains lies the world-famous city. Along the shore and over the slopes spreads the sea of houses that make this a city of more than two million souls; spreads away into the dark green fringe of the forest that flanks the bare domes and surfaces of rock. And amid the swelling waves of the dark mountain forest shine perfumed flowers and fruits the year around. Here at Rio de Janeiro mountain, sea and city unite in a perfect symphony of landscape.
>
> Kaleidoscopic indeed are the colours that greet the eye of the traveller, as his ship rounds Cap Faio and enters the wide, rocky opening of the Bay of Guanabara: before him the deep blue of the sea and the blinding white of the surf at its edge; farther back the yellow and white of the buildings, broken here and there by the dark green of trees or the blue-grey of bare rock. But unless you have looked down on Rio from the heights of Corcovado, you cannot fully appreciate the unique situation of this city. *A Cidade da Luz*, the 'City of Light', the Brazilians call Rio, and this not only on account of the nocturnal spectacle of its myriad glittering lights, reflected in the waters of the bay like strands of pearls. Everything here combines to form a wonderful harmony: the peerless setting in a tropical landscape, and the busy life of a population so privileged as to live in a city like this.
>
> Colour, light and movement are everywhere. Nothing is repeated a second time; everything clashes and yet everything marvellously harmonises in a great whole. To stroll round the city on foot—which in other great cities is often pointless and sometimes almost impossible—is here a constant pleasure; indeed, each stroll is like a fresh voyage of discovery. Go where you may in the city, every scene is like a benediction. . . . The man who comes from Rio will find every other city colourless and wan; its people dull, and its life over-regimented and uniform. The longer a man knows this city, the more he delights in it, and yet the longer he knows it, the less can he describe it.

Hauger and Wilhelmy add:

> The old Rio, with its winding alleys, its ramshackle houses, moored precariously on the slopes, is disappearing bit by bit [but see Plates 5 and 6].

Whole hills are removed and levelled, and there is no obstacle that cannot be shifted—nothing that is allowed to stand in the way, where the embellishment of the city is involved. Memorable among the sights of this tropical metropolis is the Avenida Rio Branco, truly the main artery of the organism which is Rio de Janeiro. Here the luxury trades line the street with their shops and offices; here, as on the boulevards of Paris or Vienna, the passer-by pauses to drink his coffee or his fruit juice at the round tables of the sidewalk cafés.

To the west of the city centre lie the best residential districts, where the homes are veritable palaces lying amid superb parks and gardens. Follow the Avenida Flamengo and you come to Larangeiras, the diplomatic quarter with its embassies and its clubs. Here there stands, at the end of a palm-lined avenue, the palace of the president of Brazil. In the surrounding district are to be found, besides the homes of the diplomatic community, those of Brazil's upper Ten Thousand—officials, merchants, doctors and lawyers—who live, many of them, in luxurious modern apartment houses. The façades of these buildings, unornamented yet perfectly proportioned, form a visible tribute to the excellence of contemporary Brazilian architecture. Here and there a skyscraper towers above them. If the gorgeously decorated baroque churches of Bahia are an expression in stone of tropical fantasies in the minds of a past generation, the skyscrapers of Rio form a worthy modern counterpart. They sprout upwards like the forest lianas and stand grotesque like the forest trees. They are a symbol, a recreation of the forest, set down in the city as an expression and a reminder of the forest which lies beyond the city. Modern Rio de Janeiro is far from being a desert of stone; rather, it is a forest of stone, more intimately linked with the realm of nature than almost any other city in the world.

São Paulo, which in 1963 had almost 4½ million inhabitants, is slightly larger than Rio. The city of São Paulo lies some 2500 feet above sea-level, and is the focus of a highly important economic region. It was from there that the original exploration of the mineral-rich hinterland was carried out in colonial times, to be followed later by the boom in coffee planting in the late 19th and early 20th centuries.

São Paulo is the most modern city in Brazil—apart from the still incomplete Brasilia—and its centre is crowded with hundreds of skyscrapers. Virtually every known industry is represented within the metropolitan area, and some of the city's factories are very large.

São Paulo is linked by rail and by super-highway with Santos, the chief outlet for Brazil's export trade. Santos deals with roughly a half of Brazil's exports by value, and with between one-third and two-fifths of the import trade. Before the Second World War, Santos handled 7–8 million sacks of coffee a year, almost 2 million boxes of oranges, and 11 million bushels of bananas (a crop whose cultivation has spread far and wide through the coastal plains since 1920), in addition to significant amounts of cotton and vegetable oil products. The Santos firm of Wille & Co. is the largest coffee exporter in the world.

The port has warehouse space for 8 million sacks of coffee, and there is a dockside area of more than 140,000 square yards, considerably larger than that of Rio de Janeiro. Nevertheless, it proved necessary, before the more recent difficult years of the coffee trade began, to ease the strain on Santos' port accommodation by constructing additional facilities at São Sebastião. The harbour of Santos, which lies in the lee of the island, is linked with the open sea some 6 miles away by a channel half a mile wide and 27 feet deep.

Owing to its commercial activities, the growth of Santos has been rapid ever since the middle of the nineteenth century. In 1815, its population was 5600, of whom almost two-thirds were Negroes or mulattos. By 1850, this figure had risen only to 7000. Thereafter, however, expansion was swift as coffee cultivation spread through São Paulo. By 1920, the population was 100,000; in 1934 it was more than 130,000, and in 1960 it was estimated to be about 260,000.

Fifty years ago the city, though growing, was still confined in extent to the area at the foot of Monte Serrat. In the centre of the old city lay areas of brackish swamp. Since then Santos has spread to cover the whole eastern end of the island, encircling the rocky dome of Monte Serrat and stretching out to the open sea. The old city has been restored, and drainage and reclamation have been carried out. Nevertheless, as a city Santos has little to commend it; it is dull and monotonous, for as one writer has justly remarked, 'In Santos, business is everything, and the city is nothing.'

Further south, both Pôrto Alegre in Rio Grande do Sul and Blumenau in Santa Catarina possess unmistakably European characteristics.

Pôrto Alegre, the 'joyful haven', is the most important city of the Brazilian south, with a population of 600,000. That it should make such a strongly European impression upon the observer seems at first paradoxical; the farther south one goes—that is, the farther from Europe—the more European in appearance become both landscape and inhabitants. Yet the explanation is very simple, for as we travel southwards we are passing from the tropical zone of Brazil into the sub-tropical and then into the mid-latitude zone, and thus the climate is becoming more familiar to Europeans in its features. And so it came about that Pôrto Alegre developed as a European city. Through this city runs a strong flavour of Americanism too—tall buildings and a great press of traffic—but this cannot efface the impression of European cleanliness, planning and careful administration; gardens full of flowers; suburban villas and places of entertainment; solid-looking shops. In addition, before the Second World War there were signs and labels in German to be seen everywhere, so that the newcomer was more conscious of the use of that language in the city's life than of Portuguese. Since the outbreak of the Second World War however, things have changed. The Brazilian government has insisted that Portuguese be regarded as the first language of the area, and especially of the schools. This means that Portuguese is to be the first language only, and not necessarily the exclusive means of communication, for the Brazilian government has never been over-anxious to interfere in the private lives of its citizens. They can speak and write what language they please, in their homes and clubs and newspapers.

Pôrto Alegre has a wide hinterland given over to arable farming and livestock, and is, in addition, the capital of the state of Rio Grande do Sul. In the neighbouring state of Santa Catarina, the impression of European characteristics is at least as strong as in Rio Grande do Sul; perhaps in some areas even more pronounced. You have the impression of being suddenly whisked away and dropped down in Central Europe, and you are apt to feel that your eyes are deceiving you. Here is a delightful wooded landscape of streams and hills and valleys, in the midst of which you suddenly come across a village that is Austrian, or Swiss, or German with its wide-gabled roofs, its red tiles and its short chimneys smoking merrily. And the rivers, the hills and the forests are European, not Brazilian; perhaps they will remind you of Thuringia, or perhaps of the Vienna Woods! On the streets you commonly hear nothing but German spoken; often, curiously enough, by someone you can identify at a glance as a Latin, and even more curiously, by an unmistakable mulatto. Many of these villages have long since grown to be towns—European towns —where Portuguese is the language of officialdom and of the schools, but not the language of everyday life. There is Blumenau, with its 100,000 inhabitants, and Joinville with 50,000; both of these are flourishing commercial centres, with a special interest in farm produce.[1]

Further inland and 250 miles to the north of Rio de Janeiro is Belo Horizonte with approximately 800,000 inhabitants in 1965, which superseded the old colonial gold-mining settlement of Ouro Prêto as capital of Minas Gerais in 1897, and which has developed as a fine modern city in that part of the Brazilian Highlands.

The city of São Salvador (which is often referred to simply as Salvador, and was formerly known as Bahia), with a population of 700,000, possesses an entirely different character. Through its port streamed, in the first half of the eighteenth century, untold thousands of slaves to

1   Pahlen, K., *Südamerika, eine neue Welt*, Zürich, 1949.

work on the sugar plantations. Today, sugar production is still important together with that of cacao and tobacco.

What gives this city . . . its particularly attractive appearance is its situation on the steep slopes of the coastal hills. As the traveller approaches by sea, therefore, he sees the wealth of Salvador's architectural splendours spread out before him as if it were a pattern on a carpet of stone.

Standing in the lower town, between the docks and the warehouses, you quickly smell, even if you do not see, what Salvador exports: sacks of sugar, lighters full of cocoa beans, sheds piled with bales of tobacco. . . . Like Recife, which has shared so much of Salvador's history, the city has seen the arrival of many an African slave. Bahia, to give it the older name, is the former capital of Brazil; as a capital it was displaced by Rio de Janeiro in 1763, but has remained, to some extent, the city of men of learning. It has remained, too, a religious centre; it is a city of churches and religious houses, and it is still living on the memories of its great days of splendour, in the eighteenth century.

Up or down the hilly streets, you can hardly walk a hundred yards without coming across a church or monastery in early or later Baroque style; hardly find a square which is not enriched by the façades of churches on at least three sides.[1]

The most important city and the largest port of the north-east is Recife (formerly called Pernambuco), with 930,000 inhabitants. Here, as at Salvador, it was sugar cultivation which, in its heyday, was responsible for the growth and the wealth of the city. As with Salvador, however, sugar is now only of secondary importance; it has been displaced by cotton. The plantations of the hinterland have given rise to a considerable factory and mill development in Recife. The city is the commercial centre for the whole north-east of Brazil.

In Recife one finds fully developed the life of a port-city of the tropics; a life, as Otto Maull has remarked, 'with a strong cosmopolitan flavour; busy, noisy, brawling, the gay reaction to long sea voyages; but full, too, of ugliness that can hardly be overlooked'. Wilhelmy adds: 'In the harbour of Recife are to be seen the flags of all nations; on the streets and in the shops are to be heard the speech of many peoples. Portuguese, Brazilians, Negroes and people with mixed blood of every shade live and work in this city in harmony. This mixture of races gives Recife, in spite of its modern façade, the air and character of an old colonial city in the tropics, frankly lacking the cultural tone of the great cities of central and southern Brazil.'

The last city of importance in the region is Natal, significant for its airport and its position on the transatlantic route. Since, as we have

1 Hauger, O., *Kreuz des Südens*, Brunswick, 1950.

now seen, almost all the large cities of Brazil occupy coastal or peripheral locations, we can readily appreciate the desire of many Brazilians for a capital nearer the heart of their country, in that great interior which is now being opened up. The city of Brasilia (see Plate 7) represents the realisation of this ambition.

In common with the rest of Latin America, the cities of Brazil have been growing rapidly under the process of urbanisation. People move from the rural areas to the cities in search of better economic opportunities and to secure access to educational and other social facilities. This movement of population has led to the development of extensive slum areas in each city (such as the favelas of Rio where dwellings cling to all but the steepest slopes of the city's hillsides—see Plates 5 and 6) and to excessive pressure on urban services (such as electricity and water supply and local transport facilities). These developments tend to overshadow the visual splendours of the Brazilian cities described in the earlier quotations from writers of rather earlier periods.

ECONOMIC DEVELOPMENT

Brazil's resources of both land and minerals are enormous. If development was slow at first, this was due less to a lack of resources than to a lack of population anxious and able to take advantage of the possibilities. In comparison with, for example, the U.S.A., Brazil is a nation in a very early industrial stage, whose economic development—especially that of the empty interior—is only beginning. For what are 80 million people, striving to open up a land that could support perhaps five times that number! The three great needs of Brazil today are more people educated and trained in modern agricultural and industrial technology, long-term capital investment and a narrowing of the tremendous gulf that divides the rich from the poor throughout the nation particularly by means of a fundamental land reform.

Agriculture. Agriculture employs 61% of the labour force of the country, even though the present arable area (50 million acres) represents only 2% of the total surface of Brazil, and 5% of the cultivable area. Agricultural products represent over 80% of the total value of Brazil's exports. In addition, of course, a large number of cultivators are subsistence farmers whose produce does not appear on foreign or even local domestic markets.

Today, as in the past, the centres of agricultural production lie near the coast. The following table shows the acreage and average yield per acre of the leading crops in 1958:

Crop	Area cultivated ('000 acres)	Average yield in pounds per acre
Maize	14,256	1141
Coffee	9455	403
Cotton	6501	413
Rice	6278	1397
Beans	5115	638
Wheat	3188	796
Sugar-cane	2860	36,995
Manioc	2766	11,492
Cocoa	1017	389
Tobacco	442	704
Potatoes	669	6235

A number of other crops are grown for export, among them sisal, jute, herva maté, oranges, bananas and tobacco. The main area of tobacco production is in the state of Bahia. The warm coastal zone (*tierra caliente*) produces the leaf used for wrapping cigars; higher up (in the *tierra templada*), cigarette tobacco is grown.

For a time, up until about 1901, Brazil was the world's leading producer of coffee, rubber and cacao. Since that time conditions have markedly altered. At present the main centre of coffee production is in the states of São Paulo, Paraná, Espírito Santo and Minas Gerais. In these states plantations with more than 100,000 trees are commonly found. In 1959 Brazil accounted for 43% of the world's coffee output, and remained the leading producer of this crop. Its share was formerly, however, more than two-thirds of the world trade. For a time, indeed, Brazil's whole fate seemed linked with the coffee crop; the area under cultivation expanded to such a degree that output ran far ahead of demand, and the price fell to catastrophic levels. Repeatedly, the government had to intervene by supporting the price of coffee and by buying up the unsaleable surpluses. In 1934, for example, each planter was required to place 40% of his crop at the disposal of the government, and hold back a further 30% in storage; only the remaining 30% could be offered for sale. The government then compensated the planters by offering them 20% of their production costs. Today, there has been —not for the first time—a change in the tastes of coffee consumers, as a result of which demand for the so-called 'washed' coffees of Colombia and Central America, as well as the lower grade coffees of East Africa, has increased, and Brazilian production has declined relative to the world total to take account of this fact.

As a cocoa producer, Brazil ranks behind Ghana, but with 16% of the world output its role is by no means negligible. Its sugar production represents 9% of the world total, which gives it third place, after Cuba and Indonesia. Rice is another crop of which Brazil produces more than it requires, but the output of rubber, formerly a leading export, no longer even meets Brazil's own needs. Most of the output of the remaining food crops—maize, beans, manioc—is consumed inside the country.

Brazil's production of vegetable oils and cotton has been steadily increasing. In the last 30 years, it has achieved the position of the world's fourth largest cotton producer, yet by 1950 the mills of the nation's rising textile industry were already consuming two-thirds of the output. Since the Second World War, Brazil has developed a growing export business in cotton textiles, placing its goods, for example, in the South African market.

The federal government made some effort to promote agricultural development, by establishing experimental farms, by forming co-operatives, and by founding farm colonies. Since 1951 there have been facilities for obtaining credit for the purchase of farm machinery, and plants have been built to manufacture this machinery, as well as chemical fertilisers, within Brazil itself. The basic problem of land ownership has not, however, been effectively tackled.

On the wide grasslands of the interior, ranching forms an occupation distinct from the agriculture of the coastlands. Natural conditions are generally not as favourable as in the better-known grasslands of Argentina and Uruguay, but, nevertheless, Brazil's livestock population (which in 1962 numbered 76 million cattle and 50 million pigs) is one of the largest in the world. Both frozen and tinned meat are exported, together with hides and skins.

The output of all the food products industries, in fact, now amounts to a very considerable total. Brazil's sugar refineries meet the nation's requirements, with a 10% to 20% surplus for export. The output of dairy products is increasing, while plants for extracting vegetable oils are very numerous, especially in the state of São Paulo, and Brazil ranks among the world's leading producers of cotton-seed.

Forestry. Brazil possesses immense forest resources. These forests cover some 1·6 million square miles. Little, however, has been done to exploit these scientifically; only in small areas here and there in the South and in Minas Gerais can it be said that any systematic forestry is being practised. The magnitude of the deforestation which has occurred over the past 400 years, however, has resulted in a severe deterioration of the soil resource base, and in some areas the end result is apparent in the form of exposed bedrock.

Minerals and Industry. The output of the mining industry of Brazil, once concentrated upon the production of precious metals, has changed somewhat in character. The list of its modern achievements is, however, impressive: traditionally Brazil has been a primary supplier of quartz crystals and industrial diamonds; its chrome ores are the second most important source of that metal in the western world, and it posesses iron ore deposits which, once the problem of transport has been over-come, can be worked by opencast methods over stretches many miles long. The leading producer state of these ores is Minas Gerais; they are hematite ores with an average iron content of 66% and very low sulphur and phosphorus content. Then in 1956 manganese ores were discovered in the territory of Amapá, only 120 miles from the Amazon, with which the orefields are linked by a newly built railway.

Brazil produced about 2,800,000 tons of coal in 1963, as against 21,000 tons in 1930. Unfortunately, this coal is of little use for coking purposes; it has to be mixed with higher grade imported coal. Neverthe-less, a national steel industry has been built up, and the big mills at Volta Redonda and Itabira produced some 2·2 million tons of crude steel in 1960. In much the same way, the expansion of oil production in Bahia has reduced Brazil's dependence on imports, but domestic pro-duction still provides only one-third of total demand.

The cement industry, which has also increased its output very markedly—from 770,000 tons in 1945 to 5,200,000 tons in 1963—is still not large enough to satisfy the rapidly growing domestic demand arising from the fever of construction that now rages in the cities, notably in São Paulo. Of the nation's other industries, the oldest and largest group—textiles—accounted, in 1957, for 3,200 establishments (although some 40% of these employed less than twelve workers). More than half of all the plants engaged in cotton textile manufacturers are located in the state of São Paulo.

Since 1949 the Brazilian government has embarked on successive plans for massive industrialisation on a much wider front. These plans called for large investments of domestic capital in schemes for im-proving transport, power supplies and the living conditions of the population. First priority was assigned to the improvement of the rail-way and road network—or, in the interior, to its initial establishment. The second objective was the construction of adequate electricity

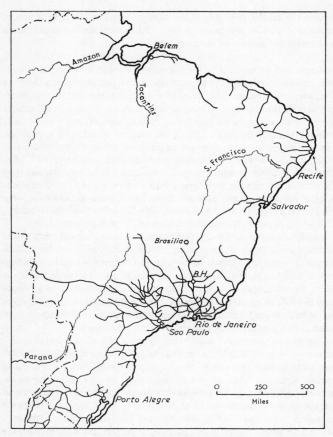

Fig. 15. Brazil: the railway network. Over 90% of the track mileage is metre-gauge. Notice (1) the way in which most of the lines thrust inland from coastal ports, and (2) how these are linked, subsequently, by lines parallel to the coast, so that a true network gradually forms in the most densely settled areas. Compare this pattern with that of the Argentine (Fig. 19).

generating capacity. In the third place, the plans were designed to increase home production of foodstuffs, and so reduce the nation's food import requirements. Private investment—both domestic and foreign—has been encouraged in manufacturing industry and Brazil is now self-sufficient in most consumer and intermediate goods. The outstanding development has been the establishment and expansion of the motor vehicle industry and associated component suppliers. In 1963 Brazil produced almost 200,000 motor cars and trucks.

Transport and Commerce. One of Brazil's main problems lies in its inadequate transport system. The official statistics reveal this deficiency. There are 22,000 miles of navigable waterways. In 1960 there were 23,500 miles of railway tracks, most of them owned by the State, but laid out on five different gauges. Even the number of motor vehicles licensed (1·75 million by 1965) and the mileage of passable highways (some 280,000 miles) are far from impressive in a country the size of a continent, in spite of a strenuous programme of road expansion. The network of airlines is well developed, and for most of the cities of the interior, the aircraft forms the one practical link with the large coastal centres. The airline Panair do Brasil was one of the pioneers of regular air services across the South Atlantic.

In spite of changes in the economy over recent years, Brazil continues, as a trading nation, to export mainly raw materials, but imports have been diversified to include materials required for industry as well as manufactured goods.

Brazil's principal trade partners are the U.S.A., Germany, Argentina and Great Britain. The U.S.A. buys about half of Brazil's exports, and provides almost two-fifths of the imports. Germany stands in second place, supplying in 1957 some 11% of Brazil's imports, and taking 8% of the exports; before the Second World War, these figures were considerably larger. Trade with the Soviet Union may increase, from its present low level, as a result of the resumption of diplomatic and commercial relations in 1962.

As a result of Brazil's development during and since the Second World War, the standard of living of some of the population has risen considerably, particularly the urban middle and working classes. At the same time, however, the cost of living has been rising steeply owing to rampant inflation; it rose fivefold overall between 1948 and 1958. In order to cure a chronic deficit in the balance of payments, import restrictions were imposed. Meanwhile, there was a continuing, yawning gap between the demands made upon the federal government and its resources to meet them.

Since 1951, continuing but largely unsuccessful efforts have been made to balance Brazil's external accounts and to meet the country's internal needs. However, there can be no question that, with its immense natural and other resources, Brazil has the means to continue its current economic development far into the future, given a real effort on the part of its population, wise hands on the political tiller of the nation and imaginative investment from private and public sources both inside and outside Brazil. Under these conditions Brazil will be one of the world's leading industrial nations by the end of the century.

CHAPTER THREE

Paraguay

Paraguay: The State and Its Regions

Western Paraguay—*Paraguay Occidental*—belongs to the great region of the Chaco. Almost the whole of this western section is a monotonous lowland, a plain of deposition built up from sand, loam and loess materials.

Along the Paraguay River there is a flood plain with swamps and lagoons. From here, the surface of the land gradually rises towards the north-west, and as it does so, the rainfall diminishes, from around 40 inches in the east to barely half that figure in the west. The mean annual temperature is high, and serves to emphasise the tropical character of the climate. The area is virtually frost-free and relief from the high temperatures comes only occasionally with the arrival of the *pampero*, a south wind that presages an advance of cool polar air. The vegetation reflects the progressive onset of aridity towards the west, for there the forest and bush of the east are superseded by more drought-tolerant plants. Thickets of pineapple plants and cacti make their appearance, and palm groves exist along the banks of the rivers.

The area between the Paraguay and Paraná Rivers (*Paraguay Oriental*) comprises the two other main regions of the country. The more westerly of the two is the richer region, with gently rolling hills terminated on the east by a fault scarp 600 to 1000 feet high beyond which lies the Paraná plateau. In the north, crystalline formations rise to the surface, while in the south there is an area of sandstone hills, the greater part of which lies below 1000 feet. By contrast with the Chaco, rainfall is greater here, and reaches 80 inches p.a. or more. This high precipitation is associated with summer heat, to create rather trying climatic conditions; Asunción has an annual mean temperature of 72° F, which compares with the 73° F of Rio de Janeiro but the extremes are greater due to Paraguay's more continental location. Outside the cultivated areas, the vegetation consists of savanna intersected by lines of *galeria* (see p. 18).

Finally, in the east lies an upland which slopes away towards the south-east and east, and which is occupied for the most part by the dense forests of the *selva* (see p. 18). Only in the north do the forests give way to savanna vegetation, a type which here comprises palms and cacti, and thus corresponds to the *caatinga* of Brazil. The forests of the south-east region are remarkable for their rich variety of trees and plants. Among these probably the best known, and certainly the most valuable economically, is the yerba maté (*Ilex paraguayensis*), the leaves and smallest twigs of which are gathered to make maté tea.

Paraguay and Its People

The present State of Paraguay can trace its origins back to the founding of Fort Asunción in 1537. Behind it stretched out a vast hinterland that reached across to the Cordillera and so formed a link with the Spanish domains of the central Andes. From Asunción, overland routes ran through the hostile world of the Chaco to the silver mines of Potosí.

But the heyday of this early Paraguayan settlement was very brief. There was a time when no city in all South America, other than Potosí and Lima, could compare with Asunción, but as time went by it was overtaken by faster-growing settlements elsewhere. Then at the beginning of the seventeenth century began the period of Jesuit missionary activity in what are now eastern Paraguay and the Argentinian territory of Misiones. Little evidence remains visible today of this attempt to organise the Indians into civilised communities with a religious foundation, and to encourage and oversee their growth with the aid of European administrators and colonists. In 1767 the Jesuits were expelled, though not without leaving behind them an interesting legacy: while in the remainder of the Spanish colonial empire it was generally the case that the Spanish and Indian populations intermarried to produce a mestizo people, yet here in Paraguay, in the areas where the Jesuits had been, the Indian strain has held its ground, and the Guarani Indians of today, pure-blooded in race, speaking their own Guarani language, and Christian in their religion, have put their own distinctive stamp on the life of Paraguay and its people.

Paraguay threw off Spanish rule at the same time as did Argentina. The country's first president, who held office from 1811 to 1840, severed its connections with the outside world, but this did not mean that the state was spared the misfortunes of international friction. In 1865 Paraguay became involved in war with Uruguay, Brazil and Argentina, and in 1933 with Bolivia—wars which devastated the country and decimated the male population, so that in 1935 the sex ratio in Paraguay was nine women to each man. A period of what one writer has called 'connubial itinerancy' has usually evened the sex ratio within a generation after these wars. There followed a destructive civil war in the years 1947–8.

In the great waves of immigration into South America during the nineteenth century, Paraguay had no share; nor had it imported Negro slaves. In consequence, more than 80% of the population of the modern state possess a mixture of Guarani Indian and Spanish blood. The present population does, however, include a few foreign elements, among which there are 20,000–30,000 Germans. Some of these migrated over the border from Brazil, to found the settlement of Encarnación in 1897; most of the remainder are Mennonites who founded a colony in the Chaco between 1926 and 1932. In addition there are groups of Italians, Swiss, East Europeans and Argentinians living in Paraguay. With regard to the Indian population, the most recent estimate is that there are probably 20,000 pure-bred Indians in the east, while in the Chaco there are probably 50,000 Indians who are virtually untouched by outside cultures.

Even up to the present day, it is almost wholly true to say that the Paraguay River separates two completely different worlds—the east, with its European influences and civilisation on the one hand, and on the other, the little-known, almost untouched west or Chaco. The over-all level of economic development in Paraguay is markedly less than that in the states that border it, and the proportion of the population living in towns is less than 20%. Some 75% of the population live within a radius of about 100 miles from the capital. Most of the country's economic activities are located in this area.

Of Asunción, Pahlen has written:

> The city of Asunción lies in an idyllic setting. It has a population of about 200,000 [1962 est. 285,000], and in spite of its tramways and its motor traffic, it is essentially a country town. Each morning early, the Indian women come riding into town, sitting side-saddle on small donkeys, and picking their way through the unpaved streets to the markets, where they will offer their wares. The streets are full of colourful characters, among whom there are far more women than men. One cannot but marvel at the grace and skill with which these women carry huge loads or pitchers of

water on their heads, without so much as touching them with their hands.

In the centre of the city, however, there are a few large, modern buildings. Here, at least, one has some impression of being in the twentieth century; there are hotels, cinemas, clubs, offices and government departments; there is a Pantheon that serves as a war memorial, a large congress hall, and a police barracks. Here, too, one finds several old churches, relics of the colonial period, and houses whose pillared façades bespeak a bygone age, while out of their gardens the most intoxicating scents are wafted; scents not only of a thousand flowers, but the soft, indefinable, heart-warming atmosphere of a gracious past.[1]

Besides Asunción, Paraguay possesses only three other urban centres: Villarrica, with a population of about 30,000, is the trade centre of the agriculturally important south-east, and it possesses a variety of processing plants for farm products; Encarnación (population 20,000) stands at the ferry point where the Central Railway of Paraguay connects with the Argentinian network at Posadas; and Concepción (population 33,000) which is a port and commercial centre.

The political structure of the state resembles that of most of the other South American republics. Legislation and justice are in the hands of a chamber of deputies and a high court. Of this structure, however, Pahlen writes:

Like all the other South American states, Paraguay is theoretically a democratic republic. With the exception of a few short periods, however, the history of Paraguay has known little of democracy. A great deal of water will have to flow down the Paraguay River before the nation is ready for this most difficult of all political forms.

But on the wide plains through which the river flows, and in the forests that line its banks, this is a question of the utmost irrelevance. The feverish political life of Asunción—where all the nation's present leaders live, and from where they will probably continue to be drawn in the future—has absolutely no impact outside a radius of a few miles from the capital. Indifferent to it all, the remainder of the population lives out its existence, encouraged in peaceful contemplation by the quiet beauty of the landscape; lives in peace and quiet as it did yesterday and the day before, and as it probably will tomorrow too.[1]

Roman Catholicism is the official religion, but religious freedom exists. Compulsory free education is a goal which, owing to limited facilities and to problems of distance and travel, has only been reached in a few areas. Asunción has a high school, and some attempt has been

1 Pahlen, K., *Südamerika, eine neue Welt*, Zürich, 1949.

made to use adult education to remedy the deficiencies in the present system. The total circulation of the country's five daily papers is less than 65,000.

The Economy of Paraguay

Agriculture. There are at present no exact statistics for the area of land under farms in Paraguay. Probably about $1\frac{1}{4}$ million acres of farmland lie within the main agricultural area of the campo, and a further $2\frac{3}{4}$ million in the scattered areas of less intensive farming. Of all the South American states, Paraguay has preserved the greatest degree of dependence on agriculture as its economic base. Nearly 60% of the population is supported either by agriculture or by forestry. Crop production is geared almost wholly to home markets. The leading crops grown are maize and manioc; apart from these, Paraguay produces rice, groundnuts, cotton, sugar-cane, tobacco and fruit. In recent years, rice production has shown the most marked advance, while the area devoted to both sugar-cane and fruit has increased, due to government encouragement of their cultivation.

In Paraguay, with its general state of economic underdevelopment, the collection of various products from wild plants plays an important part in the economy. Lumber production is in its infancy, but the output of tannin from the quebracho has attained an annual level of more than 30,000 tons of extract. Improvements in the breeding of livestock and disease control could lead to a considerable increase in the numbers of cattle reared, as could also closer control of farm operations, for there are large areas which are well suited to livestock farming. Everywhere the large farm-holding is characteristic; the great majority of the farmers own little or no land. Agricultural education for owner or tenant, is only of recent origin.

Paraguay—Livestock Population (1962 est.)

Cattle	4,500,000
Sheep	534,000
Horses and mules	337,000
Pigs	633,000

Minerals and Industry. Such industries as Paraguay possesses are based on agricultural products. The State's slaughterhouse capacity is considerable in that in 1960, for example, 200 million pounds of beef and veal resulted from the slaughter of cattle in addition to lesser quantities from sheep, pigs, and goats. There was still, nevertheless, an import of stock for slaughter from neighbouring countries. Second to meat production among Paraguay's processing industries comes the group dealing with vegetable oils—castor oil, or products extracted from ground-nuts and cotton-seed—and then, in turn, the extraction of tannin, sugar refining, soap manufacturing and, finally, cotton spinning.

The undeveloped nature of this industrial sector of the economy underlines the problems that confront the state: lack of skilled labour, poor communications, and lack of capital. The same is true of the state of development of mineral and power resources. The country's minerals are neither thoroughly surveyed nor exploited. The possibility of oil resources has not been thoroughly investigated, while out of an estimated 2,000,000 h.p. of hydro-electric power potential only about 1000 h.p. are actually developed. Electric light is found only in the larger towns; gas, water mains or sewage are not found even in Asunción. By the time the visitor reaches the suburbs, he has the impression of simply being in a country village.

Transport and Commerce. This landlocked state has communication with the coast only by way of its great rivers, whose lower course is controlled by neighbouring states rather than being under the aegis of an international central commission as are other important river systems linking separate nation states (e.g. the Danube). The Paraguay River, however, is an important traffic route, free from rapids or other obstacles, and navigable as far as Asunción and Concepción for ships of 7 feet draught. Asunción lies some 1000 miles upstream from Buenos Aires, and the big river steamers make the trip in 4 to 5 days.

The port of Asunción deals with about 4000 ships each year, and handles some 300,000 to 400,000 tons of cargo. Railway communications, on the other hand, are poorly developed; there is nothing resembling a railway network. The longest stretch of line is from Asunción to Encarnación (260 miles), and was laid by a British company. The country's total track mileage is 910 and a lot of that is solely for hauling quebracho. A road system is only now coming into being; by 1963 the country possessed about 6400 motor vehicles, of which some 75% were licensed in Asunción or its neighbourhood. Five airlines have services which call at the capital.

The position of Paraguay in international trade is far from satisfactory. The main problem is her dependence on Argentina, which is the principal trading partner.

During and after the Second World War, Paraguay had to adopt stringent currency controls and import quotas in order to maintain her trade in balance. In this, however, she succeeded; while the value of imports rose from 26·1 to 84·8 million guaranis between 1940 and 1950, that of exports rose from 20·0 to 167·7 millions. More serious are the problems of political unrest and inflation. In 1951, it was found necessary to devalue the guarani by a half. The cost of living index (1938 = 100) had risen by 1950 to 1026 (the figure for clothing was 1845, and for foodstuffs 888). Among other aid measures, the World Bank has made Paraguay a loan of $5,000,000, but continuing caution is essential for the country's uncertain economic future.

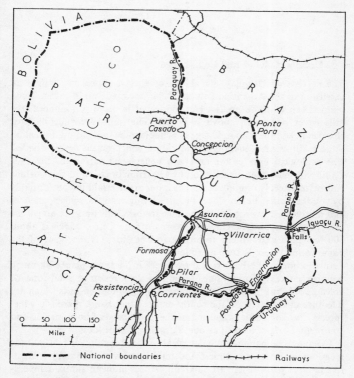

Fig. 16. Paraguay: the approaches and communications. Note how transport depends upon a combination of river and rail routes. Even the few main roads shown are not yet complete.

CHAPTER FOUR

Uruguay

Uruguay: Relief and Landscapes

The surface of Uruguay, which in some ways represents simply an extension of the Argentine Pampas, is largely made up of lowland and plain. Even in those areas where the relief is more pronounced, the hills never rise much above 1000 feet. The indication 'cuchilla' (or sharp edge) on the map of Uruguay is liable to be misleading. In reality, these features are generally broad ridges which act as water divides. The geological base of the area is a peneplaned surface of the Pre-Cambrian mass that extends southward from Brazil, and this surface cuts across steeply dipping beds. The latter are overlaid uncomformably by younger series, but in places the underlying granites, schists, gneisses and marbles are exposed at the surface to form hills that rise above the low-lying Pampas. The ridge known as Monte Cerro, which is about 500 feet high and which, according to one story, is the basis of the name Montevideo, is such an inlier.

In the north, the base rocks are overlain in some places by much younger covering formations. Layers of very resistant sandstone or volcanic sills and flows form cappings for table-topped hills which are a feature of this area. In the south, on the other hand, there is a widespread cover of Tertiary and more recent deposits, of both marine and continental origin, as well as considerable areas of loess.

Uruguay's climatic régime is typical of east coast lower mid-latitude locations with warm summers and mild winters; the country is frost-free in most years. There are small differences in mean annual temperatures and annual range between the coast and the interior; Montevideo has an annual mean of 61° F, while Mercedes on the Rio Negro has an annual mean of 63° F, by virtue of a somewhat cooler July and a warmer January. The amount of rainfall also shows some regional variations; at Montevideo it is 40 inches p.a. This fairly evenly distributed rainfall, together with the waters of the many rivers that feed the Uruguay and the La Plata Rivers, is sufficient to make cultivation and livestock raising possible throughout the entire country.

The natural vegetation is prairie everywhere except along the Uruguay

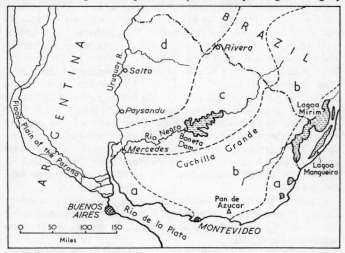

Fig. 17. Uruguay: physical divisions. The divisions are: (*a*) Coastal plains of sand and alluvium, (*b*) Granitic hills of the east, (*c*) Central plains—lowlands of the Rio Negro, (*d*) Diabase plateau of the west.

and Rio Negro, where *galeria* forests are to be found. The grassland landscape, however, is broken up here and there by lines of yatay palms. Even on the hills there is not a true forest vegetation, owing to the rocky surfaces of the ridges, but there is a sort of maquis which grows several feet high and is classified as sierra vegetation.

Uruguay and Its People

In Uruguay, the concept of citizenship is an unusual one. Foreigners can obtain citizen's rights, without relinquishing their former nationality. Anybody who can read and write, and have himself registered as naturalised is entitled, and indeed obliged, to vote from the age of eighteen upwards. The political structure is also unusual. Since 1951, in place of a president, the country has been ruled by a nine-man presidential council, whose members are elected by the voters every three years, and are not eligible for immediate re-election. This structure of government, like the surprisingly mature social and economic structure possessed by Uruguay, is an outcome of the nation's history and development.

The early history of Uruguay was the story of a conflict of Spanish and Portuguese influences. In May 1811, the country threw off Spanish rule, but Montevideo itself remained in Spanish hands for a further three years. There then followed a period of Brazilian domination which provoked a reaction from Argentina, and this, in turn, brought Great Britain to Brazil's side. In spite of—or, perhaps, because of—these international complications, the Uruguayans succeeded in establishing an independent state in 1828 (although their large neighbours only conceded final recognition of this in 1859).

There followed a brutal war with Paraguay, which inflicted immense damage on the young nation. Agricultural reform was begun, however, and in the years since 1865 the country has developed a remarkable system of social legislation. In the First World War, Uruguay took no part; in the Second, she declared war on Germany, but not until February 1945.

Uruguay's population is distinguished by the high proportion of European blood in its racial make-up. It is hard to find a pure-blooded Indian, and the Negro element is limited to the area of the Brazilian border and the capital.

As the capital of a country which has doubled in population every thirty years since 1880, Montevideo, with one million inhabitants, is also the population focus to a degree which is possibly unique among the world's capital cities. The next largest city is Paysandú, on the Uruguay River, with some 60,000 inhabitants; it is an industrial town, manufacturing meat products, soap, sugar, beer and shoes. It is followed by Salto (60,000), which has grown up at the head of navigation on the Uruguay, and is the centre for an area noted for ranching and oranges. Other towns are Mercedes (45,000), Artigas (30,000) and Fray Bentos (14,000), which is famous for its meat products.

Almost half the population lives in the vicinity of the capital. The southern provinces are relatively densely settled (an average density of about 100 persons per square mile), but in the interior and the north the figure falls to 12–15 persons per square mile. On the other hand it is these thinly populated ranchlands which provide some 80% of Uruguay's goods for export.

Two factors which have left their mark on Uruguay's social and cultural landscape are its history and the fact that a high proportion of its population is descended from European immigrants. Church and State are separated; moreover, although the majority of the population is Roman Catholic, religious freedom exists for all. Primary education is free and compulsory, and only among the older people are illiterates to be found. There are two universities and a number of vocational schools. In 1960 there were twenty-six daily newspapers published in Uruguay, fifteen of which are published in Montevideo. The nation's daily newspaper circulation totals about 750,000.

The Economy of Uruguay

Agriculture and Ranching. Some 66% of Uruguay's land is given over to livestock farming or ranching. Of the other 34% of the country, 13% is waste, 10% is under a mixture of pasture and cultivated land, and only 11% is true cropland. Wheat is the leading crop; and in comparison with the pre-war period, production has increased considerably. The explanation of this lies partly in the fact that, in Uruguay, very large holdings of land are rare; many of the great *estancias* have been converted into family undertakings and the farm labourers are protected by minimum wage legislation.

Other products of importance are oats, maize, barley and linseed. The 1961 preliminary statistics also showed that there were 8,670,000 cattle and 21,480,000 sheep in Uruguay, which gave the country a high place among the livestock-producing states of South America. By such measures as farm support prices and special freight rates on the railways, the government seeks to strengthen this position of prominence as a livestock-producing nation, although the effect of these is more than offset by the adverse impact of the exchange rate system which acts as a deterrent to exporters of wool and meat.

The processing of livestock and agricultural products forms the basis for most of Uruguay's industries. In 1960 roughly $1\frac{1}{2}$ million cattle were slaughtered. The production of frozen and tinned meat and of meat extract comprises a considerable sector of the nation's output. The linseed which is grown is mostly exported because, although there are a large number of crushing plants to produce oil, the Uruguayan housewife prefers to use imported olive oil.

Minerals and Industry. If Uruguay is favoured in terms of agricultural resources, it suffers an almost complete lack of mineral wealth and fuel energy sources. There is no coal and—as yet—no petroleum has been discovered. Water power has been harnessed at the Boneta Dam on the Rio Negro, and this scheme, which supplies electricity to the capital, will be followed in the future by others utilising the considerable hydro-electric power reserves. Petroleum is imported into Uruguay and processed in a state-owned refinery.

Uruguay was affected, as were all the South American republics, by the closure of her regular sources of supply of manufactured goods —the U.S.A. and Europe—during the two World Wars. By 1946 Uruguay was producing, with her young woollen textile industry, wool, cloth, and clothing for export. The cotton goods industry is at present limited to supply of the home market, as is the rubber industry; in 1950 the country's own plants produced four-fifths of the rubber goods consumed. Other industries, particularly consumer goods industries, have been developed, though invariably on a scale limited to the small domestic market. Almost 25% of the labour force is employed in manufacturing industry—a higher percentage than is now employed in agriculture (21%).

Transport and commerce. Uruguay's surface configuration presents no very serious structural obstacles to the development of communications. However, the track mileage of the State's railways is less than 2000 miles. In 1948, the government bought from British ownership four sections of track with a total length of some 1500 miles; before this date the State owned only the few remaining short lines. The system is in process of modernisation, but it faces increasingly serious competition from road transport. The principal commodity carried by the railways is cattle.

The network of serviceable roads in 1960 had a total length of some 5300 miles, used by about 50,000 private and 48,000 commercial vehicles and is focused on the port of Montevideo, which is the country's most important outlet to world markets; in 1948, it handled some 8 million tons of shipping. Uruguay's own merchant fleet is very small, but it is being encouraged by government legislation which stipulates that a minimum percentage of the country's exports must be carried in Uruguayan ships. There is also a network of air services, operated by various local lines.

On the whole, interchange of goods within the country is between Montevideo—where most of the industry is located—and the interior, whilst Uruguay's foreign trade, of the greatest importance to her economy, is still principally with her oldest trading partner, Great

Britain, although trade with the U.S.A., and also with Western Europe, is growing in value. Her exports are almost all agricultural products, while imports are extremely varied—numerous raw materials, machinery, motor vehicles, textiles and a host of other manufactured goods. The country's volume of trade has increased fourfold since 1939. (See Plate 9.)

In what has already been written, the main features of Uruguay's economy can be recognised. The backbone is formed by the vast meat products industry, which is important on a world scale. Since the State's principal sources of revenue are customs duties and profits from exchange transactions, its government must maintain a very close watch upon world market trends. Uruguay's highly developed social welfare system is very costly to operate. Even before the Second World War, the government had introduced trade and exchange controls. The State was forced to intervene in a situation in which the level of incomes was rising steeply, but the general price level was rising even more sharply. Maximum prices are fixed for all essential commodities, and, in addition, the state subsidises prices of certain basic items.

The Swiss author, Pahlen, writes:

This is Uruguay, the country which writers who describe it are unanimous in giving the best character possible; the country with which no one finds fault, and which is often compared with those showpieces of the Old World such as Denmark. In my opinion, however, a comparison with Switzerland is more telling. Both are lands sandwiched between larger neighbours, each of which exercises an undeniable influence upon them, yet without being able to rob them of their individuality, or the people of their unique character. Both are lands crossed by vital lines of international communication: lands with a stable currency and a solid economic base; lands which, although not essentially rich, have achieved, through years of peace and wise administration, a high level of general well-being. [See Plate 10.] They are lands of democratic rule and advanced social standards, free from marked contrasts, and unified by their landscapes— there by the mountains and here by the plains; lands with great international prestige, with few of their peoples either very rich or very poor, and with a pace to their life which is neither too fast nor too slow. They are progressive without being haughty; cultured without being snobbish.[1]

1 Pahlen, K., *Südamerika, eine neue Welt*, Zürich, 1949.

CHAPTER FIVE

Argentina

_____

Argentina: Regions and Landscapes

The great wedge-shaped area which is Argentina[1] stretches from the Tropic of Capricorn in the north to the high latitudes of Tierra del Fuego in the south, and from the main chain of the Andes in the west to the Atlantic. In terms of European measurement, this north-south extent corresponds to the distance from London to Timbuktu.

Within this area, three main physical divisions can be recognised: the lowlands, the Patagonian Plateau (the Meseta) and the mountain west (Fig. 18). Each of these can be sub-divided into smaller regions and each embodies within its borders different conditions for settlement, agriculture and communications.

(1) THE LOWLANDS

The Argentine Lowlands form the southernmost part of the great structural lowland which, as we saw in Chapter 2, separates the eastern highlands of South America from the Andes. The axis of this great trough is represented by the line of the Paraguay-Paraná river system.

The Paraguay River rises in the Brazilian state of Mato Grosso, and as a lowland river it is navigable far up towards its head-waters. North of Corrientes it joins with the Paraná, bringing a huge volume of water down from the Brazilian Highlands. At this point the river already has a width of more than a mile and a half, and a flood plain 15 to 20 miles wide. After receiving the additional flow of the Uruguay River, it expands into the shallow, silt-laden waters of the Rio de la Plata, an estuary that attains a width of more than 100 miles and covers an

1 The name means land of silver; the Indians who were encountered in a few places by the earlier explorers wore silver ornaments.

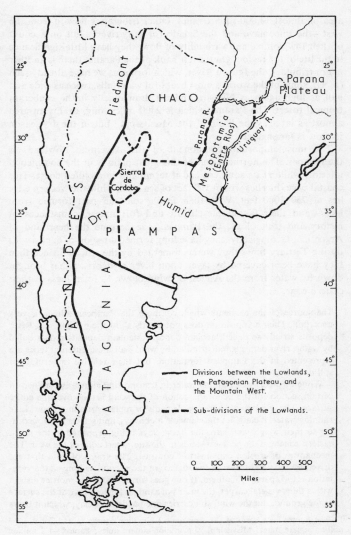

Fig. 18. Argentina: major geographical regions and sub-regions.

area of almost 14,000 square miles. Other tributaries flow in from the west—the Pilcomayo and the Salado (or salty river)—but on account of their low volume and variability of flow, they have little significance in the life of the region. On the left bank of the Paraná, there is another major tributary, the Iguaçú River, which forms, as we have already seen (p. 33), some of the world's most beautiful waterfalls, twice as wide and half as high again as Niagara and set dramatically in the exuberant tropical forest. The Paraná, which is 2400 miles long, drains an area almost as large as the basin of the Mississippi,[1] but in the dry season its flow is far smaller.

The most important component of the Argentine Lowlands is the Pampas. The northern end of this great plain is in the continental interior, while at its southern end it terminates in a cliffed coast. This coastal edge thus lies within 100 feet of sea level, while the western edge lies at 750–1000 feet. With their fertile soils—in part formed from loess—and their favourable climate and fortunate circumstances of history and technology, the Pampas have become the heartland of Argentina. Geologically, they have long formed a region of deposition; during Tertiary times they were submerged by the sea, and since then they have been covered by layer upon layer of debris, either brought down by water from the Andes, or wind-blown to form loess at their eastern edge.

> The source of the elements which compose the Pampean alluvia is very uncertain. Their composition does not clearly show their origin. . . . River deposits strictly so called, aeolian deposits, aeolian deposits redistributed by water, river deposits redistributed by wind—all these different types are represented in the Pampean formation, but their relative importance is still disputed.
>
> While the agency of running water in transporting alluvia is confined to certain sections of the plain, the action of the wind is seen over the entire surface. The wind everywhere supplements or replaces running water. Like running water, it classifies the elements it conveys, and selects them according to their weight and size, the finest clays being deposited in the moist eastern zone and the coarsest sands in the sub-desert zone of the west. The mechanism of erosion explains this contrast. The grains of sand that are driven by the wind travel at the surface of the ground as long as the vegetation is too sparse to fix them. If one goes further east, to a moister district with a thick vegetal carpet, the grains of sand no longer move at the surface of the ground, but the wind still carries fine particles of clay, which it bears

1 The figures are: Basin of the Amazon—2·7 million square miles; Congo—1·4 million square miles; Mississippi—1·4 million square miles; Paraná—1·2 million square miles.

to a great height. . . . It is during dry seasons that the deposition of clay is at its greatest. Darwin mentions that after the droughts of 1827–1830 in the area round the Paraná, the boundary marks were buried under dust to such an extent that one could no longer recognise the limits of the various land holdings. Apart, however, from these sorts of floods or storms of dust caused by the *pampero*, the summer atmosphere is clearly laden with dust, which colours the skies in the east of Buenos Aires province, as far as Entre Rios.[1]

In the climate of the region Atlantic influences are the most pronounced. Annual rainfall diminishes from the coast (Buenos Aires, 38 inches) going inland (San Luis, 20 inches; Mendoza, 8 inches). Summer is in general the season of maximum precipitation, but seasonal distribution, unreliability and intensity of rainfall are all important climatic factors in this part of the world, where agriculture plays so dominant a role in the economy.

Buenos Aires has a January (summer) mean temperature of 74° F and a July mean of 49° F. A particular menace is the famous *pampero*, an outbreak of cold polar air. Heralded by the gathering of huge banks of cloud in the south, this wind sweeps across the level plains with great force, bringing outbreaks of torrential rain. The north wind, too, is a familiar feature of Argentinian life, blowing hot and dry from the interior, and reminiscent of the *sirocco* of Mediterranean lands.

These great plains, which were sparsely-inhabited grasslands when the Spaniards arrived in the sixteenth century, are today some of the country's best-developed lands. The explanation of their treeless character has not yet been established for certain; sixteenth-century descriptions, for example, speak of limited tree growth encountered by the early explorers. There may be some evidence here to support the theory, mentioned earlier, that the continent is becoming progressively drier. But it is also probable that burning by the Indians contributed to the destruction of any woody growth, thereby encouraging grasses.

In terms of land use, the extensive pastoral activities of a former era on the Pampas have today been forced out to the margins by the expansion of cultivation. Agricultural lands now occupy most of the former grasslands within a half-circle around Buenos Aires with a radius of some 250 miles. Within this belt there live, on less than a quarter of Argentina's land area, three-quarters of her population.

The second component of the Argentinian Lowlands is the Gran Chaco (or 'great hunting-ground'). This comprises the northern end

1 Denis, P., *The Argentine Republic*, London, 1922, pp. 167–70.

of the lowlands, west of the Paraná. It is, in reality, a transition belt between the open grasslands of the Pampas to the south, and the tropical rain-forests of Brazil to the north. In form, most of its surface is occupied by very young flood plains. Its climate is continental; summer temperatures are high (80–85° F) and winters are cool. Lying as it does on the fringe of the tropics, the region experiences a long dry season.

This is the habitat of the quebracho tree, valued originally for its termite-resistant wood, and today more for its tannin extract. Over much of the Chaco, forest alternates with savanna or grassland. The forest is dense; the trees are mostly stunted and gnarled, and less than 40 feet high, with a thick, thorny undergrowth below them. The grasslands of the Chaco are beginning to give way before the advance of cotton cultivation. In the driest areas, too, are to be found giant cacti, while in the more humid north, the dry forest of the Chaco becomes more varied in character and includes, for example, palms and other varieties of plants characteristic of the tropical rain-forest.

The third component of the lowlands is the region between the rivers Paraná and Uruguay called Mesopotamia, or Entre Rios. Across this area the rainfall increases from 40 inches in the west, north-eastwards into Brazil. Here, in consequence, the transition is completed between the park-like landscapes farther south, with their prairie openings, their acacias and their mimosa, and the true tropical rainforest, with its endless variety of plant life, that lies to the north. The surface is somewhat more undulating than elsewhere within the lowlands, with low ranges of hills in the territory of Misiones which form a link with the Brazilian Highlands beyond. It is here that yerba maté grows, the leaves of which are steeped in water to make the national beverage, maté tea.

The southern tip of this region between the rivers has long been, in terms of human geography, a part of the developed steppe lands farther south, and it is intensively cultivated.

(2) THE PATAGONIAN PLATEAU

The second main sub-division of Argentina is the Patagonian Plateau, which lies to the south of the Pampas. Its surface represents an old sea floor, uplifted to its present position and still projecting, as a continental shelf, for some scores of miles out beneath the present surface of the Atlantic. Its surface has been deeply scored by the action of such rivers as the Rio Colorado and Rio Negro. In contrast with the lowland which adjoins it on the north, it is an erosion surface, and it falls, in a series of steps, towards the sea on the east. It is a region of meagre rainfall and, consequently, supports only a limited range of plant life. The distribution of this rainfall, however, provides another point of contrast with the lowlands further north, for in Patagonia precipitation decreases from west to east. At the base of the Cordillera there are some 20 inches per year; on the Meseta itself the figure is 8–10 inches, and on the Atlantic coast generally less than 8 inches. In this region, in fact, the dry zone of the continent spreads from the north-west to overlap the more humid area under Atlantic influences.

Here, as on the Pampas farther north, one of the most significant of the climatic elements is the strength of the winds. Antoine de St-Exupéry, who flew the pioneer air routes in this area, describes their force in this way:

I had taken off from the field at Trelew [43° S, 65° W] and was flying down to Comodoro-Rivadavia, in the Patagonian Argentine. Here the crust of the earth is as dented as an old boiler. The high-pressure regions over the Pacific send the winds past a gap in the Andes into a corridor fifty miles wide through which they rush to the Atlantic in a strangled and accelerated buffeting that scrapes the surface of everything in their path. The sole vegetation visible in this threadbare landscape is a series of oil derricks looking like the after-effects of a forest fire. Towering over the round hills on which the winds have left a residue of stony gravel, there rises a chain of prow-shaped, saw-toothed, razor-edged mountains stripped by the elements down to the bare rock.

For three months in the year the speed of these winds at ground level is up to a hundred miles an hour. We who flew the route knew that once we had crossed the marshes at Trelew and had reached the threshold of the zone they swept, we should recognise the winds from afar by a grey-blue tint in the atmosphere at the sight of which we would tighten our belts and shoulder-straps in preparation for what was coming. From then on we had an hour of stiff fighting and of stumbling again and again into invisible ditches of air. This was manual labour, and our muscles felt it pretty much as if we had been carrying a longshoreman's load.[1]

Conditions at ground level are described by Pierre Denis:

The climate determines the character of the soil in Patagonia. The rounded pebbles of granite and eruptive rock, so often described since the time of Darwin, sometimes free and sometimes embedded in red sand or limestone, are spread over the tableland like aureoles round the masses of rock, and they are particularly abundant in the coast region. . . . It is the wind that explains the concentration of the gravel at the surface. It separates the pebbles from the more mobile material about them. Wherever the outcrop-strata contain pebbles, the wind eventually converts the place into a field

1 St-Exupéry, A. de, *Wind, Sand and Stars*, London, 1939, pp. 64–5.

of shingle. It has done this with the terraces of the Limay. The Tertiary marine deposits of the coast region are rich in pebbles torn from the rocky promontories of the shore; hence the extent of stony soils in the coast region. The wind similarly strips naked the angular stones, of local origin and incompletely worn, round the isolated rocks of the desert tableland or on the flanks of the secondary ravines.

On the other hand, the bedding action of the wind creates deposits consisting of small and uniform elements from the sand of the dunes to the finest dust. The lightest particles, caught up repeatedly by the squalls and carried to a great height in the atmosphere, go beyond the Patagonian region and reach the bottom of the Atlantic or the plain of the Pampa.[1]

Volcanic activity in the Andean Cordillera to the west has resulted in the partial filling by lava flows of the trough at the foot of the mountains, while glaciation has produced numerous moraines and a widespread drift cover. At the eastern edge of the area, the coastline is for the most part cliffed, and provides few harbours for shipping.

The forests that cover the lower slopes of the Andes terminate at the western edge of the Patagonian Plateau, to be replaced by thorny scrub, briars and bristly grass, which afford only the poorest of grazing for livestock. The river courses on the plateau, it is true, are lined with better grasses and clumps of trees, but apart from the foothill zone of the Andes, where irrigation agriculture is possible, the area is of little value except for sheep-raising. Indeed, considering the natural handicaps of the area, sheep-ranching has been developed quite intensively. The ranches are of enormous extent, and the produce is shipped to market by way of the few ports on this inhospitable coastline. Lack of effective communications in the interior poses a serious obstacle to further development.

(3) THE MOUNTAIN WEST

The western part of Argentina falls wholly within this physical province, and the area can be sub-divided into two distinct sections.

(a) *The foothill (Monte) section* lies intermediately between the Pampas and the Andes. It consists of low ranges, varying in height from 2500 feet in the west to 800 feet in the east, underlain by Paleozoic formations and forming a general piedmont slope away from the mountains. The southern limit of this section lies roughly along the Rio Negro. The particular feature of this area is its aridity; it is covered with a dry steppe vegetation of thornbush, scrub, cacti and coarse grass. Here

1   Denis, P., op. cit., pp. 123–4.

and there sand-dunes and pebble-strewn surfaces give the landscape an appearance of true desert; elsewhere there are salt playas or sinks (*salinas*) with the typical salt desert scrub vegetation. Only by irrigation can these dry lands be effectively cultivated. Around Mendoza and San Juan citrus orchards and vineyards cover former desert areas. Farther north, in Tucumán, irrigated plantations produce the bulk of Argentina's sugar-cane, in rotation with rice and lucerne. Outside these oasis areas, the dry piedmont is given over to extensive pastoralism.

(*b*) *The Argentinian Andes* lie at the extreme western edge of the country; indeed, for most of their length, their main watershed forms the western boundary of Argentina. In the north-west, the mountains reach heights of 15-18,000 feet, culminating in the towering peak of Aconcagua (22,834 feet). The intermontane plateaux are dry, and often contain salt flats. The population is sparse everywhere, except in the irrigated piedmont zone already mentioned. Farther south, where the mountains are lower, is a region of impressive beauty; a land of lakes and forests that is being developed to attract tourists and so to produce some economic values from an area which, in the past, has been largely unproductive (see Plate 11). As Kühn has written,

> As one crosses the eastern foothills of the Andes, which are watered by the orographic rainfall, the landscape alters very rapidly; the splendid forests end abruptly and, as suddenly, hills and valleys seem to be overrun with low scrub, thorns, candelabra cacti, all combining to create that landscape of yellows and browns which is so characteristic of the dry mountain steppes.[1]

THE ISLANDS

In a physical sense, Argentina includes, besides the three main sections which have been described, a number of islands. These include Tierra del Fuego, Staten Island, and the Falkland Islands. The latter form the subject of a long-standing political dispute with Britain regarding ownership. They consist of two main islands, separated by the narrow Falkland Sound, and almost 200 lesser islands. They lie on the continental shelf that stretches eastwards into the Atlantic, and they are composed of surfaces of almost bare rock smoothed and rounded by erosion. Grass and heathland make up the vegetation; there are no trees to break the monotony of the landscape.

The islands lie in the path of the cold Falkland Current, and this has a marked effect on the climate. The mean temperatures of both the

1 'Argentinien' in *Handbuch der Geographische Wissenschaften*, Potsdam, 1930.

warmest and the coldest months lie between 48° and 50° F. Rain falls on two days out of every three. Under these stringent circumstances, sheep-raising has come to be the most suitable occupation for the inhabitants.

Since they were discovered in 1592, the islands have changed hands several times. Port Stanley has a good harbour and has become a useful port of call and an important base for whaling. The islands came into Argentina's possession in 1820, but in 1832 they were taken over by Great Britain, and Argentina, which could offer no military resistance to this action, has not ceased since to protest against it. The same is true of the area claimed by the State as the 'Argentinian Antarctic' (Antartida Argentina)—the sector of Antarctica lying south of 60°S between the 25th and 74th meridians of west longitude.

Argentina and Its People

HISTORICAL

In the first decades after the discovery and occupation of the Rio de la Plata region by Spain, a number of towns were founded as a necessary condition of successful settlement in Indian territory, but it was the middle of the eighteenth century before the Spaniards effectively strengthened their hold on this eastward-facing part of their American empire. In 1776 Buenos Aires became the seat of a viceroyalty. The land was torn by feuds and uprisings, most of them evolving, in this period, as social or political revolts against individual members of the land-owning aristocracy. However, when the British Navy made two surprise attacks on Buenos Aires in 1806 and 1807 they were foiled by the unexpectedly strong resistance of the local population. In the great struggle with Napoleon in Spain, Argentina decided not to take either side, but to try to gain independence. In José de San Martin the independents found a leader.

After independence there followed years of struggle and open warfare between Buenos Aires and the outer territories. It was not until Juan Manuel de Rosas seized power during an outbreak of violence in 1829 and became, in 1835, the virtual dictator of Argentina that the national territory came under central control. The nation entered upon an expansionist phase, and efforts were made to enlarge its borders in the north-east and the south, but all efforts to do this in the north-east met with determined resistance from Brazil and Uruguay. Only in the south, on the Pampas, and in the face of Indian opposition, did expansion occur. The exhausting struggles of these early years brought the country to the edge of the political abyss. After Rosas, governments followed each other in quick succession, and boundary questions had to be settled by foreign arbitration. By 1890 the country was bankrupt.

This proved to be the nadir of Argentina's fortunes. From this point onwards, there began a steady improvement, based on the opening up of new sections of the Pampas, the spread of the railway network, enclosure of the land based on the use of barbed wire, the expansion of both crop acreages and livestock population, and the coming of refrigeration for transporting meat to Europe. The population now spread from areas which had become congested to the new lands; exports increased year by year, and with them the significance of Argentina in world affairs also increased. With her predominantly white population and her marked sense of national consciousness, Argentina was thus able to embark upon consistent and methodical promotion of her interests in the political sphere. By 1929 Argentina was one of the strongest and richest countries in the world, but the effect of the Great Depression (1923–33), the further dislocation of international trade caused by the Second World War and the economically disastrous régime of the dictator, Perón, from 1944 to 1956, followed by a period of weak, ineffective government have today placed Argentina in a precarious position.

POPULATION AND SETTLEMENT

The population of Argentina has increased fourfold during the past century. This great empty land, in which wide stretches of fertile land were available within middle latitudes, attracted large numbers of immigrants, most of them from Europe. Argentine law, in fact, permits the immigration only of white peoples, so that with the sparse Indian population decimated by years of struggle with the whites, there has arisen in Argentina a situation which is unique in South America: almost 90% of the population are of European descent, and some 20% were actually born in Europe. Immigrant elements have amalgamated to a striking degree to produce one homogeneous Argentinian people.

The country as a whole is still underpopulated for full development; in particular, the rural population is much too small. In consequence, Argentina is most eager to encourage new farm settlement; indeed, the opening up of new lands, as in a number of other South American states, is a matter of the utmost emergency. However, the long-standing arrangement whereby the country has imported seasonal labourers—especially Italians—for the harvest period has militated against such permanent settlement as have the political and economic difficulties of the post-war period.

There are other obstacles also. In the areas best suited for new development, in terms of both physical conditions and ease of access, most of the land has long been divided into latifundia, whose owners will rent holdings for a few years, but refuse to sell. As a result, the tenant, knowing that in a short time his lease will fall in, uses the land he rents without regard for its future. Such an arrangement holds little attraction for the European settler. As one writer has expressed it:

> The German's ambition is to possess his own land and his own home. To him it is unthinkable that, somewhere on the Pampas, without even the comforting shade of a tree, he should sit out a period of three or five years in a wretched hovel, perhaps with a wife and family as well, with no other prospect before him than that, wind and locusts permitting, he may be able to wrest from this foreign soil enough profit so that, when this dog's life ends and he must move on, he may have something saved up to take with him to the place where the whole business will begin again.

There is still good land available elsewhere, to be sure, but it is in remote areas and generally in regions where Europeans might find the climate unattractive.

The settlement of the Pampas. The occupance history of the Pampas differs in several respects from that of the world's other great mid-latitude grasslands. In the years before Argentina became independent, the Pampas, like the grasslands of North America, were the scene of a clash between two races and cultures, similar to the better-known conflict between cowboys and Indians farther north. On the Pampas, the warlike Indian tribes were opposed by the half-breed *gauchos* and the place of the North American buffalo herds was taken by the wild horses of the Pampas, which the *gauchos* hunted for their hides.

Beset as it was by political troubles, the new state of Argentina was too preoccupied to undertake a determined move to settle the Pampas for several decades after independence, and Indian raids continued along the frontier of settlement. When expansion finally began in the 1870's, it was the product of several favourable circumstances: (1) final removal of the Indian menace by the campaign of 1879–84; (2) government-sponsored immigration from the 1860's onwards, to provide settlers; (3) growth of the railway system which here, as in North America, was the main agency of colonisation; (4) the opening of the port of Buenos Aires in 1889 (loading and unloading goods in the shallow estuary off the city had previously involved a tedious and often hazardous problem of trans-shipment); (5) the beginnings of refrigerated transport for meat, about 1875, making it possible for Argentine meat to reach the continent where there was a market for it—Europe.

Thus it came about that the last quarter of the nineteenth century saw a phase of rapid development on the Pampas as the railways, many of them built with British capital, thrust forward across the smooth surface of the region. Whereas all settlement had previously been located in relation to river routes, the railways provided new links with inland areas (see Fig. 19).

The subsequent development of the Pampas became a story of competition between three different forms of land use: sheep raising, cattle raising (as opposed to the old cattle *hunting* of the *gauchos*), and agriculture. This conflict of land use, in an area suited physically to all three of these forms, also developed into a social conflict between Creole pastoralists and immigrant cultivators.

Of the three, sheep raising came first. It was the sheep ranchers who followed the border patrols out into Indian territory, and products of the sheep headed the list of Argentina's exports until 1890. But this first phase was short-lived, for while sheep thrive on the Pampas they were less profitable than cattle and were thus forced off the Pampas and into the drier margins—Patagonia and the foothills of the Andes, where they could still be raised successfully.

The decisive factor in driving the sheep from the central Pampas was the introduction of alfalfa in the 1890's. This crop increased the cattle-carrying capacity of the grasslands five- or sixfold. Before 1890 cattle had roamed wild and little effort had been made to improve the breed; now, with a market for meat in industrial Europe, and a means of reaching it—by refrigerated ship—new incentives to improvement and increase of the herds were at work. The grasslands were divided —in the first instance by the government—into huge ranches or *estancias*, on which the cattle could be fenced and controlled, and where alfalfa could be raised as a feed crop. (See Plate 12.) These *estancias* were in the hands of a Creole aristocracy of ranchers, to whom the ownership of cattle was a status symbol, and for whom other forms of agriculture were inferior occupations.

But before the Pampas would produce satisfactory alfalfa crops, it was found desirable to break the ground by first planting wheat. To do this, the ranchers brought in immigrant farmers, to whom the land was rented for four to five years for the express purpose of planting a wheat crop. At the end of the period of lease the tenants were obliged to move on, and to find another tenant-holding where the same process was then repeated. Thus Argentina became a great wheat exporter almost by accident, and at the cost of much social unrest and discontent.

Meanwhile, the third type of land use—a genuine agriculture—was developing in the La Plata lowland. This began in earnest in 1856, when the government established agricultural colonies in the Santa Fé area. From the first, it was essentially in the hands of immigrants, and it was largely confined to areas outside the cattlemen's territory since the immigrants had little hope of acquiring land (other than on the leases already described) within that area. In time, however, there grew up what has become the Argentine 'Corn Belt' centred on Rosario, and a region of genuine—one might almost say 'intentional'—and stable wheat farming out on the drier margins of the west and south, beyond the cattle lands.

The immigrants. The conditions which we have been considering serve as a partial explanation of the fact that, as noted on p. 95, while immigration into Argentina has been heavy, there has also been a very large return movement of the immigrants. Of the 9·8 million persons who immigrated during the period 1857–1944, 5·4 million or 55% later left again; only 4·4 million remained. By country of origin, these movements for the most important period of immigration—1857 to 1914—created the following situation:

Country of Origin	Immigrants 1857–1914	Remaining in Argentina, 1914
Italy	2,300,000	930,000
Spain	1,500,000	830,000
France	214,000	79,000
Russia	161,000	94,000
Turkey and Syria	136,000	64,000
Austria-Hungary	87,000	38,000
Germany	62,000	27,000
Great Britain	55,000	28,000
Switzerland	33,000	14,000
Portugal	26,000	14,000
Others	126,000	239,000
TOTAL	4,700,000	2,357,000

In 1914 the population of Argentina was some 7,900,000.

This movement to and from Argentina is seen also in the annual statistics, which show the net movement for each year:

	Immigrants	Emigrants	Balance of Immigrants (+) or Emigrants (−)
		(Figures are given in thousands)	
1910	290	98	+ 192
1913	302	157	+ 145
1915	83	148	− 65
1919	70	68	+ 2
1923	209	61	+ 148
1936–40*	406	380	+ 26
1941–5*	332	321	+ 11
1947	452	406	+ 46
1950	692	532	+ 160
1955	52	29	+ 23

* Annual average for period.

We must now turn to the other features of Argentina's population geography. One of the most striking of these is the division of the population into urban and rural elements. In the years stated, the balance was as follows:

	Urban (%)	Rural (%)
1869	28	72
1895	38	62
1914	53	47
1947	58	42

By 1947, 39·3% of the total population lived in only eight cities of more than 100,000 inhabitants. In 1962 probably three-quarters of Argentina's people lived in towns of more than 3,000 inhabitants. Not only does the farm population suffer under the restrictions upon land tenure described earlier, but the rural housing situation also discourages settlement on the land. The agricultural census of 1937 classified 4% of the rural housing as adequate, 40% as usable, and 56% as 'defective', a euphemism perhaps better translated as 'unfit for human habitation'. Most of these houses have less than three rooms. An altogether fresh incentive must be provided, if rural settlement is to become more attractive in the future as the national interest demands.

Compared with the Argentinians of European descent, the remaining elements of the population are insignificant. There are a small number of Indians—the Guarani in the north, and the Patagonian Indians in the south. The few Negroes who were brought in as slaves have long since merged into the population. There remain the Gauchos, a mixture of Creole and Indian; a half-wild people who roamed the Pampas as wandering herdsmen of the great droves of equally wild cattle. They used the lasso and the bola (a leather thong with round weights at its ends, which, when thrown, wraps itself around the legs of the cattle and brings them down). Today those gauchos who remain lead a more orderly life, though a hard one, as *peones* or farm-servants.

What has been written regarding social backwardness in Argentina's rural areas, however, must not be allowed to obscure the fact that the government has made the most strenuous efforts to improve social conditions, in the first instance by education. Schooling is free and compulsory between the ages of six and fourteen, and in 1958 there were some 17,920 primary schools with 2·9 million pupils. There were also over 2,500 high schools with half a million pupils, and 134 universities and colleges with 153,000 students. In the rural areas, nevertheless, there is still a considerable number of illiterates.

Population estimates for Argentina forecast a figure of 28 millions for 1975, and 48 millions for the year 2000. Although this rate of population growth is significantly lower than in all other countries of Latin America (except Uruguay), it still represents a formidable increase and underlines the need for long-term planning by the government, particularly in the sphere of land use.

THE CITIES OF ARGENTINA

One-third of Argentina's population lives in greater metropolitan Buenos Aires. It is a commonplace to hear it said that Buenos Aires *is* Argentina. From its earliest beginnings, the city was overwhelmingly European in character. Those beginnings were slow; not for centuries after its foundation did the real growth of the city begin.

Today the port of Buenos Aires—a largely artificial creation that provides a dredged depth of water to 20 feet—handles some 20 million tons of cargoes annually. Four-fifths of the country's imports and one-third of the exports pass through this veritable 'Gateway of Argentina'. Lying as it does 140 miles from the open sea, it affords also a good break of bulk point for cargoes to or from ports on the navigable Paraná and Uruguay Rivers.

The already considerable industrial growth of Buenos Aires is partly given over to processing the country's raw materials and partly to the manufacture of a variety of consumer goods previously imported. Some of these manufactured goods are exported. The city is also the hub of the railway system, from which the lines fan out, north, west and south. This greatest of all South American cities today covers an area which in shape resembles a rather flattened star with four points, and in size extends over some 300 square miles. The areas of present growth are 15 miles from the city centre, and of the 300 square miles covered by the modern urban sprawl, all but 20 represent growth since the beginning of the present century. The last 20 years, in particular, have seen the transformation of the city centre, through the erection of tall blocks of buildings, and the construction of great radial traffic arteries, avenues of exceptional width cutting across the older gridiron pattern of the original street layout.

It was in the year 1536 that 'Puerto de Nuestra Senora Santa Maria de Buen Aire' was first founded, by Spaniards who chose the name as an expression of gratitude to the patroness who had prospered their voyage. But like a number of the other early Spanish settlements, it could not survive against the hostility of surrounding Indian tribes who feared for their hunting grounds. The second attempt, in 1580, proved more permanent but the settlement, poorly located on a low-lying shore, remained relatively insignificant as long as the settlements on the Pacific side of the continent continued to dominate the Spanish Empire. In 1776, however, the Spanish government withdrew its previous embargoes and permitted all the South American ports to trade directly with Spain. Buenos Aires then became the seat of a viceroy who was independent of control from Lima.

After the war of independence, the city became the base for the nation's dictatorship (see p. 94), and in 1880 the city was organised as federal territory and made the official capital of the republic. The role of provincial capital of Buenos Aires province passed to the city of La Plata, founded in 1882 and consciously modelled on Washington in the U.S.A. By 1903, Buenos Aires had passed the million mark.

Today there are some 6·7 million people within the entire metropolitan area. Of these, approximately a million and a half are foreigners, including probably 400,000 each of Spaniards and Italians, 100,000 Frenchmen, 30,000–40,000 Germans and the same number of Britons. Argentina takes pride in the fact that it possesses the largest city of the Latin world; a city of distinctive character, in which great obelisks replace the triumphal arches of European cities, and serve, together with hundreds of well-placed statues, to recall to the nation the great moments of its past. (See Plate 13).

Compared with Buenos Aires, all Argentina's other cities are relatively insignificant. However, Mar del Plata (200,000) plays an important, if seasonal, role; although it is 200 miles from the capital, it acts as a kind of suburb by the sea, and in summer may hold as many as half a million visitors from Buenos Aires. Farther south, Bahía Blanca (115,000) has become the point of export for the southern Pampas, and ships a large proportion of the nation's wheat. The other towns of the Atlantic coast are all small; they are simply collecting and supply centres for the sheep ranchers of Patagonia.

The situation in the north and north-west of Argentina is different. Along the Paraná, a line of cities has grown up. The most important of these—the second city of Argentina—is Rosario (671,000). It lies 250 miles upstream from Buenos Aires, is accessible to ships of 12,000 tons burden, and is thus the point where the grain of the northern Pampas can be handled most easily and cheaply. For the same reason, it has built up agricultural processing industries—milling, brewing and tanning.

As far as Rosario, there is a 22-foot channel; beyond the city the depth decreases to 12–15 feet, so that Santa Fé (190,000) further upstream plays a role similar to that of Rosario but on a smaller scale. Paraná (110,000) is the focus of a great grain-producing region, and Posadas (44,000), the chief town of the forested Misiones Territory, is a centre of maté production. Corrientes (100,000) and Resistencia (90,000) are local market centres, the latter specialising in cotton from the Chaco.

There is a further group of towns along the eastern foot of the Andes, some of them at elevations of 2,000–3,000 feet. A number of these are oasis cities, for this is a region of irrigation, and they have developed as agricultural production has increased in an area that was formerly useless. Among them are Salta (100,000) and Tucumán (250,000), the latter a fine modern city and a centre for sugar-cane growing. Santiago del Estero (90,000) was the earliest Spanish settlement in the interior (1533). Finally, Mendoza (110,000), with the snow-clad peaks of the Andes towering behind it, has become famous for its wines and its fruit, and is achieving a new reputation today as the location of one of Argentina's largest oilfields.

Between the Andes and the Paraná, on the eastern slope of a range of low hills, stands Argentina's third city, Córdoba (600,000). Its streets contain many buildings that are reminders of the great days of the Spanish Empire, when Córdoba was one of the chief centres of Spanish influence. It retains its cultural influence to the present day, and is in

Plate 1 (*top*). Latin America: the colonial period. Morro Castle, built by the Spanish during their long occupation of Puerto Rico, guards the sea approaches to San Juan (background), and serves as a reminder of centuries of piracy and of European rivalries in the West Indies.

(Courtesy: Pan American Airways)

Plate 2 (*bottom*). The Craft Industries of Latin America: the work of this expert Chilean basket-maker contrasts sharply with the heavy industry now developing in many parts of the continent (see Plates 33 and 38).

(Courtesy: Lan–Chile Airlines)

Plate 3. Brazil: Rio de
Janeiro, with the Sugar
Loaf in the background
(see Fig. 14).
(*Courtesy: Braniff Airways*)

Plate 4. Brazil: the coastal
hills. The imposing Rock
of Gavea towers over
the modern road winding
along the outskirts of
Rio de Janeiro.
(*Courtesy: Departamento
de Tourismo e Certames, Rio
de Janeiro*)

Plates 5 and 6. Two views of a Rio de Janeiro favela, 1964.
(*Courtesy: K. E. Webb*)

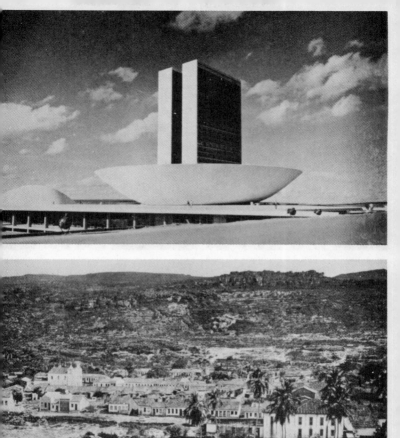

Plate 7 (*top*). Brazil: Brasilia, the new federal capital, which is being created 600 miles inland from the old capital at Rio de Janeiro, is a city of strikingly modern layout and architecture. The view shows Oscar Niemeyer's structures for the Brazilian Senate and Chamber of Deputies.
(*Courtesy: Braniff Airways*)

Plate 8 (*bottom*). Andaraí, a town of some 3500 inhabitants set amidst the 'Diamond' landscape of Bahia, Brazil (see p. 48).
(*Courtesy: Aerofilms for Ewing Galloway*)

Plate 9 (*top*). Uruguay: Montevideo and its harbour.
(*Courtesy: Pan American Airways*)

Plate 10 (*bottom*). Uruguay: Punta del Este, an exclusive seaside resort.
(*Courtesy: Pan American Airways*)

Plate 11 (top). Argentina: in the Lake District. A panoramic view
of Lake Moreno, near Bariloche (see Fig. 20), which may well remind
the observer of Switzerland or the Canadian Rocky Mountains.
(Courtesy: Braniff Airways)

Plate 12 (bottom). Argentina: one of the palatial estancias of the
Pampas—a ranch home in the vicinity of Buenos Aires.
(Courtesy: Aerofilms for Ewing Galloway)

Plate 13. Argentina: the Avenue 9 de Julio in Buenos Aires, looking towards the Plaza Republica with its 220-foot obelisk
(Courtesy: Pan American Airways)

Plate 14 (*top*). Chile: hunting seals in open boats among the miniature icebergs off Chile's southern fiorded shores.

(*Courtesy: Lan–Chile Airlines*)

Plate 15 (*bottom*). Puerto Montt: Angelmo Cove on the Tenglo Channel— a view of Chile's southern 'Lake District'.

(*Courtesy: Chilean Nitrate Agricultural Service*)

Plate 16 (*top*). Chile: a beach scene at Viña del Mar, near Valparaiso.
(*Courtesy: Lan–Chile Airlines*)

Plate 17 (*bottom*). Chile: drilling holes in *caliche* in preparation for blasting. A scene in the nitrate area of Chile's Atacama Desert.
(*Courtesy: Chilean Nitrate Agricultural Service*)

Plate 18. Chile: a ski-ing resort hotel 10,000 feet up in the winter sports region of the Andes on the highest part of the railway linking Mendoza, Argentina, to Santiago, Chile. (*Courtesy: Lan–Chile Airlines*)

Plate 19. Bolivia: Uru Indian fishermen on Lake Titicaca. Their boats are constructed of reeds, and if left in the water for too long will become waterlogged and sink. They must be brought ashore periodically and dried. (See page 140.)   *(Courtesy: Pan American Airways)*

Plate 20. Peru: the Machu Picchu ruins, set amid precipitous slopes, recall the former glories of the Inca Empire. The prominent peak is Huaynu Picchu which also has stone ruins on its summit.

(*Courtesy: Canadian Pacific Railway*)

Plate 21 (*top*). An Indian village or 'communidad' on the shores
of Lake Titicaca. (*Courtesy: Canadian Pacific Railway*)

Plate 22 (*bottom*). Peru: a scene near Arequipa. In the background, the Andean peaks rise to over 19,000 feet, while this region at
their foot is one of intensive agriculture.

(*Courtesy: Canadian Pacific Railway*)

Plate 23. Peru: Tiobamba, with its old Spanish church, and Mt Chicon rising in the background. Note the immense labour which has been expended in terracing the slopes. *(Courtesy: Canadian Pacific Railway)*

Plate 24. Peru: the Ragra mine of the Vanadium Corporation of America on the shores of Lake Punrun. Notice the extreme barrenness of the mountain slopes which have little soil cover and even less vegetation.
(Courtesy: Standard Oil Co. (N.J.))

Plate 25. Peru: transporting ore on llamas from a mine on the Altiplano to the railway. Each animal carries a load of only about 100 lb. (*Courtesy: Standard Oil Co. (N.J.)*)

Plate 26. Peru: women labourers at the Morococha mine. Among the Indian populations of the Andes, women have always shared the work of the men, and although they do not go underground, they work as surface labourers in the mines. These women are chewing wads of coca leaves, which tend to suppress a sensation of hunger or cold. This practice is widespread on the Altiplano.   *(Courtesy: Standard Oil Co. (N.J.))*

Plate 27. Peru: a highway through the Andes from Lima to Cerro de Pasco. Trucks of the kind shown here, carrying oil, wool, etc., and also passengers, are the backbone of the Peruvian transport system.

(Courtesy: Standard Oil Co. (N.J.))

addition an important route focus, with a thriving commercial community and a growing manufacturing sector including motor vehicle assembly plants.

The Economy of Argentina

It was in 1930 that the following statements appeared in a geography of South America:

> Argentina has the prospect of becoming, thanks to her favourable position, fertile soils and healthy climate, one of the world's leading producers of agricultural and livestock products. . . . With the help of a friendly attitude to other nations, an energetic white population, and a political climate which is now reasonably stable, she has become the leading trading nation of South America, and is responsible for one-third of the total volume of business in the continent.[1]

Since 1930 Argentina's economy has undergone, to an even greater extent than those of other South American states, profound changes which are still continuing. The overall effect of these changes has been to create economic problems and associated social and political tensions which place the country in a difficult position. The country's most pressing need is to achieve continued economic growth and rising living standards for the mass of the population within the fundamentally changed economic structure.

AGRICULTURE

In the great fan-shaped area of Humid Pampa which borders the Rio de la Plata on the west, and extends into Argentinian Mesopotamia—a fan whose hinge is Buenos Aires—there lies the agricultural heart of Argentina. The two principal farm occupations are the production of grain crops and fat stock. The soil is rich in humus, although with the less intensive farming techniques characteristic of the New World, the yields per acre are lower than in Europe. Wheat, maize and fodder crops occupy most of the cropland, but cotton, linseed, sugar-cane, sunflowers, groundnuts and rape are also grown. The farm units are generally large, but it is here that there has grown up the peculiar Argentinian system of tenancy (see p. 96), whereby some 70% of the farm area is at present being cultivated by tenants on short lease. Only recently has the legal minimum for these leases been raised to five years. By contrast, there are very few middle-sized or small holdings.

1 Harms *Erdkunde: Amerika*, 5th ed., 1930.

The present land-use figures for Argentina show that 41% is pasture land, 36% is forested and 11% is under cultivation. The spread of cultivation has corresponded closely with the extension of the railway network. In 1895, Argentina exported roughly a million tons of wheat. In 1961 the wheat production was 4 million metric tons, of which the greater part was exported.

Although the production of individual crops in the Pampas has fluctuated greatly over the years, as the following table shows, the trend for main crops has been downwards. Whilst fluctuations are due partly to climatic factors and partly to market conditions, the downward trend for main crops arises partly from a change-over from single-crop or single-purpose farming to mixed farming with lucerne[1] pastures and partly from adverse government policies towards the production and export of agricultural commodities.

ARGENTINA: Annual Average Production
of Selected Crops
(in mill. tons)

	1934/38	1944/48	1954/58	1961/64
Wheat	6·63	5·06	6·52	5·56
Maize	7·89	4·68	3·76	4·95
Linseed	1·70	0·86	0·51	0·74
Oats	0·75	0·71	0·91	0·73
Barley	0·50	0·83	1·10	0·73
Rye	0·25	0·36	0·76	0·42
Sugar	0·41	0·60	0·72	0·78

Agricultural diversification into crops intended mainly for domestic consumption has been rather more successful. In 1955, for example, her sugar refineries (41 processing cane, and 1 dealing with sugar beet) had an output of 584,000 tons of sugar, and she harvested 1½ million tons of potatoes and 37,500 tons of tobacco, and a cotton crop of some 120,000 tons.

The importance of Argentina's livestock production rivals that of her field crops. As we saw in Chapter 2, the first Europeans found no large

1 Lucerne, or alfalfa, is an extraordinarily useful member of the clover family; its roots are exceptionally deep, and it is consequently able to subsist in areas of very low rainfall. In addition it is a nitrogen fixer, and thereby enriches the soil in which it grows. After being grazed, its rate of growth is very rapid, so that the stock—which in Argentina remains in the open fields at all seasons—is provided with fresh fodder in both summer and winter. Alfalfa will generally yield 4 or 5 hay crops a year; in well-watered fields as many as 9. Its carrying capacity is five times as great as that of the natural range grasses.

animals in South America that they could use other than the llama and its relatives and the llama cannot pull a plough. As time went on, however, European animals were introduced, particularly cattle. In the first decades after their introduction, they multiplied very rapidly. With little restraint or attention, many of them ran wild, acquiring in the process a useful resistance to climatic conditions. These half-wild cattle were less valuable, and were known as *criollos*.

Originally, ranching on the Pampas was carried out on the open range, but soon there began to appear the barbed-wire fences of huge *estancias*, some of which were as large as whole countries in Europe. With this enclosure of the ranges, it became possible to separate the stock and to begin improving the breed. Ranching was placed on a permanent footing, and the numbers of cattle rose from 22 million in 1895 to 37 million in 1922, and some 45 million in 1960. Owing to the skilful way in which the *criollos* have been crossed with some of the best European breeds, the quality of Argentina's stock has risen very markedly. The statistics reveal that today more than 70% of the cattle are of good breeding quality. The numbers of milking cows, however, must appear very small to European eyes, when compared with those of beef cattle—the former number only 4 million head; they supply mainly the urban markets.

In the early days in Argentina, it was hides and skins which were the sought-after livestock products, rather than meat. Today, as the table of exports on p. 294 shows, meat is the more important commodity. Since 1950 the whole cattle industry has been subject to government supervision. In that year, some 9·4 million head of cattle were slaughtered, and of the resultant meat products four-fifths were consumed within the country. Today, Argentina has the highest annual per capita consumption of meat in the world—about 220 pounds, compared with 160 pounds in the U.S.A. (This, of course, restricts the possibilities of exports.) Furthermore, Buenos Aires possesses the world's largest meat-packing plant; it has a daily capacity for processing 5000 animals.

Sheep raising in Argentina is an activity which has been increasingly forced out to the remoter margins by agriculture and cattle raising. There are more than 46 million sheep, most of them of good breeds, and producers of both wool and mutton. They are to be found in Tierra del Fuego and Patagonia; in the drier, southern part of the Pampas where rainfall is insufficient for crops; and in the Argentine Mesopotamia. Most of the sheep, especially in the southern areas, are raised on huge *estancias*, which naturally involve very large amounts of starting capital, but also yield high rates of return. Argentina's share of the world's wool output has been maintained far better than the country's share of wheat, maize and meat production.

The Argentine grasslands also provided, in the early days of European settlement, a kind of equine El Dorado for the horses of the Spanish *conquistadores*, many of which had escaped and run wild on the Pampas. Statistically, the horse has held its own in Argentina much better than in North America. Today there must be some 5·5 million horses in the country, and these have been kept in use for field work until quite recently as there has been little incentive to mechanise agriculture and, in any case, shortage of foreign exchange has limited the import of farm machinery.

With the rise in certain agricultural sectors and the steady increase in population, Argentina has developed a number of subsidiary branches of her farm economy. There is, for example, a big demand for vegetable oil, and this was formerly met by the production of linseed. Today, the linseed is exported and the domestic demand is met by the processing of sunflower seed and olives. Then again, flour milling has increased, and the output largely goes to supply the domestic market. The distribution of the flour-milling industry, incidentally, reflects accurately the distribution of the nation's population: the province and city of Buenos Aires are responsible for more than a half of the total output of flour.

The government of Argentina has recently undertaken to improve the quality of the country's dairy products. Among these, the most interesting is casein, of which Argentina is responsible for almost half the world's production. The significance of this fact lies in the use of casein, which is the protein of cheese, as the base for a number of modern plastic materials.

MINERALS AND INDUSTRIAL DEVELOPMENT

The mineral resources of Argentina are somewhat limited, a fact of which the country has become increasingly aware. In 1928, there began the exploitation of a coalfield in the Rio Turbio district, a short distance north of the Strait of Magellan, and a railway line was specially built to link it with the port of Gallegos on the remote coast of southern Patagonia. The position regarding iron ore has also been unsatisfactory until very recently when new deposits were discovered.

Certain other minerals are, however, to be found among the mountains of the west and north-west. Thus there is manganese in the northern Sierra de Cordoba, and wolfram (tungsten) in the Sierra de San Luis. Copper, lead and zinc are found at heights up to 12,000 feet in the Cordillera of the north-west. To provide materials for the great volume of building construction which has been a feature of recent years, cement is produced from the chalk of the Sierra de Olavarría in Buenos Aires province. The country also possesses supplies of marble and of mica. Since 1951, all mining has been under state supervision.

To meet the deficiencies in domestic energy production, Argentina imported coal and oil in large quantities until very recently. Annual coal output was 283,000 tons in 1960, against requirements of over 2 million tons, and in 1956 oil production was 4·4 million tons, as compared with annual requirements of about 9 million tons. However, large reserves of oil were known to exist in several parts of the country and in 1958 various private companies were invited to help Y.P.F.—the State oil concern—to increase output as quickly as possible and to provide facilities (tankers, pipelines) to move it to the markets. As a result, by 1962 Argentina's production of oil had increased threefold from 5 to 15 million tons per annum and the country was virtually self-sufficient. At the same time, natural gas output has rapidly increased and the consumption and import of coal has been falling away as industries and other users have turned to oil and gas.

Most of Argentina's industries manufacture consumer goods. In terms of employment, the food products and beverage industries account for 22% of the total, the textile industry for 17·5%, and the metal goods industries (including machinery and vehicles) for 9%. Recently the country has obtained a number of assembly plants for European and U.S. manufactures imported in a semi-finished state. (These include motor car assembly plants which, in spite of initial difficulties, may become one of the most important industrial sectors of the economy.) Argentina's own principal raw materials are livestock and agricultural products, and these are processed in the meat-packing plants and the spinning and textile mills. The long-standing export of frozen meat (dating from the installation of refrigeration facilities in the 1870's) has now been supplemented by the meat-canning industry. Today Argentina ranks as one of the world's largest meat suppliers. The hides remaining after slaughter of the livestock are also exported, after being tanned with home-produced tannin from the quebracho forests.

The number of Argentina's industrial workers, which was 490,000 in 1937, has now arisen to approximately 1,400,000.

COMMUNICATIONS AND TRADE

In Argentina, natural conditions are relatively favourable for the creation of routeways. There are quiet, navigable waterways that penetrate from the core area of the state to its northern borders, and the vast plains are an open invitation to railway construction. It was the railway lines, most of them built with British capital, which were the original agents of settlement on the Pampas, and to which the earliest settlements clung; indeed in Argentina, perhaps more than anywhere else, settlement followed the railways.

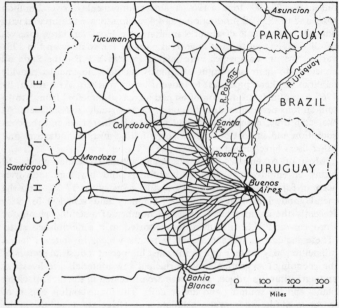

Fig. 19. Argentina: the railway network. Notice the convergence of routes on Buenos Aires and, to a lesser degree, on Bahía Blanca indicating the development of the system as a means of moving the products of the Pampas to the export ports. Notice, too, the complete barrier effect of the major rivers, the Paraná and Uruguay, on rail movement.

On the whole, the rapid development of the railway network militated until recently against the growth of a good road network. Today, Argentina possesses nearly 30,000 miles of track—easily the largest mileage of any South American state. In 1948, the Argentinian government bought out the foreign holdings in the railway system, and thus became the owner of the whole network of broad-, standard- and narrow-gauge lines. This network spreads out like a fan from Buenos Aires, and its shape is the clearest possible indication of the purpose for which it was designed: not so much to facilitate the interchange of products within the country as to speed the movement of goods between the expanding frontier of settlement and the port of entry from, and shipment to, Europe.

In Argentina's communications, both external and also internal, air services play an increasingly important role. There are no less than 170 airfields in the country, although many of these, of course, are merely unsurfaced runways. Buenos Aires Airport, on the other hand, some twenty miles from the city centre, is one of the largest airfields in the world and can accommodate the largest jet airliners. In addition the city has the advantage of an airport only two miles or so from the city centre. This is used by domestic services.

Inland navigation on the main rivers of the north is excellent, but, as we have already seen, it is limited to the main waterways because of the unreliable flow of their right-bank tributaries. The Patagonian rivers, Rio Negro and Rio Colorado, are navigable only in sections. Coastal and ocean shipping, on the other hand, have made good progress in recent years. Most of Argentina's merchant fleet consists of ships built since 1940, and her gross tonnage in 1962 was more than one million, of which about a third represented oil tanker tonnage. Only 17% of the total, according to 1950 figures, was passenger tonnage. The government has set itself the aim of being able eventually to ship at least a third of Argentina's exports under her own flag.

To conclude this chapter on Argentina's economy, let us recall the main problems which have already been cited, and which confront the nation in the immediate future. Both official plans and private efforts must be concentrated—and indeed are—upon ending the prolonged period of economic stagnation during which Argentina's share of Latin America's gross domestic product has fallen from over 25% to less than 18%. These plans and efforts include: (1) decentralisation from the cities, especially Buenos Aires, (2) relief of the present industrial concentration at the ports, (3) the opening up and full settlement of marginal lands at present only sparsely settled, and (4) provision of the necessary loans and credits to finance future agricultural and industrial expansion.

CHAPTER SIX

The Lands of the Andes: Introduction

(1) The Physical Setting

The Andes or Cordillera run parallel with the west coast of South America for a distance of nearly 4000 miles. They form a gigantic chain, seven times as long as the Alps, up to 500 miles wide, surmounted by a multitude of snow-clad peaks, and running across the territory of several states. These countries stretch—except in the case of Chile—from the Pacific Coast, inland across the mountains and into the great central lowlands of South America. Considering the variety of relief and the effects of the Pacific on its coastlands, it is not to be expected that these states show any uniformity of landscape between their eastern and western borderlands. This diversity between east and west we shall shortly examine in more detail.

The Himalayas, it is true, are higher than the Andes, and tectonically similar. But they cannot rival the Andes for interest and variety of their natural and cultural landscapes. The Himalayas lack the sweeping range of conditions that is to be found in South America: from humid lands to arid; from uninhabitable mountains above the snowline to tropical rain-forests; from jagged peaks and snow-capped volcanoes to broad plateaux; from coastal fjords to mountain basins choked with detritus; from powerful rivers to swampy areas, sumps and salt pans.

The eastern slope of the Andes, though steep, is generally accessible. That on the west is often wall-like as it plunges down to the Pacific—indeed, below the Pacific, for the precipitous slope continues to the bed of the Atacama Deep. Earthquakes are frequent, and bear evidence of continuing movements in the earth's crust. There are, in addition, some twenty to thirty volcanoes which are still regarded as being active.

This great north-south line of the Andes can be divided into three parts. In the south is a section formed simply of the main and subsidiary chains of the mountains; one of these chains has become detached, and forms a string of islands along the Chilean coast. The central section covers northern Chile and Argentina, western Bolivia and southern Peru, where the mountains merely form rims for broad, high plateaux. The third section, that of the northern Andes, consists of a number of parallel ranges enclosing smaller basins, and fanning out towards the north to embrace broad valleys that lead down to the Colombian and Venezuelan coasts.

But the real diversity of Andean landscapes is much greater than this simple threefold division suggests; a diversity based, as we saw in Chapter 2, on height and aspect, moisture and temperature. The *southern* Andes act as a great divide between the two populated and developed areas of the Central Valley of Chile and the Argentine

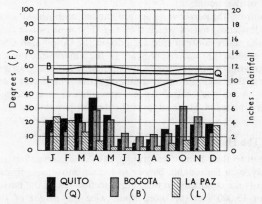

Fig. 20. The Andes: temperature and rainfall diagrams for three Andean stations—Quito (9350 feet, Lat. 0°), Bogotá (8700 feet, 4½° N), and La Paz (12,000 feet, 17° S). Notice how the monthly mean temperature for Quito is constant throughout the year, just as it is for other equatorial stations at sea-level; the mean is depressed by altitude, but the régime is the same.

Piedmont. In the *central* Andes, on the other hand, it is the high plateaux, rimmed with mountains, which are the economically and culturally developed regions. While the eastern slope of the central Andes is covered with rain-forests, the western slope is dry; here, in fact, is to be found one of the driest areas on the earth's surface—the Atacama

Desert. The aridity of the coastlands in these latitudes spreads far into the mountains of Peru; this is the region of the *puna* (see p. 19), an open grassland with limited bush and scrub vegetation. It is also a region where the altitudinal limits of plant life and human activity are tested. Here there has grown up the highest large city in the world, La Paz (11,900 feet). The tree line in parts of the western Cordillera is at 15,000 feet or above, and in Peru there are human habitations at altitudes of as much as 17,000 feet. In these dry, sub-tropical latitudes, under the influence of stable descending air, the snow line lies very high also; in places at 19,000 feet. Glaciers are few and permanent snow cover is limited to the highest peaks. Going south, however, the snow line falls to about 3000 feet in Tierra del Fuego and glaciers become much more numerous. Those on the west side terminate, in many cases, in fjords on the Chilean coast; on the east, they end in glacial lakes along the foot of the mountains.

By contrast, the *northern* Andes are flanked on both sides by humid tropical lowlands, out of which they rise. The west side is the wettest part of the entire continent; at Quibdó, in the Colombian Choco, the rainfall is some 400 inches per year. In the mountains, the short dry *puna* vegetation gives way to the moister, taller *paramo* grassland type. The snow line and the upper limit of settlement descend to lower altitudes. As in the central Andes, nevertheless, it is the mountain basins and plateaux which support the densest population.

(2) The Human Setting

In relation to their human geography, the Andes serve, first and most obviously, as a formidable barrier to human movement from east to west across the continent. In the central section few of the passes are at less than 13,000 feet (or more than twice the height of the most important Alpine passes). Even to reach the high plateaux from the coast is an undertaking that confronts the railway or road engineer with tremendous problems. He has to surmount obstacles at elevations which not even the funicular railways of Europe attain. Even although the capacity of some of the earlier railways through the Andes is no longer equal to the needs of today, yet the boldness of their conception and the splendid way in which they accept the challenge thrown down to them by nature merit for them a special mention. Such lines run from Punta Santa Elena up to Quito; from Callao and Lima to Oroya; from Mollendo, via Arequipa, to Puno; from Arica to La Paz; from Antofagasta to La Paz, and from Valparaiso, over the Andes, to Mendoza and Buenos Aires (see Plate 18). The Mollendo-Puno line reaches a height of over 15,000 feet. Road building poses equal problems for east-west movement, while in the north-south direction, although the technical problems are somewhat less severe, distances are great, and resources have so far proved inadequate to the task of developing a satisfactory road network. It will be some time yet before the Pan-American Highway is completed, as an all-weather, modern artery of commerce, throughout the length of the Andes.

But in the human geography of the Andes there is a more fundamental consideration: why these mountain lands should be so densely settled—indeed, why they should be inhabited at all. This enigma is well expressed by Arthaud and Hébert-Stevens, as follows:

At first sight—as no explorer since the sixteenth century has failed to observe—the presence of a population in the Andes at a mean altitude of 13,000 feet and a temperature below 10 degrees Centigrade (50° F) appears as a challenge to nature. It is readily understandable that a few scattered tribes of Eskimos should dwell in the Arctic regions, but it is hard to understand how any organised communities can maintain themselves in a territory five times the size of France and as high as Mont Blanc. Yet only yesterday, at this altitude, they managed not only to feed themselves but to build colossal cities by shifting blocks of stone weighing ten tons or so. At the present day they toil in mines extracting gold, silver, copper and tin, while a tourist newly arrived in La Paz is out of breath if he walks upstairs, and is liable to faint at the wheel while driving over some of the 16,000-feet-high mountain passes. European or American mining or hydraulic engineers are obliged to take certain precautions and to follow a certain regimen; even so, they rarely stay in the country more than two or three years.

It is true that the Indian, with his expanded thorax, his abnormal ratio of white to red corpuscles and his rapid circulation has adapted himself to his environment. But the mere statement of this fact is no answer to the question: Why this challenge to nature? Why did man choose a land where conditions of life seem less favourable than elsewhere, less suited to give birth to civilisation? And if we consider the pre-Columbian civilisations as a whole, why was it that the descendants of those yellow emigrants, who, forty thousand years ago, crossed the then ice-bound Bering Straits, preferred to settle on high and almost inaccessible plateaux: the Toltecs and Aztecs on the Altiplano of Anahuach, the Chibchas on the Altiplano of Cundinamarca, the Aymaras round Lake Titicaca, whereas only a few tumuli have been found in the fertile plains of the Mississippi?[1]

1 Arthaud, C., and Hébert-Stevens, F., *The Andes: Roof of America*, London, 1956, pp. vii–ix.

Whatever answer we may offer to this historical conundrum, there can be no doubt that, once settled in this mountain environment, the Andean peoples have been strongly influenced by it. As the same authors continue:

> The civilisation of the Andes is a mountain civilisation, and there are few countries where the configuration of the landscape has exerted so powerful an influence on the inhabitants and their evolution. Outwardly the Andes present the appearance of a simple chain closely following the outline of the Pacific coast, and forming a spinal column to the huge belly of the Amazon basin. But in reality the monotonous expanse of their high plateaux conceals an extremely complicated network of basins and widely separated valleys, and it was in these bowls and holes and cracks that the population concentrated. And just as the Alps range through France, Italy, Switzerland and Austria and are inhabited by Dauphinois, Savoyards, Piedmontese, Vaudois, Tyroleans, etc., so in the Andes we find a hundred tribes, the best known being the Chibchas in Colombia, the Paltas and Caras on the Equatorial plateau, the Urus round Lake Titicaca, the Aymaras on the Bolivian plateau, the Quechas in southern Peru. But the distortion of the principal languages into dialects and *patois*, from valley to valley, is even greater than in the Alps, so that the Andean civilisation might be compared to a Harlequin's coat whose three or four basic colours form a patchwork, the pieces, in the case of the Andes, being valleys and basins whose artificial bond of union is provided by religion or the state; so much so that every time one crosses a mountain pass one has the feeling of crossing a frontier.
>
> The Andes afford a striking illustration of the isolation and dispersion of mountain peoples, whether or not they belong to the same race, religion or nation. The ascendancy of the mountain over man is much greater than that of the sea or the plain. It crushes him with its ramparts, by the unending and almost insurmountable obstacles with which it confronts him, infecting him in the end with a 'valley complex'. With no horizons, with the very sky bounded by the mountain crests, a valley is a small closed world providing very simple and elementary object-lessons: a slope in the shade for one crop, a slope in the sun for another; a torrent, an occasional lake, and high above all a tutelary peak. On its summit dwells Inti the all-powerful creator, in its depths dwell the demons . . . Its menacing bulk, now far now near, forecasts the weather and the crops, sums up all the mysteries of life and death; and under its name the several communities gather together.[1]

1   Arthaud, C., and Hébert-Stevens, F., op. cit., pp. ix–xii.

CHAPTER SEVEN

Chile

Chile: Its Structure and Regions

The shape of the state of Chile is unique: 2600 miles long and, for the most part, little more than 100 miles wide. Nevertheless, Chile possesses —as the other Andean states do not—clear natural frontiers. The great barricade of the Andes forms her eastern border, a climatic and vegetational divide that gives Chile, between the mountains and the ocean, almost the character of an island. Her northern boundary lies close to the sharp bend in the main Andean chain; her southern extremity is storm-lashed Cape Horn. The north–south extent of this single, uniquely-shaped country is as great as the distance from Seattle to Miami, or from Copenhagen to Lake Chad.

The Chilean Andes consist, in the south, of a single main range, but at the latitude of Aconcagua (the western hemisphere's highest peak at 22,834 feet above sea-level) they divide into two, and in places three, ranges. On the Pacific side, there is a lower coastal range between the Cordillera and the sea; it rises to a maximum elevation of 8800 feet, but is broken by numerous river valleys running westwards. In central Chile, it acts as an enclosing wall on the west for the 500-mile long Central Valley, but farther south it runs out into the Pacific, to form the 3000-odd islands of southern Chile, much as the Coast Ranges and Olympic Mountains of the north-western U.S.A. become, in their extension, the islands of the British Columbia coast.

The main chain of the Andes diminishes in height towards the south and is cut by deep incisions and interrupted by the indentations of the fjord coastline. Snowfields and icecaps become more frequent on the peaks, and glacial lakes line the eastern, or Patagonian, foothills. South of the Strait of Magellan, the Andes of Tierra del Fuego swing

115

towards the east. They end in Cape Horn and Staten Island, and are then continued by the line of a submarine ridge which reappears in the Falkland Islands and South Georgia.

The present Andean relief is the product of several phases of mountain building. There have been a number of periods of uplift and depression of varying intensity, and today there are mature erosion forms to be found at great heights in the mountains. More recently, both glaciation and volcanic activity have played an important part in moulding the landscape. To the south of Aconcagua, the chain contains a large number of active volcanoes—Tupungato, Maipo and Osorno, for example—but these lie remote from the main populated areas. The area is subject, however, to frequent earthquakes, as a reminder that the latest phase of mountain building in the Andes is by no means over. Fractures and folds in which there is a displacement of as much as 40,000 feet bear eloquent testimony to the magnitude of the forces involved. Geologically speaking, this is a landscape which nature is still fashioning. Here is St-Exupéry's description:

> The pilot flying towards the Strait of Magellan sees below him, a little to the south of the Gallegos River, an ancient lava flow, an erupted waste of a thickness of sixty feet that crushes down the plain on which it has congealed. Farther south he meets a second flow, then a third; and thereafter every hump on the globe, every mound a few hundred feet high, carries a crater in its flank. No Vesuvius rises up to reign in the clouds; merely, flat on the plain, a succession of gaping howitzer mouths.
>
> This day, as I fly, the lava world is calm. There is something surprising in the tranquillity of this deserted landscape where once a thousand volcanoes boomed to each other in their great subterranean organs and spat forth their fire. I fly over a world mute and abandoned, strewn with black glaciers.
>
> South of these glaciers there are yet older volcanoes veiled with the passing of time in a golden sward. Here and there a tree rises out of a crevice like a plant out of a cracked pot. In the soft and yellow light the plain appears as luxuriant as a garden; the short grass seems to civilise it, and round its giant throats there is scarcely a swelling to be seen. A hare scampers off; a bird wheels in the air; life has taken possession of a new planet where the decent loam of our earth has at last spread over the surface of the star.
>
> Finally, crossing the line into Chile, a little north of Punta Arenas, you come to the last of the craters, and here the mouths have been stopped with earth. A silky turf lies snug over the curves of the volcanoes, and all is suavity in the scene.[1]

1 St-Exupéry, A. de, *Wind, Sand and Stars*, London, 1939, pp. 85–6.

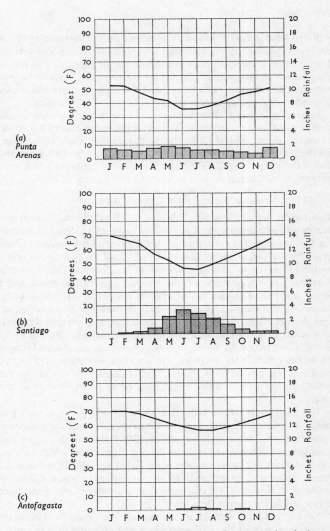

Fig. 21. Chile: temperature and rainfall diagrams for three stations in the south, centre and north: (*a*) Punta Arenas (53° S), (*b*) Santiago (33° S), (*c*) Antofagasta (23½° S) respectively.

River development is naturally restricted by the abrupt rise of the Andes in the east. In any case even the largest rivers, such as the Rio Loa in the dry north, do not reach the sea at all in some years due to evaporation of their waters. The southern rivers carry more water, but are often in the nature of torrents, and the whole country has a bare 200 miles of navigable waterway.

In terms of human activity and the conditions bearing upon economic development, we can recognise four main regions of Chile: the north, or desert region; central Chile, the most intensively cultivated region; southern Chile, a land of farms and forests and, finally, Patagonia and Tierra del Fuego. Fig. 21 illustrates the climatic contrasts which exist between three Chilean stations separated by 30 degrees of latitude.

(1) NORTHERN CHILE: THE DESERT REGION

This region lies north of the valley of the River Aconcagua, and is everywhere extremely arid. It is subject, however, to dense cloud and sea fog, the so-called *garuas*, which is the result of the presence of the cold Peru Current. But this bank of cloud, which is so often visible on the coast, almost never brings rain inland. Thus it is that northern Chile forms one of the world's most pronounced desert areas, and it is a matter of observation that its aridity seems to be increasing with the passage of time. Even in the driest areas, of course, here are occasional downpours, but these may only occur at intervals of several years, and the desert is totally bare of vegetation in many areas. Along the coast, due to slightly more humid conditions brought on by the coastal fogs, there may be a sparse vegetation made up of cacti and various bulbous forms. This is succeeded, inland, by the wholly barren area, and this in turn gives way to arid steppe on the east.

The north is usually sub-divided, on economic grounds, into two parts—the Greater North and the Lesser North, with the boundary between them lying roughly at 28° S. The former is the driest and broadest part of Chile, and includes the desert sinks from which nitrates, salt and borax are produced. The latter includes the highly mineralised region between Copiapó and the Rio Aconcagua, where rainfall is rather more abundant, but still unreliable, and where oasis agriculture is possible in the river valleys.

Northern Chile was long known as the World's Chemistry Laboratory. Among the resources which won this title for the region, the most important are the Atacama nitrates. In the heart of the desert, in an upland valley which runs parallel with the Andes for some 500 miles at between 3000 and 6000 feet, there lie the great nitrate beds of international fame. The region is almost entirely bare of vegetation, and what little cultivation there is depends on irrigation water.

Nowhere else in the world's deserts are there such immense beds of salts as here. Even the most soluble compounds are found in a bone-dry condition. Organic matter does not decay, but such objects as the bodies of dead animals undergo rapid dehydration and turn into stone-hard mummies. Another curious feature of the desert is that its surface retains the marks of chance events for many years; the wheel marks

of a vehicle may remain clearly visible for a decade or more. This is partly because chemical weathering, which would break up surface materials, is very slow here; partly, also, it is due to the fact that there is little loose sand to cover such marks, for the sand is held by the salt pan in a hard crust. This crust provides an admirable surface for the movement of vehicles, and the mineral railways were laid on it with the minimum of preparation for the road-bed.

Surprisingly, although the desert is for the most part an area where the silence of death reigns, it is not entirely lifeless. There are sea birds which have the curious habit of flying 30–40 miles inland to nest; to these nesting-places they must, of course, carry every bite of their food from the coast. The only reasonable explanation would seem to be that there used to be sweet-water lakes in this region, to the site of which some instinct makes them return. It is certain that the salt beds contain in large numbers the

Fig. 22. Chile: the nitrate region.

petrified remains of birds that must be some thousands of years old.

The famous nitrate deposits, many of them several square miles in extent, are strewn along the northern end of the upland valley, between 20 and 50 miles from the coast. Most of the deposits are to be found along the eastern foot of the coastal mountains in a belt 2–3 miles wide, where there is neither rainfall nor plant growth. The nitrate beds (known as *caliche*) lie near the surface, but beneath detritus which is cemented into hard layers by salts. (See Plate 17.) The beds have a thickness of up to 3 feet; in a few cases as much as 6 feet. To be workable, the nitrate beds must have a thickness of at least a foot. The beds are brightly coloured, grey, yellow or violet, and contain up to 70% of saltpetre. A content of 25%, however, was considered good and anything above 12% was worth working in the heyday of the industry. Slabs are blasted loose, broken up with hammers, and carried to the processing plant, which is known as the *oficina*, and usually employs 500 to 1000 workers. Here the material is crushed and dissolved in boilers. The brine crystallises out, and the product is pure Chile saltpetre, sodium nitrate ($NaNO_3$), which is used principally today as fertiliser.

Most of the *oficinas* are in the north, where groundwater is available; otherwise it is necessary to pipe water long distances from the Andes to the processing plants. By-products from the plants are nitric acid, iodine and borax.

The chief port of shipment for the nitrates is Iquique. From the port there runs the so-called nitrate railway, which links all the main *oficinas*. Other mineral-shipping rail lines run to less important points of shipment, such as Antofagasta and Taltal.

In the years before 1914 Germany was Chile's best customer for nitrates, while the U.S.A. purchased an almost equal quantity. The growth of the heavy chemical industries since that date has, however, altered and reduced the structure of demand, as Fig. 24 shows.

(2) CENTRAL CHILE

Central Chile is the country's farming region. It lies between the Rivers Aconcagua and Bió-Bió, south of Concepción. It contains the most fertile sections of the Central Valley, and is sometimes described as Chile's granary and fruit store. Here, there is a combination of fertile volcanic soils with a climate which, with the addition of irrigation water (mainly by sprinkler), permits the cultivation of sub-tropical fruits (Fig. 23).

Much of this region is under the plough, while the remainder is

Fig. 23. Central Chile: physical features. The shortage of precipitation in the Chilean heartland around Santiago is stressed by the insertion of the 10 and 20 inch isohyets. The line X-X marks a significant divide in Chilean geography. North of this line, most crops are grown under irrigation, and the flanks of the Central Valley are given over to stock raising; south of the line, crops are generally unirrigated, and the flanking slopes are under forest.

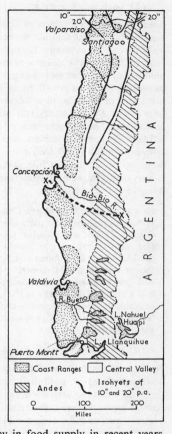

often park-like in character, with remnants of an original forest cover. However, clearance of this cover has been carried out all too ruthlessly, so that much of the arable land has suffered from erosion, and it has been necessary to start afresh and to pay due regard to conservation practices.

The traditional dominance of the large land-holding, the *hacienda*, has been altered slightly in recent years by a growing number of small properties. The fact remains, however, that land use intensity and productivity per acre in the Central Valley is higher on the smaller property than on the large haciendas which are worked less effectively than they should be —a fact which played an important part in Chile's inability to maintain domestic self-sufficiency in food supply in recent years.

The climate has the Mediterranean characteristics of winter rain and summer drought (see Fig. 21). Much of the scanty flow of the rivers is used, as we have seen, for sprinkler irrigation. It is generally agreed that the landscape of this central region of Chile, with its woods and its green fields, is a most attractive one. Its prosperity in the recent past has been enhanced also by the development of coal and lignite workings.

(3) SOUTHERN CHILE

Southern Chile is a region of farms and forests. South of the central region, the annual rainfall increases very rapidly. In the latitude of Valdivia (40° S) it averages 120 inches p.a., with a mean annual temperature of 53° F. The season of maximum precipitation remains the winter, but the other seasons are much less dry than in the north. The proportion of forest growth in the landscape increases. A short distance north-east of Valdivia, there begins also a line of glacial lakes along the foot of the Andes as they run south. These correspond to the Patagonian lakes, on the other side of the chain. The largest of these lakes is Llanquihue, with a surface area of 285 square miles. Behind it, the volcano Osorno (8700 feet) raises its snow-capped peak. Indeed, the landscape of southern Chile, with its mountains, lakes and glaciers, is very reminiscent of Switzerland; some observers consider it even finer.

How can I describe southern Chile without being a writer of romances? It is a land of the most magical-looking mountains; peaks like those of Osorno, Llaima and Villarica, snow-capped, perfectly formed volcanoes, that seem to rise straight up out of still, dark lakes—such peaks exist nowhere else save in Japan and New Zealand. It is a land of forests too; forests with great old monarchs of trees—giants rather—that ten men with hands linked cannot encircle, trees thirty generations old. And then it is a land of lakes; lakes of the most improbable colours—turquoise or emerald, or leaden, or steely—and waterfalls, too, that burst out of the forests and brush to plunge in wide, wild arcs into the depths below, foaming and raging. (Knoche.)

(4) PATAGONIA AND TIERRA DEL FUEGO

As they approach the southern tip of the continent, the Andes steadily decline in elevation, until their peaks are at only 6000–7000 feet. Both the fjord coastline with its fringe of islands and the mild climate are reminiscent of Norway. Precipitation is heavy—at least 100 inches per annum—and includes considerable amounts of snow. Here, in super-humid climatic conditions, the forest cover is dense. It is composed, for the most part, of conifers (*Araucaria*), but includes also evergreen beechwoods, a vegetation type which, in the northern part of the region, flourishes at heights up to 4500 feet. The forests are virtually impenetrable, on account of the dense undergrowth of luxuriant, bamboo-like grasses and giant ferns.

This region, forest covered and barely explored, is almost uninhabited. The sparse population is to be found mainly on the plateau steppes, where sheep raising provides a livelihood. Through the centre of the region, separating Patagonia from Tierra del Fuego, runs the Strait of Magellan. It is roughly 350 miles in length, and in places it provides a channel for shipping which is both narrow and dangerous. Nevertheless it is preferred by sailors to the stormy passage round the rocky projection of Cape Horn, except at times when sea fog blankets the Strait, and the open sea route is necessarily followed.

Tierra del Fuego, with its heavy snowfalls, its glaciers and its cold winters, possesses all the characteristics of an area of sub-polar climate. In sheltered spots, however, beech woods, and even poplars, can be found. The island was given its name by Ferdinand Magellan, who discovered it as well as the Strait which bears his name, in the course of his circumnavigation of the globe in 1519. As he passed through the Strait, he saw at night the bonfires of the Indians on shore, who had the habit—maintained to the present day on board fishing vessels—of keeping their fires burning in order to save themselves the labour of relighting them in that damp climate. The inhabitants of the island eke out an existence in these inhospitable conditions, and seem rather less well adapted to their habitat than the Indians of the North American Pacific islands. While they have a surprisingly highly developed ethical basis for their culture, the material development is very slight. Even today, there are some groups of them who subsist, with inadequate clothing, tools and weapons, on what they can catch or snare from the beech bark canoes that virtually form their homes. It should be added, also, that the number of Indians in the area is rapidly dwindling, and that the last few decades have witnessed the disappearance of several tribes. (See Plate 14.)

Chile: Land, Population and Economy

HISTORY AND SETTLEMENT

Chile became independent of Spain in 1810–11. But its history as a nation can hardly be said to have begun until twenty years after that date, when there at last appeared on the national scene a statesman —Portales—of real merit, who set the country's finances in order, reorganised the administration, and laid the basis for Chile's future development. Expansion of settlement took place and, around the middle of the century, the frontiers of colonisation were successfully thrust forward into the south, due largely to the wholehearted efforts of European colonists and to an agreement reached with the unconquered Araucanian Indians.

As the nation which was actively working the Atacama nitrate deposits, Chile was plunged early into the maelstrom of South American political and economic life. The fact that Peru and Bolivia both exercised sovereignty over parts of the nitrate region which were being exploited from Chile led to a declaration of war in 1879. There followed the so-called Nitrate War. In this Chile was victorious, and in 1883 received from Bolivia the port and hinterland of Antofagasta, and from Peru the province of Tarapacá. As a result, Bolivia was cut off from the coast. (A short-lived arrangement, whereby Bolivia was granted access to the Pacific by acquisition of the area around Arica, was later nullified. Bolivia has subsequently attained access to the Pacific via the Arica–La Paz railway, and 'in bond' arrangements for handling Bolivian imports and exports in the port of Arica.) On the east the boundary with Argentina was fixed in 1902, after British arbitration had saved the two countries from war. Chile's only outstanding territorial dispute concerns the Antarctic, where she claims the sector between 54° and 90° W.

Up to the beginning of the present century, most of the occupied land, particularly that in the Central Valley between Santiago and the Rio Bío-Bío, was held in large estates. Large-scale land ownership in this area persists and gives rise to much social unrest in the rural areas from which there has been a steady drift of population because of the absence of real economic opportunities for most of the people. Additionally, the growth of the mining industry in the north and the development of manufacturing around Santiago have led to the growth of an industrial proletariat. A significant middle class has also arisen in the urban centres. These developments have favoured the development of both liberal and left-wing political parties. In 1890 the reform programme of a liberal president led to revolution. Parliamentary democracy triumphed, but still the struggle continued intermittently. The great depression of 1929–33, which almost annihilated the nitrate industry, provoked a fresh outbreak of unrest. Since that time, Chile has been governed, for the most part, by parliamentary coalitions.

In the Congress all shades of political opinion, from communist to conservative, are represented. The present constitution has been in force since 1925, and it resembles in essentials those of the other South American states; universal franchise exists for those who are over 21 and who can read and write. Since some 50% of the population live in towns, where educational facilities are well developed, the number of those entitled to vote is constantly increasing, and represents one of the highest proportions of the population in any South American nation.

The composition of Chile's population is peculiar among the American republics. In terms of numbers, the Spanish Creoles form an important sector of the population, although by far the greater part are of mixed Spanish/Indian parentage. There are virtually no Negroes, but 20–30% of the population claim pure European descent. Among these, the Germans form an important element, at least judged by the strong role they have played in the expansion of settlement into the southern forested part of the country. Alfred Hettner has described the task which some of these German colonists performed, in the following terms:

> The life of the settlers was marked, from the first, by immense hardships and serious deprivation. Practically everything they needed—food, clothing, tools—had to be carried on their backs from the newly established port of Puerto Montt to their new homes, and they were obliged to use the same means to get their own produce to outside markets. They lived in crude huts and had to be content with a wretched diet, and then before they could sow their first crops they had the Herculean task of clearing the dense forest from their land.
>
> At last came the time when their harvests were sufficient at least to meet their own needs, and then as the years passed by, they were able to produce butter—famous throughout Chile—potatoes, and spirits distilled from them, honey and wax, for sale in Chile or even in Germany, and so to purchase in exchange the goods they so badly needed. In place of the first crude dwellings they could now build attractive houses, in style, layout and gardens closely resembling those of their homeland. The Germans of yesterday have become the Chileans of today.[1]

In that part of Chile which lies south of Concepción, these German settlers found a climate and vegetation which—apart from the wildness of this virgin territory—struck them as familiar. The idea of planned colonisation of this area originated with an engineer, Philippi, who came to Chile in 1838, collecting specimens for museums in Prussia. Later, he became a major in Chilean service and, with the approval of the young republic's government, he recruited immigrants in Europe. The first families who came forward were Germans from Hesse who were chiefly artisans. After a four-month voyage, via Cape Horn, they landed at Corral, the port of Valdivia, in 1846. In the years that followed, some 700 other families emigrated, and by 1922 these families and their descendants numbered roughly 15,000 persons.

In these early days, the immigrant population was concentrated in the three areas of Valdivia, Osorno and the shore of Lake Llanquihue, where farmhouses encircled the lake, and the mountains towered behind

1 Hettner, A.

them, thus strongly resembling a landscape in Alpine Europe. The new generation of colonists, however, had their eyes on lands farther south. Once the Chilean government had established its control over the Araucanian Indians and their territory, many of the younger colonists moved south. Although they were never very numerous, their contribution to the establishment of civilisation in that remote region was outstanding. In contrast with the rest of the country—and indeed, with most of South America—where large estates predominated, they demonstrated the economic and social vigour of a community of progressive small farmers. They became a prime force for good in the culture of their adopted homeland. As one Swiss writer has recently reported:

> The most commonly-heard language in southern Chile is not Araucanian or Spanish but German. It is spoken by people who have not a single drop of German blood in their veins. Furthermore, the style of building is not Spanish or Moorish, but German, and the familiar eaves and gables greet the traveller in Valdivia, Osorno or Puerto Montt. And yet the inhabitants, with their blue eyes and fair hair, have thought of themselves, for many years now, as Chileans. That they still feel tied by bonds of sympathy to the land of their forefathers, whose customs they follow and whose songs they sing, is understandable. But when their real fatherland calls for their services, they stand ready to a man. And their real fatherland is Chile (Rohrbach.)

All through Chile, there is a pronounced drift of population to the cities and towns. This has tended to concentrate the country's population in central Chile and in the northern end of the southern region. In the north, there are only three towns of any size—the ports of Arica, Antofagasta and Iquique. Arica (with roughly 20,000 inhabitants) and Antofagasta (100,000) not only serve Chilean hinterlands, but also handle much of Bolivia's traffic to and from the outside world. Both are enclosed by the desert, and Antofagasta would never have expanded even to its present moderate size were it not the regional focus of the north and a port of shipment for nitrates. Iquique (60,000) also owes its continued existence in this fiercely dry environment to the mineral wealth of its hinterland, particularly nitrates.

In central Chile, conditions for urban development are entirely different and much more favourable. Here, there is a cluster of splendid cities whose growth is rapid and continuous. The capital, Santiago, is today a city of over a million and a half inhabitants. In a sense it should be considered together with its port, Valparaiso (285,000), which is the point of entry for some 75% of the country's imports. (It is, however, significant that the proportion of Chile's *exports* handled by Valparaiso is smaller and is diminishing.) The port was founded in the mid-sixteenth century, but up till 1830 it consisted of little save a waterfront and a foreign quarter. Its growth dates from about 1830, when it began to serve both as a base for the whaling fleets and as a port of call on the long sea route from Cape Horn to California. It was from Valparaiso, too, that the supply vessels sailed to the northern ports with food for the desert mining communities.

Santiago, the fourth largest city of the continent, is peculiarly favoured in situation and climate. From September until April, the skies above the city are blue and cloudless. Only occasionally, beyond the distant peaks of the Andes, is there a thin bank of clouds to be seen. All through the summer, temperatures here in the city at 1500–1600 feet, are pleasantly warm and the air is dry, without any excessive heat, except perhaps at noonday in December and January. Even then, the low relative humidity makes the heat entirely bearable. While its summer maxima reach 90° F, Santiago's winter temperatures seldom fall below 40° F.

The appearance of the city has changed considerably in recent years. This is particularly so because it is largely due to the adoption of reinforced concrete that it has proved possible to overcome the earthquake menace in construction of large buildings. Today, in addition to modern and spacious residential areas, there is a business district where skyscrapers are springing up.

The third largest city in Chile and the regional capital of southern Chile is Concepción (170,000). It lies 8 miles above the mouth of the Rio Bío-Bío, and is an important commercial centre with a large foreign colony. Its port, Talcahuano (65,000) is the finest in Chile. Inland, Temuco (1962 population about 100,000) has grown to be the focus and market centre for a rich agricultural district. Valdivia (1962 population about 70,000) is known as the busiest city in southern Chile. It came into its own particularly after the arrival of the colonists in the south, and these colonists continue to play an important part in its life and commerce. The same may be said of Osorno (1962 population about 70,000). The remaining towns of southern Chile are Puerto Montt (45,000), a focus of local shipping routes on the southern coast (see Plate 15), and Punta Arenas (33,000), most southerly of all the world's towns, which is well known as an exporter of mutton and wool.

THE ECONOMY OF CHILE

In considering Chile's economic structure, it is well to begin by recalling the somewhat violent changes which it has undergone before attaining its present form. Chile was formerly one of the world's main suppliers of manufactured fertilisers. In the last years of the nineteenth century, however, the advance of scientific knowledge made possible the laboratory production of synthetic nitrates and thereby basically altered the demand for these fertilisers in the countries of Europe and North America. This development, however, may well prove to have been in the long-term interest of Chile, since it forced upon her the diversification of her economy, and the development of other activities less dependent on world market conditions.

The major natural divisions of Chile which were described in the last chapter remain valid as the basis of a division of the country into its main economic regions. In the arid north, mining is the principal activity; in the centre and south the emphasis is on agriculture and livestock raising, while in Chilean Patagonia economic activity is still little developed, in a region which was formerly totally unexploited.

Agriculture and livestock raising. The principal area of cultivation lies in the central third of the country. The total area of Chile is roughly 183 million acres, and in 1955 the area in farms was 33 millions, of which some 23·5 million acres were classified as meadows and permanent pasture. Of the remainder, 40 million acres are under forest and woods. To what extent the designation 'unfit for farming' can justly be applied to the rest of the country is a matter for investigation.

An outstanding feature of Chile's agriculture is the great variety of production possible in a country that stretches from tropical to subpolar latitudes. With the exception only of the hot humid conditions of the tropical rain-forest, Chile provides an almost complete range of life zones and environments. In consequence, we do not find in Chile, as in some other South American states, an agriculture based on a small group of export crops, but one which is genuinely diverse. If irrigation can be extended in the future, both the area under crops and the yields per acre will increase.

To this need for further irrigation to overcome the meagre rainfall of the important central Chile farming area can be added the need to intensify agriculture on the large estates which exist in all areas except the recently colonised south if agriculture is to expand.

There have been recurrent demands in Chile for a land reform programme, for in contrast to the great holdings—626 were more than 5000 hectares (roughly 12,300 acres) in extent and the average size of these was actually 54,000 acres—there were almost 90,000 farms in the country less than 5 hectares (12·3 acres) in extent, and the average size of these was only 3·9 acres. In addition to these contrasts in land holdings there are also large numbers of landless labourers. Overall, therefore, agriculture in Chile faces many difficult economic and social problems and the 34% of the population engaged in farming receive only 18% of the national income.

One aspect of the inefficiency of agriculture is its inability to feed the steadily increasing population of Chile. It has been necessary in fact to import foodstuffs, particularly wheat, sugar and beef cattle, and this in spite of the fact that wheat—which occupies about half the cropland——is a major product of Chile. The cultivation of sugar-beet is promoted by the government as a means of reducing the cost of Chile's imports. The country is, however, self-sufficient in potatoes, whilst other products such as lentils, beans and wines are produced in sufficient amounts to allow some surplus for export in certain years.

Cattle raising in Chile suffers from the handicap of a shortage of good pasture, and in fact Chile draws some of its beef cattle for slaughter from Argentina. In southern Chile, on the other hand, sheep raising is the most important farm activity. In 1950 the province of Magallanes contained almost a half of the total of 6½ million sheep in the country at that date. Punta Arenas, the only town of any size in the southern tip of the continent, has made itself a name, as we have already seen, as a shipping port for mutton and wool. The province is also the source of 70% of Chile's valuable wool exports. A third, rather curious form of 'livestock raising' was introduced into Chile by the German immigrants—large-scale bee-keeping. Today the products are exported far and wide throughout the world.

Fishing is of importance to a country with so long a coastline as Chile, and although development has been slow, the country has gained an important place in the whaling industry and has recently developed a very successful fish meal industry based on the large-scale availability of fish just off the coast of the northern part of the country.

Since the end of the Second World War, government economic policy has focused on the need to strengthen the whole agriculutural sector of the economy by means of a national plan for farming. The main points of this programme are: (1) Rural education, (2) Extension of the irrigated area, (3) Mechanisation and scientific agriculture.

It is, however, beyond question that in order that such a programme should be implemented, there must also be an improvement in the communications network. In a north-south direction, the sea route naturally forms the main axis of movement, but to link the interior—even of this narrow land—with the coast a great deal remains to be done. In particular, the great forest area of southern Chile must be opened up and made accessible for economic development; at present, significantly enough, the centre of Chile's forests products industry is not in the forested zone itself but in Santiago. Moreover, a programme of radical and fundamental land reform is probably a basic prerequisite for significant development of the agricultural sector of the economy.

Minerals and industrial development. Until recently the industries of Chile have been related rather closely to her agricultural production; they consist, for the most part, of such manufactures as flour milling, canning food and wine production. In the economy in general, and foreign trade in particular, mining remains more important than industry.

Up until the First World War, Chile dominated the world market in nitrates. The revenue from nitrate production was so large that taxes were almost unknown. By 1959, although nitrates and copper together still made up three-quarters of Chile's exports by value, the nitrates industry, suffering from the competition of synthetic products, had greatly diminished in importance (see Fig. 24).

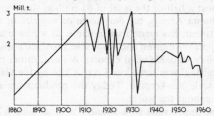

Fig. 24. Chile: output of nitrates, in millions of tons, 1880-1960.

The nitrate industry is becoming increasingly mechanised although it still employs 50,000–60,000 workers. But today only a proportion of the industry's profits remain within Chile, in the form of taxes; the larger part is received by the British and American companies which extract the nitrates. By contrast, copper production is increasing in both volume and value; by 1959, Chile was the world's second largest producer after the U.S.A., excluding the Soviet sphere (see Fig. 25). Indeed, according to some estimates, Chile possesses one-third of the world's reserves of copper. The copper deposits lie in relatively accessible locations near suitable harbours, and a recent new agreement between the Chilean government and the foreign owned (mainly U.S.) copper companies should provide the basis on which the rapid expansion of production and exports can be based.

Besides these two leading minerals, Chile produces a number of others in smaller quantities. One of these is iodine, of which the country is responsible for 70% of world production. Then, too, Chile shares the desire of other South American states to acquire its own heavy industries, and in this connection it is estimated that she possesses about 1000 million tons of iron ore for future exploitation; at present only one set of blast furnaces is in operation. While coal production has risen steadily since 1939 (to a 1960 figure of 1·42 million tons), it has not thus far proved possible to obtain a good coking coal, so that this grade of coal must be imported. On the other hand, the past decade has seen oil strikes in Tierra del Fuego such that the country now provides about three-quarters of its requirements, and there is virtually unlimited hydro-electricity potential. In 1960, some 682,000 metric tons of iron and steel were produced by the country's Huachipato plant, near Concepción. Meanwhile, a copper refinery had been established, 400 miles north of Santiago, and had gone into production

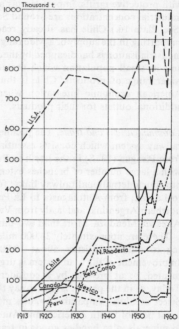

Fig 25. Copper Production: the output of Chile, in comparison with that of other major world producers, by thousands of tons, 1913–1960.

in 1952. The refining of copper in Chile is likely to be greatly expanded in the next decade under the terms of the new agreement with the copper companies.

It is apparent that the government and people of Chile are making strenuous efforts to secure for their country a place among the industrialised nations of South America. In this struggle, Chile possesses the considerable advantages of a wide variety of agricultural and mineral resources and of a diligent, enterprising population. Up until the present, the main industrial emphasis, as we have already seen, has been on consumer goods manufactured from agricultural raw materials, and these industries have been encouraged by the state in the usual way—with protective tariffs, import quotas and currency controls. The main industrial concentrations are around Santiago and its port, Valparaiso. (See Plate 16.) Chile has already reached the point where it is self-supporting in the supply of a wide range of consumer goods, but further industrialisation is handicapped by the country's out-of-the-way location and its small population which provides an insufficient market for a wider range of products. Chile is thus a strong protagonist of Latin American economic integration whereby new industries could find additional outlets for their products.

Communications and trade. The peculiar shape of Chile has produced a railway system which consists essentially of a single longitudinal line, from Pisagua (19° S) in the north to Puerto Montt (42° S) in the south, with a large number of branches extending to the east and west. Chile has four international railway links: from Arica, in the extreme north, to La Paz; from Antofagasta to La Paz; from Antofagasta to Salta in northern Argentina, and lastly from Valparaiso and Santiago to Buenos Aires via Mendoza. More than two-thirds of the mileage is state-owned.

There are approximately 34,000 miles of roads in Chile, and according to official statistics about 12,000 miles are all-weather roads. Improvement of the road system is urgently needed, even if it is supplemented, as at present, by a considerable traffic of coastal shipping. Today, as in the past, it is true to say that the Pacific Ocean is the Main Street of Chile. Valparaiso handles more tonnage than any other west coast port of South America, and Antofagasta, in addition to its traffic in minerals, also handles goods in transit to and from Bolivia—traffic which it shares with Chile's northernmost port of Arica which has recently developed an industrial base under the stimulus of 'freeport' status. The country possesses a well-developed system of airways.

The trend towards industrialisation which has been described, and which is evident in the details of Chile's trade, arises very naturally out of the past experience of a state whose exports have long been dominated by mineral products and whose economy was therefore very sensitive to international trade and business conditions. In recent years, imports of consumer goods into Chile have declined in favour of imports of raw materials for manufacture and of capital goods.

Like most other nations, Chile faces many economic problems. For example, the volume of money has been enlarged to make possible reforms and industrial planning, but has grown out of alignment with actual production. The result is that prices have risen faster than wages, and the consequent unrest and strikes have merely depressed production levels still further. It is a thought-provoking fact that, during the years 1938–51, government expenditures increased thirteenfold, while on the production side the quantity index of the national product merely doubled. Since 1951 there has been little or no improvement in this position, and today the average standard of living in Chile is probably very little higher than it was some 30 years ago.

CHILE'S ISLAND POSSESSIONS

Chile possesses two small groups of volcanic islands, which lie remote in the Pacific and are of little economic importance. The Juan Fernandez group lies some 400 miles west of Valparaiso, and represents an igneous intrusion rising from great depths. Among the group, Robinson Island, with 300 inhabitants, is known to the outside world, for it was here that, in the years 1704–9, the Scottish sailor Alexander Selkirk lived through the experiences which provided Daniel Defoe with the basis for his *Robinson Crusoe*.

Easter Island (so-called because it was discovered on Easter Day), is a bare, treeless island lying over 2000 miles west of Chile in the South Pacific. It has a rocky shore which makes it extremely difficult of access, and it is inhabited only by a few scores of islanders. But it is the location of famous stone statues, some of them nearly 40 feet high, whose origin is shrouded in mystery. There are several hundreds of them, and in a particular valley they are commonly found with their heads all pointing in the same direction. Nearby, there are still to be found the stone chisels and picks of obsidian, lying in the quarries from which the builders hewed these huge chunks of lava. One of the great secrets of man's history is locked up in this remote pinpoint of land in the heart of the Pacific.

CHAPTER EIGHT

Bolivia

Landscapes and Regions of Bolivia

Bolivia, like Paraguay, is an inland state, but its seclusion is even greater than that of Paraguay, which at least has its river link with the outside world. Roughly two-thirds of Bolivia's territory, however, lies east of the Andes: that is, in the remote interior of the continent. On the west, Bolivia comprises the mountains and the high plateaux of the main chain of the central Andes—the 'roof of the New World'. Even after travellers and goods have made the difficult descent from these heights the territory of Chile blocks the route to the Pacific.

The whole of Bolivia possesses a tropical climate, modified strongly by elevation and surface configuration. In general, the amount of rainfall increases from south to north. Thus on the high plateaux we find salt desert in the south giving way to the better-watered country around Lake Titicaca; on the eastern slope of the Andes we find sub-tropical woodland giving way to evergreen tropical rain-forest, and in the eastern lowland there is a transition from dry Chaco-type grassland in the south, through savanna, to the rain-forests of the Amazon.

The natural division of Bolivia, as suggested by Carl Troll, is best made between (a) Mountain Bolivia, comprising the Altiplano, the Western Cordillera, the North-Eastern Cordillera and Yunga zone, and the Eastern Bolivian Highland, and (b) Lowland Bolivia.

(a) MOUNTAIN BOLIVIA

The heartland of Bolivia is the Altiplano, the great central plateau of the Bolivian Andes, which stretches across eight degrees of latitude, and is enclosed by the Cordilleran chains on the west and the north-east. The Altiplano is actually composed of a large number of high-altitude basins separated by mountains 14,000–15,000 feet high. These plateau areas are generally higher in the north than in the south. It is in the north that Lake Titicaca lies, 12,500 feet above sea-level, and 860 feet deep. From the lake, fresh water flows through the area known as the Desaguadero to Lake Poopó. Farther south, these freshwater lakes give way to salt pans and salt lakes, and it is not, therefore, surprising that the south is virtually uninhabited, while settlement is still spreading in the north. It is from this northern region that Bolivia's railway extends, by two different routes, from La Paz to the Pacific ports in Chile.

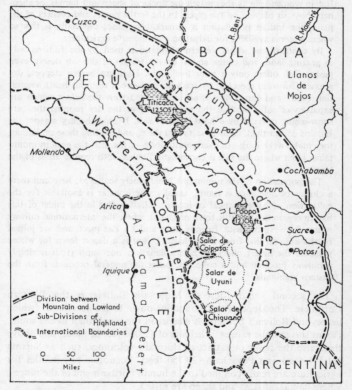

Fig. 26. The Central Andes: the major physical divisions, showing the Cordillera and the area of interior drainage.

This contrast between north and south is, as we have already seen, a product of the climate. The landscapes of north and south are described by Troll as follows:

Terraced like vineyards along the Rhine, the fields rise above the shores of Lake Titicaca. Here barley is grown, and potatoes . . . indeed, wheat and maize are produced too. Around the farmsteads stand the dark-green quinoa bush, and the quishuara, with its leaves that remind one of the olive tree. Otherwise the landscape is empty of trees. On the bare hill-sides above the cultivated fields, and on the yellow-brown steppes of the plateau, Indian women spin as they watch the flocks of sheep and llamas, or shepherd boys sit playing on the pipes. In the fertile nooks and corners of the plain, the Indian population is remarkably dense; especially is this so where water is available for irrigation and intensive agriculture.

By contrast, the whole western Altiplano is used by the Indians only as grazing land, and in the south, on the fringes of the salt desert, even pastoralism offers only a poor livelihood. Here are barren steppes, dry grasses (*Iru-Ichu*) scorched by the sun, dark-green resinous heath vegetation (*tola*), and sandy desert, all interspersed with the *salars*, which are expanses of salty mud in the wet season; in the dry months they are snow-white, covered by a hard crust of salt. During the dry season, the Indians collect thick slabs of salt from them, and loading these on llamas, they make week-long—or even month-long—trips into the eastern mountains, from where the salt is carried still further, into remote areas of the tropics.

The population of the mountains is extremely scattered; here and there a cluster of dwellings is found, usually where water is available for the cultivation of barley, wheat or lucerne (alfalfa). But in the midst of this barren region lies the little town of Uyuni, where the international railway routes from Antofagasta, Buenos Aires and La Paz meet, and are joined by the mineral line from Huanchaca. Uyuni is a desert town for whose presence the desert offers neither explanation nor support; it is simply a railway junction and a collecting point for mineral products from the eastern highlands.[1]

The second sub-division of Mountain Bolivia is the Western Cordillera. The slope of the mountains down to the coastlands (which lie beyond Bolivia's borders) is steeper in the north than in the south. Passes traverse the ranges at heights of 12,000 feet or more, and above them rise the cover of extinct or dormant volcanoes, such as Sajama (21,391 feet) and Payachata (20,750 feet). Economic possibilities for agriculture are really confined to the humid northern end of the ranges, where llamas, alpacas and sheep are raised.

1   Troll, C., 'Die Andenländer'.

The North-Eastern Cordillera forms the third section of Mountain Bolivia. The mountains are deeply dissected by the headwaters of the Rio Beni, which have cut into them in valleys of great natural splendour. They bear various local names such as Cordillera Real. This range dominates the region, with its 18,000-foot peaks and its heavily glaciated summits, and it is crowned by the great mass of Illampu (21,490 feet). It effectively divides two contrasting habitats. On the western side of the range, there are settlements of shepherds and pastoralists lying in the upland steppe zone at heights up to 15,000 feet. The eastern side, on the other hand, is virtually uninhabited. On this east side the moss forest of

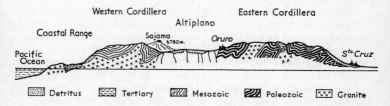

Fig. 27. The Andes: schematic profile along the 18th parallel of south latitude.

the mist zone (see p. 150) reaches heights of over 11,000 feet. Below it, in these latitudes where the Andes are at their broadest, we find the tropical zone of the *Yungas*, which comprises the *tierra caliente* and *tierra templada*. Each *tierra* produces its specific crops, including the coca leaves which seem an almost indispensable narcotic to the Indians in alleviating the pain of cold and hunger, while the products of the Altiplano find a ready sale here. In this region neither railway nor road construction has ever made much headway due to the extremely hazardous and costly nature of such work in an area of precipitous slopes and low productivity.

The last section of Mountain Bolivia is usually known as the Eastern Bolivian Highland. It is a mountain region dissected by deep valleys, and enclosing numerous basins and plateaux where the population is quite densely concentrated and agriculture is carried on. These areas of settlement are well watered, and produce valuable supplies of maize, fruit and wine. The towns of Sucre, Cochabamba and Tarija have all grown up in such basins, to be important centres within the region.

(b) LOWLAND BOLIVIA

The lowlands of Bolivia, beyond the Andes, form the larger part of the territory of the state, but they are also the most sparsely populated part. A comparison of lowland northern Bolivia with the Altiplano reveals the immense range of conditions to be met with within the country's borders. On the Altiplano, the mean annual temperature is 50–58° F. In the interior lowlands, conditions vary from the hot and humid climate of the *selvas* in the north to the extremes encountered in the savannas of the Chaco in the south-east—very high temperatures, frosts and a rainfall which averages 36–40 inches p.a. but varies by 20–25 inches from year to year.

The town of Santa Cruz lies approximately at the point where the forests of the north and the savannas of the south merge into one another. In the plains of the Rio Beni valley, there is a very marked dry season between May and October. This whole great expanse of lowland lies below 1000 feet, and thus reflects the gentle gradient of the Amazon on its 1500-mile journey to the sea. The best sections of the lowland, at least with regard to the prospects of growing rubber, lie in the so-called Acre territory which Bolivia sold to Brazil in 1903 and which became a Brazilian state in 1962.

Bolivia: Land, Population and Economy

HISTORICAL

The territory which has, since 1825, been known as Bolivia was originally called Alto Peru (Upper Peru), and formed a part of the viceroyalty of Lima. The new state took its name from the great leader for independence in South America, Simón Bolívar. Later on, efforts were made to combine it with Peru, but they failed. Then trouble arose with Chile. After a brief flare-up in 1864, there was a lull until 1879, when the Nitrate War erupted as a result of Chile's opposition to the payment of nitrate taxes, in the then-Bolivian Atacama, by enterprising Chilean exploiters.

Bolivia was defeated in the war; its mountain peoples proved unequal to the demands made on them by the desert war, and Chile took possession of the nitrate region. In place of its former territories stretching to the Pacific, Bolivia had to be content with two railway lines, linking it with Arica and Antofagasta on the coast. Then in the second half of the nineteenth-century Bolivia also lost territory to its great neighbour Brazil. Between 1932 and 1938 (the Chaco War) further territory was lost to Paraguay. The mountain region known as Puna de Atacama had already been ceded, in 1898, to Argentina; Bolivia had no further interest in the area after the loss of the Atacama Desert. In 1929, an agreement between Bolivia and Chile diminished Bolivian hopes of securing the return of a corridor of territory along the Arica–La Paz railway, and thereby of gaining access once more to the sea. Repeated negotiations on this point have produced no result, and relations between the two countries continue to be strained over this long-standing problem.

The internal and external affairs of Bolivia were long dominated by the great mining companies and the large landowners. It was only in 1952, following a revolution pledged to change the fundamental structure of Bolivian society, that the country at last secured a government avowedly opposed to these interests. The revolution was only the second one in Latin America (the first had been in Mexico in 1910) which set out to change fundamentally the structure of society. A new constitution which recognised the rights of the Indians forming the overwhelming majority of the population; a basic land reform involving the redistribution of the land to the peasants; the nationalisation of the tin mines—these were three of the main elements in this revolutionary process which brought political stability to Bolivia until 1964.

POPULATION AND SETTLEMENT

More than half the population of Bolivia is of pure Indian extraction. In the northern Bolivian highlands, many of the Indians speak Quechua, the language used over much of the central Andean region. The language of most highland Indians in Bolivia is, however, Aymara. At the time of the Spanish penetration, the Quechua-speaking peoples possessed the most developed civilisation of any tribe within the great Inca Empire, and they still adhere rigidly to many customs dating from that period (*ca.* A.D. 1300–1500). There exist, for example, groups of these people who hold their land in communal ownership, who live in self-contained communities (*communidades*) under a leader, and in this fashion work, harvest and celebrate their festivals.

Once again it is the configuration and particular climate of the mountain that accounts for this natural socialism. In a valley no cultivation is possible without the building of terraces to hold up the earth and above all without irrigation. In the mountains a peasant is bound to his neighbours by ties of mutual dependence. If he neglects his own portion of terrace, or deflects all the water for his own use, the whole community will suffer. This elementary solidarity of the peasants has been preserved in the Andes since prehistoric times by the *ayllu*, a kind of collective farm.[1]

With the arrival of the Spaniards, after 1530, this ancient form of society was replaced by the European feudal system. The American lands were divided between a few large owners, and the native population on each estate became *pongos*, or in effect serfs, whose labour went with the ownership of the estate. Relics of this feudal régime are to be found to this day in the tenant labour of the so-called *fincas*.

The Bolivian Indians are a talented people, but their advance into the modern world was slow until the 1952 revolution. Even now most important positions in business and mining are held either by whites or by mestizos, among whom there is a strong European element. However, Bolivia has not experienced, as have other South American states, a real immigrant wave from mid-latitude lands; there are few areas considered sufficiently attractive for such colonisation, and in these the presence of a considerable Indian population complicates the issue.

Among the Indians themselves, there are considerable differences in modes and standards of living. Perhaps the most interesting group is formed by the Urus of Lake Titicaca:

> Under the pressure of more highly organised tribes, the Urus—who have never possessed either chiefs or sorcerers—arrived by stages on the shores of Lake Titicaca, whence they were driven by the Aymaras to take refuge in the marshes. There they built themselves islands of stacked reeds, and there they have remained, retaining their language, their customs and religion, a segregated people despised and at the same time feared on account of their miraculous origin [in the eyes of neighbouring tribes] and their peculiar way of life in the midst of the waters.
>
> There they have invented a 'reed civilisation'. Houses, boats, nets, mats, and even clothing not so long ago, are all made of reeds, whose pith and bulbous roots also provide a kind of gruel and drink. Over great stretches called *totora* the reeds teem with shrimps and with nesting birds—ducks, gulls, flamingoes, woodcock and moorhen. The Urus gather the eggs, and hunt with a very primitive weapon made of two wooden balls roped together: the rope breaks the birds' feet, and the balls float and prevent them from rising off the water.[2] (See Plate 19.)

The density of population in Bolivia is shown in Fig. 28. It is obvious from the map that the area of population concentration is small. In any

1   Arthaud, C., and Hébert-Stevens, F., *The Andes: Roof of America*, London, 1956, pp. xvii–xviii.
2   Arthaud, C., and Hébert-Stevens, F., op. cit., p. 133.

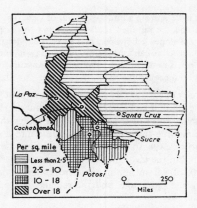

Fig. 28. Bolivia: population density, by
departments, 1950.

event, more than three-quarters of the population live at altitudes above
10,000 feet. La Paz, the capital, lies at almost 12,000 feet, in a basin
high in the Cordillera Real and just below the eastern border of the
Altiplano. Troll describes the scene:

> The profound impression made upon the foreign visitor by the basin in
> which La Paz lies is produced not merely by the grandeurs of the scene,
> but also by the suddenness with which it comes into view, at a point where
> there is nothing to lead him to anticipate it. Before him, a wide
> monotonous, detritus-strewn plateau slopes gradually away and up towards
> the bare brown foothills of the distant snow-clad Cordillera. Then all
> at once he is looking down into a valley, scooped out in the plain, with
> steep sides and a depth of 1500 to 2000 feet. On the other side of the valley,
> towards the north, the surface of the plain continues briefly beyond the
> interruption provided by this great hollow. To the east, across a valley
> which grows deeper as it runs away from the observer, there opens up a
> magnificent view of that superb peak, Illimani. The slopes of the basin are
> scored by erosion, and cut into all sorts of gullies and folds, and beneath
> the sparse vegetation cover, the bare rock is visible—glistening grey, or
> bluish, or even a glaring red. Over the smoother slopes there spreads the
> fawn-coloured vegetation mantle of the *puna* steppe on the higher ground,
> while at lower elevations the grain fields, laid out in regular patterns,
> gleam yellow in May and June when the sparse vegetation of the *puna* is
> withering away after the rains. The whole floor of the valley and the lower
> river terraces are occupied by La Paz, its sea of buildings laid out here for

inspection, as it were, from a bird's eye point of view. The gridiron pattern of the streets and the red-tiled roofs spread out to the perimeter of the basin, where the slopes get steeper, and there the pattern breaks up; the trees that line the suburban avenues are replaced by clumps of eucalyptus, and one sees roads and railways winding their way up the slopes, out of the basin and onto the Altiplano.[1]

This capital city of La Paz has usurped the dominant place once held by Sucre. As a capital, it lacks central position, but on the other hand it lies at the crossing point of the two principal routes through Bolivia: the great diagonal line from Peru to Argentina and a second—as yet incomplete—from Chile to Brazil. The growth of La Paz has been particularly rapid in the past three decades, and today it has a population of 348,000, of whom about one-third claim to be white, nearly a half are of mixed parentage, and the remainder are Indian. Pahlen describes the city:

> In recent years, La Paz has acquired a number of large multi-storey buildings, as well as an impressive university block; it has achieved well-surfaced boulevards, good hotels, modern shops and a swarm of motor cars. But it has also retained, even in the city centre, much of the old-world charm of its colonial mansions, with their projecting wooden balconies that serve to shade the narrow streets a little from the dazzling sunlight. It possesses, too, those wonderful old churches in monumental baroque, with their splendid doorways and dim, treasure-filled interiors. Here at last is a great South American city which has nothing stereotyped about it. All the streets are hilly (for the floor of the valley is hummocky), and none of them is straight. There are corners and alleys to delight the artist, relics of a former era, and one half expects to see some Spanish grandee emerging from the doors of these houses.[2]

Today, La Paz is the centre of the political, economic and cultural life of Bolivia. It possesses attractive suburbs where, in interesting contrast to most cities, the villas and houses are situated by preference not on the highest sites available, but on the lowest, in order to obtain whatever shelter can be found for the cultivation of trees and flower gardens and to minimise the effect of altitude.

Cochabamba (90,000) is Bolivia's second city, with rail and road links to La Paz over the salt flats via Oruro, and other road links with the region east of the mountains. The town lies at 8000 feet above sea-level in the Eastern Cordillera, and is the centre of a densely populated agricultural district. Oruro (82,000), lying at 12,300 feet, is an important

1   Troll, C., 'Die Andenländer.'
2   Pahlen, K., *Südamerika, eine neue Welt*, Zürich, 1949.

junction of road and rail routes. Around the town are important silver and tin mines. The famous old silver city of Potosí (54,000), which in the sixteenth and seventeenth centuries must have had a population of about 200,000, survives today as a tin-mining centre. High up, on the flanks of the 15,400-foot 'silver mountain', the remains of buildings and squares and the traces of old streets are reminders of the great days of Potosí; days when this city could proudly compare itself with those of the Spanish homeland.

The development of Sucre (60,000), still officially Bolivia's capital city, has gone on very slowly, now that it has lost its old functions. What is left, however, to this old city is its reputation of being one of the most attractive in Bolivia. Lastly, the only large city of lowland Bolivia is Santa Cruz de la Sierra (67,000) amidst the eastern foothills of the Andes. Founded as early as 1560 by Spaniards from Asunción, it stood on the old silver road to the Rio de la Plata. Today, it has regained a certain importance with the construction of transport facilities from Bolivia to Corumbá, on the Brazilian side of the Paraguay. This link with the more powerful eastern neighbours has set the stage for Bolivia to achieve a fuller exploitation of the resources of her eastern territories.

THE ECONOMY OF BOLIVIA

There is an ironical saying in Bolivia that the country is 'a beggar on a throne of gold'; a sparse population lives in poverty amidst rich natural resources. There is a striking discrepancy between the occupational structure of the population and the foreign trade situation: 70% of the work force is employed in agriculture—mainly of a subsistence type—but over 90% of the country's exports are products of mines. The national economy, in fact, is based on mining the varied resources of this mineral-rich land. And this dependence on exporting mineral wealth renders Bolivia susceptible to world commodity market fluctuations in much the same way as does the dependence of other Latin American states on agricultural exports.

Agriculture and livestock raising. The area farmed makes up about 2% of Bolivia's total land surface, and most of this farmland is to be found on the Altiplano, at heights up to 13,000 feet where conditions are hardly ideal for most crops. Agricultural techniques are, for the most part, exceedingly primitive, although a start was made with mechanisation and with more intensive methods on some of the big estates, or *fincas*—semi-feudal institutions where the Indians were obliged to work for the estate owner for three days per week—until they were broken up after the 1952 revolution. This redistribution of land to the former landless Indians led to an apparent decline in agricultural output—although this may have been due to greater food consumption by the Indians now working their own land. In any case, by the early 1960's the former level of output had again been achieved.

Conditions in Bolivia permit the cultivation of almost all the crops needed for the country's food supply, but in fact the production of foodstuffs does not cover requirements. In the highlands, where the population is relatively dense and the standard of living low, the Indians grow wheat, maize, barley, beans and potatoes, as well as a variety of vegetables. The lowlands east of the Andes, on the other hand, could be used for the cultivation of almost any tropical crop, but they remain largely undeveloped although some colonisation and experi-mentation is now being initiated partly through a programme of British technical assistance. About 40% of Bolivia is forested. The exploitation of these forests, however, is hindered by the low density of population and the lack of transport facilities.

Centuries of cultivation of these same farmlands and unwise farming methods have worn out the highland soils. The remarkable irrigation works built by the Incas are today in ruins. Efforts have been made by agencies of the United Nations to improve this agricultural situation and increase production, especially in the sphere of livestock raising. There are 7·2 million sheep in Bolivia, 2·2 million cattle, 1·2 million goats, half a million pigs and some 2 million llamas, alpacas and vicunas, but the wool-bearing animals provide less than half of the country's wool requirements, a serious deficiency where so much of the population lives on a high plateau and under such generally cool climatic conditions, and one that could be relatively easily overcome with modern techniques.

Minerals and industry. The industries of Bolivia are generally limited to simple forms of consumer goods production, designed to meet internal needs only. Most of this very limited industrial development has taken place in and around La Paz, where food processing and canning have made considerable progress in recent years. Flour milling and canning are the most important branches of industry; then follow brewing and textiles. The raw materials for the latter must be in part imported.

By far the greatest part of the national production is provided by minerals. These account for 80% of government revenue and some 90–95% of the value of exports. The leading product today is tin. This was not always the case; we have already seen how, in colonial days, it was the silver mines of Potosí that created there the greatest city in the Americas and provided the revenues of Spain. Then a century ago, vast deposits of tin were uncovered, and since the turn of the century it is tin which has been the principal source of wealth. But there is a long list of subsidiary products, among them antimony, copper, lead, zinc, tungsten, bismuth, manganese, iron, mercury and sulphur. The chief mining areas are in the vicinity of La Paz, Oruro and Potosí, and in these are to be found some 6% of the population—50,000 miners with their families. The work is very exacting and productivity is low, due partly to the altitude and its effects and partly to the low degree of mechanisation in the mines and partly to the inefficient organisation of the nationally owned enterprise which suffers from a lack of capital and modern know-how. Some of the mines are at heights up to 18,500 feet.

Both oil prospecting and oil production are on the increase. New discoveries both by Y.P.F.B., the State oil company, and by Gulf Oil indicate the possibilities of oil exports in the near future. Initially these will move via a pipe-line which already exists down to the Chilean port of Arica through which Bolivian trade has complete freedom of movement. The country's hydro-electric potential has never been accurately assessed but is thought likely to be more than sufficient to meet foreseeable demands.

With all this, the number of industrial establishments in Bolivia doubled between 1940 and 1950 (although most of them were small) and the number of workers in them increased from 12,000 to 20,000. But there are very serious obstacles—problems of labour, capital supply, markets, transport—in the way of any more far-reaching industrialisation, which might involve capital goods or even the finishing of consumer goods manufactured within the country.

Transport and commerce. In Bolivia, lack of transport facilities is a basic hindrance to all economic development, even although considerable improvements have been made in this respect in recent years. The fundamental difficulty is, of course, the mountainous terrain and the consequent cost of all construction. It was British capital which built the railway linking La Paz with the coast, and British interests were dominant in railway ownership until the State took over responsibility. There are approximately 1500 miles of railways, all to be found either on the high plateaux or else linking these with the coast. There are reported to be 13,000 miles of roads, but little more than 2500 of these can be classed as 'all-weather'. In Bolivia, as in other Andean and Central American states, the Pan-American Highway is intended eventually to form the backbone of a developed road system. At present the pack animal is the standard means of transport over much of the country, and in this respect air transport is making it possible, in many areas, to by-pass the intermediate stages of transport development between these two extremes of the primitive and the modern.

Mineral exploitation, the mainstay of Bolivia's economic position in world trade, was largely in the hands of big foreign corporations until the industry was nationalised after the 1952 revolution. In 1946, Bolivia produced 46% of the world output of tin. Since that date, however, its share of world production has steadily diminished, as the South-East Asian tin producers (of which the chief is Malaya) have recovered from wartime conditions and reasserted their position in world markets. Lead production, although almost equal to that of tin by weight, has a value only one-tenth as great.

The structure of Bolivia's foreign trade, then, is notably unbalanced. Before the Second World War, Great Britain was the principal buyer of Bolivian ores (providing a market for up to 80% of all ore exports). In the post-war years, the U.S.A. became Bolivia's chief customer, and now consumes about half of the ore exports. More than a half of Bolivia's imports are manufactured or processed goods, and about a quarter consist of prepared foodstuffs. The remainder are textiles, agricultural and mining machinery, iron and steel goods, electrical equipment, office equipment, and chemicals.

This heavy dependence on exports of minerals inevitably renders Bolivia highly susceptible to the effects of fluctuations in world commodity prices. In the depression years of the early 1930's, this dependence became clear; between 1925 and 1932 the average income in the country declined by one-fifth. In the 1930's, minerals made up between 90% and 98% of the export total, declining in 1960 to only 78%. On several occasions political unrest has been checked by timely discussions between the Bolivian government and the United States government whose financial aid to Bolivia is indispensable in the present economic situation. Even here, in this under-developed land, the effects of currency controls, increases in the volume of money in circulation, and wage disputes make themselves felt.

CHAPTER NINE

Peru

Peru: The State and Its Regions

The name of Peru calls to the twentieth-century mind a nation that
stretches from the Pacific across the Andes to the forests of the Amazon.
But there was a time when this same name applied to virtually the whole
Spanish Empire in South America, from the Pacific and the Caribbean
to the Atlantic and the Rio de la Plata. It was in the modern Peru that
this great empire survived longest, when the time for its dissolution came.

As it runs from north to south across Peru the Andean belt broadens,
the narrow longitudinal valleys open out and then merge to form, in
the south-east of the state, a region of upland basins like that across the
border in Bolivia. The whole state can be divided into three physical
provinces: 1. The coastal zone (*costa*); 2. The mountains (*sierra*);
3. The forest lands of the eastern Andean slope and the Amazon lowland (*montaña*).

(1) THE COASTAL ZONE

The coastlands of Peru vary considerably in width from point to point,
but are almost uniformly a dry zone. They form, in fact, the northern
end of the great desert belt that stretches diagonally from north-west
to south-east across the Andes into Patagonia. The longshore winds
over the Pacific are virtually rainless since above the cold Peru
Current the great stability of the chilled air reduces convection, and
consequently precipitation, to a minimum.

There are slight differences in local surface configuration along the
coast. From the north the *costa* narrows towards the Rio Santa; thereafter the slope of the Andes becomes steeper and movement along the
coast more difficult. Particular importance attaches to the valleys

of the southern coastlands where the rivers have built themselves broad outwash plains and these form oases of productive agricultural land in the midst of this desert region.

The most southerly section of the coastal zone, beyond Pisco, is noted for the way in which the coastal mountains plunge steeply down to the sea from heights of 4000 feet and over. Behind the mountains stretches an area of high, barren plains (*pampas*). Of this coast, Troll writes (article, 1951, and in Lauer, Schmidt, etc., 1952):

> The south-east trade winds which one would expect to find in these latitudes are here encountered only at a considerable distance from the coast. In the vicinity of the coast, and over the shore itself, the south-easterly trades are transformed into steady southerly or south-westerly winds; that is the winds blow slightly *on-shore*. To do this they originate as warm winds, but then must blow across the cold Humboldt Current, where cooling occurs and fog constantly forms (as is the case in comparable locations in other continents). On the landward side, however, there is a difference in the cloud-forming process between summer and winter. In winter the flow of the cold current is stronger and the land is no warmer than the sea. Under these conditions, the fog envelops the coast more densely and these fogs are known as *garuas*. Whenever the on-shore airstream is forced to rise, either by the wall of the Cordillera, or, indeed, by any lesser relief obstacle, raindrops form. This means that in southern Peru only the immediate vicinity of the coast—the lowest terraces on the seaward side of the coastal mountains—is entirely arid. Higher up on this same seaward side, between 2000 feet and 4000 feet, the fog belt is at its densest. This in turn means that on the leeward side of the mountains is a true dry zone —that of the pampas. As far north as the eleventh parallel these winter *garuas* are a regular occurrence. Further north—as far, say, as Trujillo— the *garuas* are sufficiently pronounced to turn the hillsides green only in certain years, while further north they do not occur at all in winter. The *garua* is a heavy mist which now and then turns into a fine drizzle. This drizzle is just enough to make streets and footpaths muddy, without being enough to wash the dirt away. The coastal fog and mist hang low over the coast ranges, and extend seaward above the shoreline itself so that the inhabitants of the ports on this coast have, as a matter of routine, to endure a daily weather cycle of leaden grey skies in the mornings, and sometimes in the afternoons too. Occasionally there is a sprinkling of rain falling from the overcast sky, but it is too slight in amount to be of any service. In spite of the constant impression that rain is threatening, the region is arid in the extreme.

(2) THE MOUNTAINS (SIERRA)

The mountains of Peru are dissected and divided into a number of components. The Western Cordillera forms the watershed between Atlantic and Pacific streams, and also forms the rim of the basin which drains to Lake Titicaca. On the shores of Lake Titicaca, conditions of settlement are similar to those which have already been described in the Bolivian section of the basin. Farther north, around Cuzco, the ranges converge and enclose deep valleys. North of Cerro de Pasco, in particular, three main ranges can be distinguished, with two of the main headstreams of the Amazon—the Marañon and Huallaga—flowing northwards between them. The third headstream, the Mantaro-Ucayali, has cut its way far back into the Andes, and rises south of Cuzco.

By contrast with these east-flowing rivers, those which drain to the Pacific possess nothing like the same length or volume of flow. Some of them, however, flow parallel with the Cordillera on the landward side, before breaking through to the Pacific in deep-cut valleys. The relief on this seaward side of the mountains is, in fact, everywhere steep and rugged, especially behind Lima. West of Lake Titicaca lies Ampato (22,796 feet), a peak almost equal in height to Aconcagua.

Here in the mountains elevation and proximity to the equator produce a distinctive natural landscape (see Plate 23). Southern Peru is dry; the *puna* is the characteristic vegetation type and the llama is native to this region. Farther north, however, rainfall increases and the vegetation changes to a humid *paramo* type, the *jalca*. Here the snowline drops below 16,000 feet and as it descends, so too do the zones of cultivation. Finally, in northern Peru, there comes a point where the evergreen rainforest of the Amazon Basin spreads right across the mountain region to the Pacific slope.

Throughout the whole mountain region the climate supports a wide variety of crops and activities. Even here, however, the effect of the Humboldt Current in depressing temperatures can be noticed. Cuzco has a mean annual temperature of only 50° F and night-time frost is frequent. The daily range of temperature is everywhere wide and frost can occur on the Altiplano (12,000–14,000 feet) practically every night throughout the year.

The true 'high steppe' or *puna* climate of central Peru has been described by W. Sievers as follows:

> Out in the open in such a town as Pasco the midday sun is oppressively hot but one has only to step into the shade to feel frozen. . . . The winter is pleasanter than the summer since in summer at these altitudes the precipitation generally falls as snow or hail. The rainy season begins with very heavy thunder-storms occurring daily over a period of several weeks and often ending with drifting snow. The dry season, on the other hand, which

lasts from May to September, is marked by clear weather with occasional storms and low night-time temperatures brought on by very rapid radiation.

The highland of southern Peru was the core area of the Inca Empire, traces of which still remain both in the landscape and in settlements.

(3) THE FOREST LANDS AND THE ANDEAN SLOPE (MONTAÑA)

In this region, as in the mountains, climatic conditions are extremely varied and in detail are a product of altitude and configuration. Much of the eastern Andes is heavily dissected. The forest boundary of the *montaña* is found at great heights. Thus while there is a mist-zone forest at between 10,000 feet and 12,000 feet, at the lower edge of this the rain-forest begins at once without any transitional belts (although in the valleys patches of savanna may frequently occur). In this territory, so difficult of access and so little known, the average rainfall is 100 inches p.a. and the mean annual temperature is 80° F or above. This is an area of which the coca bush and the cinchona tree are natives. Here stands the city of Iquitos, Peru's outpost on the Amazon.

Peru: The Land and Its People

Peru is widely regarded as the original cultural heartland of South America. Cultural development had been under way for about 4000 years before the coming of the Spaniards. As in many of the long-settled parts of Europe much of the cultural history still remains to be pieced together from archaeological evidence. Remains of successive epochs lie jumbled together, or on top of one another. On the mountain outpost of Machu Picchu there are to be found well-preserved remains of early Indian building construction (see Plate 20), while the art and architecture of the Incas were subsequently dominated by Spanish designers of both religious and secular buildings. And today motor roads follow through the mountains some of the lines of old highways, which were the arteries of movement of a tightly knit, highly organised people who knew of neither horse nor carriage, yet who conquered and ruled effectively over an immense empire.

THE EMPIRE OF THE INCAS

The Inca Empire stretched, as Fig. 29 shows, from the border of present day Colombia and Ecuador southwards, far beyond the Tropic of Capricorn and into what is now Chile and north-western Argentina. It embraced the lands of a large number of Indian peoples, previously organised into a system of local states. The Incas (or Children of the Sun) themselves—heirs to a long cultural tradition in the area—formed the aristocracy and they elected one of their number as an absolute monarch, the Inca, who was accorded divine honours by the people. Like the Aztecs in Mexico, the Incas were conquerors—although it is

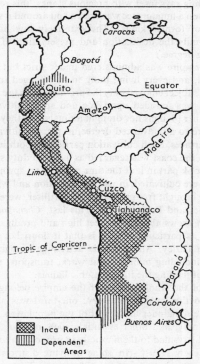

Fig. 29. The Inca Empire: its extent immediately before the Spanish Conquest in 1531.

interesting to note that some of their victories were achieved without bloodshed. As they expanded their territories in the twelfth century, they probably overwhelmed several other well-developed Indian groups, appropriated the best of their cultures, transformed other parts and adopted them. Quechua was the official language of the empire. They had, properly speaking, no written language, although a type of picto-graph narrative form resembling newspaper cartoon strips existed.

The heart of the whole great empire was the sacred city of Cuzco which boasted a Temple of the Sun literally roofed with gold. Here the people came to worship a golden sun as big as a cartwheel and decorated with surrounding rays inset with precious stones; this represented their deity. On the sun a human face was drawn and around it sat the mummi-fied corpses of former kings. (The extremely low humidity of the highlands permits the desiccation and preservation of organic tissue to an amazing degree.)

The whole empire was administered under strict but well-conceived laws. All land, and every living thing in it, belonged to the Inca, and the individual subject enjoyed only the privilege of its use. The livelihood of the people was founded upon hoe and stick cultivation (for they possessed neither ploughs nor draught animals) but they had developed hoe agriculture to an advanced degree, in places cultivating by means of irrigated terraces. Such cultivation carried on both in the mountain basins and on the coast was regarded as a sacred duty so that even the Inca himself took part in it at the time of the great spring festivals. The crops which were cultivated, in part by irrigation and with the applica-tion of guano brought from the coast for fertiliser, were usually maize, beans, potatoes and Peruvian rice. This last, *Chenopodium quinoa*, is a shrub which grows about three feet high and produces a mealy seed like a cereal; its particular quality is that it flourishes at even greater altitudes than barley. All economic activity was regulated in detail by the state, including mining, road work, transport, military service and the task of tending the indispensable llamas.

One-third of the whole output of the empire belonged to the Inca and went into the imperial treasury; one-third was allocated to the priests and the remainder to the rest of the population. These received their food supply, and other essentials such as wool, community by community, distributed to them exactly in proportion to the number of members in each family. (In some outlying districts traces of this primitive communal organisation still persist.) There was no money, nor were there any taxes, yet the Incas possessed gold and silver in untold quantities.

On a certain day in the year all the men who had reached the age of twenty-five since the last year had to marry; no question of emotion or affection arose. The community saw to the construction of a simple dwelling for the newly-weds. After one year of marriage every man became liable for state labour duty until he reached the age of fifty.

This labour was never very onerous as the supply of labour was more than adequate, but it had to be performed in order to obtain title to a food allocation. No one could move from one place to another without permission. Begging was forbidden. The idle were whipped out of the community. Personal freedom there was none, nor any opportunity for the individual to better himself; on the other hand there was no poverty and no dissatisfaction for lack of the material necessities of life. According to the size of his family so each man received a piece of land of sufficient extent, and the water required for its cultivation was precisely measured out to him. Neglect of duty was a punishable offence. Here, then, was a community in which the state not only supplied all-embracing welfare services but also acted as guardian to the individual to a degree unknown elsewhere.

Crafts and industries were highly developed. The Incas were extremely skilful makers of gold and silver ornaments of beautiful design. They knew how to make bronze out of copper and tin and how to work it into knives, axes and so on. They wove excellent cloth and their pottery was well made and tasteful. In fact, the relative degrees to which the intricate weaving and pottery designs were abstract or realistic has helped cultural historians reconstruct earlier phases of the pre-Conquest period of Peru. They were also ingenious builders; using quarried stones and adobe, they built temples and houses, aqueducts, huge dams and well-made surfaced roads (really elaborate footpaths since there were no wheeled vehicles), which they lined with trees. (See Plate 20.) The Inca roads, centuries old but still in being in parts today, ran throughout the whole empire linking its settlements. Two ran north-south—one along the coast and one in the mountains— with east-west link roads at regular intervals. Along the roads were way-stations called *tambos* for the benefit of official messengers, or for the llama pack trains upon which the movement of goods depended. The news or post service of the Incas and their transport organisation were far superior to anything in Europe at the same period. For the postal runners to make unofficial or unnecessary stops *en route* was a punishable offence.

It was shortly before the arrival of the Spaniards that the Inca state, traditionally held to have been founded four centuries previously by Manco Capac, 'the son of the sun god', achieved its maximum extent. But in a few short years, between 1531 and 1535, this great empire, torn by internal strife, was overthrown by Francisco Pizarro and a mere handful of followers, whose advance brought down the régime.

The Scene of Pizarro's Encounter with the Inca

The descent of the sierra, though the Andes are less precipitous on their eastern side than toward the west, was attended with difficulties almost equal to those of the upward march; and the Spaniards felt no little satisfaction when, on the seventh day, they arrived in view of the valley of Caxamalca, which, enamelled with all the beauties of cultivation, lay unrolled like a rich and variegated carpet of verdure in strong contrast with the dark forms of the Andes that rose up everywhere around it. The valley is of an oval shape, extending about five leagues in length by three in breadth. It was inhabited by a population of a superior character to any which the Spaniards had met on the other side of the mountains, as was argued by the superior style of their attire and the greater cleanliness and comfort visible both in their persons and dwellings. As far as the eye could reach, the level tract exhibited the show of a diligent and thrifty husbandry. A broad river rolled through the meadows, supplying facilities for copious irrigation by means of the usual canals and subterraneous aqueducts. The land, intersected with verdant hedge-rows, was chequered with patches of various cultivation; for the soil was rich, and the climate, if less stimulating than that of the sultry regions of the coast, was more favourable to the hardy products of the temperate latitudes. Below the adventurers, with its white houses glittering in the sun, lay the little city of Caxamalca, like a sparkling gem on the dark skirts of the sierra. At the distance of about a league farther across the valley might be seen columns of vapour rising up towards the heavens, indicating the place of the famous hot baths, much frequented by the Peruvian princes.[1]

Under the Spanish rule, the Indians were reduced to slaves and an untold quantity of precious metals was removed by the new overlords. Soon many facets of the original culture of the Indians were things of the past, and life offered the miserable slaves little but the prospect of hard labour in the mines or in the fields now owned by the Spanish conquerors.

HISTORICAL

It was in Peru that Spanish rule in South America survived longest. Part of the reason for this fact is to be sought in the close ties between the Indian population and the Church; consequently in the wars of liberation the Indians were to a large extent opposed to the liberators' ideals. This attachment to the Spanish rule continued even after Upper Peru (now Bolivia) had formed itself into a separate and independent territory.

1 Prescott, W. H., *History of the Conquest of Peru*, London, 5th edn., 1857, Vol. II, pp. 38-9.

The modern economic development of Peru began with the exploitation of the guano of the Chincha Islands. Foreign capital was invested in this industry and in plantation agriculture in the coastal zone, where a number of crops were grown. The state's economic centre of gravity shifted from the mountains to the coastal area. Meanwhile, Peru had become involved in several border disputes with Bolivia and Chile and these led finally to open warfare. Internally, conditions were little more peaceful; there were constant changes of government and policy. Clashes have occurred up until recent times between, for example, the large landowners and the Army on one side and the A.P.R.A. (Alianca Popular Revolucionaria Americana) on the other. These popular movements and unrest are aimed at social and economic reform, in the first instance in favour of the Indians, who comprise about half of the country's population, but who have never really participated in its economic and political life. To date, however, the traditional ruling class has been able to maintain its dominant position and Peru remains one of the most socially backward countries of the continent. The prospects for the peaceful evolution of the situation are not bright.

POPULATION AND SETTLEMENT

Peru is divided into 134 provinces which form 24 departments, and from which representatives are elected to sit in the legislature. As members of the latter, these deputies are barred from holding any executive office. The franchise is open to all adult males who are literate (a small percentage of total adult males), and voting is compulsory. Women have the right to vote only in certain local elections.

Some 46% of the population was classified as Indian in 1955. Negroes and Asiatics made up less than 1% of the total, and the remainder was composed of whites and mestizos—mostly the latter. The number of Europeans and North Americans is very small, but they control the country's economic life out of proportion to their numbers, and possess their own schools.

The distribution of the population is shown in Fig. 30, and its principal feature is the absence of urban centres, apart from Lima where almost 10% of the population is to be found. (The percentages for 1870 and 1925 were 3% and 4% respectively.) Of the growth of Lima, Wilhelmy writes as follows:

> The rapid growth of the recent decades has made Lima [1,800,000 in 1962] the most important city of South America's Pacific coast. Today, therefore, it has won back for itself that old position of supremacy which, as the

Cuidad de los Reyes, it possessed during the days of the Empire, but subsequently lost. In spite of all the reconstruction which has been carried out in the old city, Lima has by no means become a typical, cosmopolitan South American capital. On the contrary, it has retained, to a degree seldom found elsewhere, the appearance which it owes to its four centuries of history.[1]

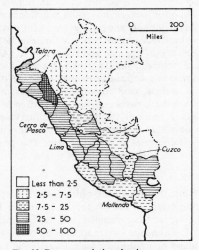

Fig. 30. Peru: population density per square mile, by departments, 1950.

Pahlen adds to this description:

Lima was founded on a wonderful site, in a green valley, beside a river, sheltered by the gentle outliers of the Great Andes, whose snow-clad tops can be seen in the far distance. It is not so near to the sea that its heat becomes too humid; on the other hand, it is near enough not to forget its connections with the outside world.

Today, Lima is an attractive, modern city. But wherever you go, you are reminded of the past—the remoter past by an excellent museum; the more immediate past by the streets themselves. Here you find many a building constructed in colonial style and bespeaking a centuries-long history. Within the city are to be found a large number of churches, almost all of them containing some relic of interest; most of them are built in that baroque style which, with its mixture of faith and power, seems to express

1 Wilhelmy, H., *Südamerika im Spiegel seiner Städte*, Hamburg, 1952.

so aptly the nature of the old Spanish colonial rule. In the cathedral rests the body of Pizarro, the man who, in the name of one empire, destroyed another; he lies in the heart of his city, to which he gave streets and squares and churches. Pizarro's streets today are asphalted, and the houses he built have long since been destroyed by earthquakes, only to be rebuilt in yet more attractive style. He may not have thought in terms of motor transport, or concrete office blocks, but it is to him that Lima owes at least its gardens; gardens which he foresaw and planned.

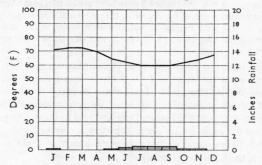

Fig. 31. Peru: temperature and rainfall diagram for Lima.

In spite of its tropical setting (it lies at 12° S), Lima enjoys a pleasant climate. The warmest month is February, with a mean temperature of 73° F, and the coolest is August with 61° F. Thus while its summer weather corresponds roughly with that of Buenos Aires, the winter—which in the Argentinian capital can be distinctly cold—is much milder in Lima. However, during this winter weather—if one can call it that—the city itself is often overshadowed by a damp veil of mist which clings to the valley and softens the outlines of hills and of buildings, so that they look as if they had been painted by an impressionist artist. But a few hundred feet higher up the hillsides, where many of the more well-to-do have their villas, the sun shines brightly above the mist below.

There are some splendid buildings in Lima, as befits a city with such a history. Among them is San Marcos University; it was founded in 1551, the first university in America, when the city itself was only sixteen years old. Its library grew rapidly to become the largest in the continent for a while, and among its distinctions in research has been the groundwork of the study of South American Indian languages. And for several centuries Peru was not merely the bastion of Spanish culture in the New World; it was also the outpost of Christendom.

Lima is the undisputed cultural capital of Peru. Here are published the most influential newspapers, and here there has come together, in recent years, a group of truly native artists, to form a colony of their own, where formerly the artistic life depended on the presence of visitors and foreigners. Today Lima is the home of a fine national orchestra, and its musicians have produced a gratifying number of genuinely Peruvian compositions, in which Indian influence can be detected. In the sphere of literature, too, where little progress has been made since colonial times, recent years have seen the publication of works with truly Peruvian themes, many of them concerned to defend or vindicate the Indians and their past.

But in spite of this, the Indians themselves have no part in this burgeoning national culture; indeed, the degree of the individual's participation seems to vary directly with the amount of European blood he has in his veins. It is not easy to eradicate in a few years the cultural effect of centuries of serfdom.[1]

No description of Lima, however, is complete without reference to the central tenement slums and the acres of squatter settlements—the barriadas—on the outskirts. These have resulted from the rapid influx of Peruvians into Lima in search of jobs and social facilities. No government up to 1962 was willing and able to tackle the problems —let alone the basic causes—of this process of urbanisation, but the slums and the barriadas are now as much a part of Lima as are the remains of the Spanish colonial past.

Lima's port, Callao (210,000), today forms virtually a single, continuous urban area with the capital. The country's second city, Arequipa (130,000), which possesses some splendid buildings dating from the Empire, grew up on the route between its port, Mollendo (18,000), and the settlements on the Altiplano around Lake Titicaca. The former 'holy city' of the Incas, Cuzco, which was ravaged by an earthquake in 1950, today has a population of over 70,000, and is still held in almost the same esteem as formerly by the Indians. One of the world's highest towns is Cerro de Pasco (23,000) which lies at 14,300 feet. Scattered through the mountains there are other towns at great altitudes, which are mining settlements—towns like Oroya (15,000) which, besides its copper mines, possesses an important railway junction. Far to the east, in Amazonia, lies Iquitos (55,000), awaiting the day when development will begin in earnest in the great lowland hinterland. On the coast there are a number of industrial towns, such as Trujillo (70,000) and, as the most westerly of Peru's ports, Talara (40,000), with its oil-field and refinery.

The contrast is very marked between these cities, which are mostly products of the outside influence of world commerce, and the rest of the country. It is essentially the same contrast that divides the small

1 Pahlen, K., *Südamerika, eine neue Welt*, Zürich, 1949.

group of the rich from the great mass of the people, who merely eke out their livelihood (see Plate 21). It will require the concentrated efforts of generations of Peruvians to bridge this gap, even on the educational front. Technically, education is compulsory between the ages of seven and fourteen, but quite apart from problems of distance and transport, this requirement, for the present, remains largely theoretical. Neither the provision of school buildings nor the training of teachers is at present even keeping pace with the increase of population. According to a calculation made in 1948, less than half the children of school age were actually receiving instruction. In 1958, among a population of 10 million, there were twelve leading newspapers publishing 430,000 copies in all.

The Economy of Peru

The economic position of Peru is substantially related to its physical background. The official policy is to encourage a more intensive agriculture among the Indians in the mountains and on the coast, in order to achieve a higher standard of living, but the plans have in general not been translated into effective action, involving as they must a radical and fundamental system of agrarian reform. At present, the country does not cover its own requirements of either food or consumer goods. About 60% of the labour force is engaged in agriculture, but while this latter provides some 60% of the value of Peru's exports, it accounts for only about 40% of the national product. Three-quarters of the exports are still raw materials, but there are, as has already been mentioned, plans afoot to increase food production and establish agricultural processing industries.

Agriculture. The main regions of commercial cultivation in Peru are found in the irrigated valleys of the *Costa*, where export crops are grown. In the rain-forest areas, beyond the Andes, there has so far been little agricultural development, apart from sporadic attempts to establish plantations. In the mountains cultivation is patchy, and the region's main shipments are animal products and, of course, minerals.

Among the agricultural products from Peru which enter world trade are cotton—the Peruvian variety is a valuable long-staple type—cane sugar and rice. The principal cotton area is the valley of the Chincha. Sugar-cane—most of which is grown on large estates—is the second most valuable product, and for this crop Chile is an important customer. The cultivation of rice is hampered somewhat by periodic droughts.

In recent years there has been evidence of new developments in cropping (see Plate 22); cereals in the mountains, and the production of vegetables and root crops, fruits and coconuts. Peru also produces tea, coffee and cocoa in sufficient quantities to meet the country's own requirements.

Pastoral farming is centred on sheep raising, but it is everywhere restricted by the low carrying capacity of these largely arid lands. The production of animal fats does not even cover the country's requirements. The fisheries of the Pacific Coast which were underdeveloped, particularly considering the wide variety of types of fish to be found in these waters, have recently undergone very rapid expansion and the export of fishmeal has now become one of the most important foreign-exchange earners. Guano, formerly an important export, is today produced in quantities which do little more than supply Peru's own plantations with fertilisers; the beds of this valuable material, which in some places formerly lay 100 feet deep, are largely exhausted. The forest products industries are, owing to the immense transport difficulties in the *montaña*, in their infancy.

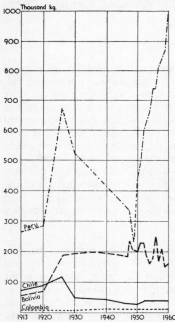

Fig. 32. South America: silver production by countries, in thousands of kilograms, 1913–60.

Minerals and industry. Among the principal exports of Peru are a number of minerals: petroleum, lead, copper, zinc, silver and gold. Smaller in quantity, but no less significant in terms of world trade, are the output of bismuth and of vanadium. (See Plates 24 and 25.) The mining industry is dominated by foreign capital and management, especially from the U.S.A. Owing to the presence of coal supplies (around Oroya), it has been possible to undertake the smelting of copper before export.

Industrial development has gone on quite rapidly in the last fifteen years. Industry now employs about 20% and accounts for significantly more of the national product. But the factor which persistently hampers industrial progress is the lack of any sizeable demand for manufactured goods among the Indian population. While their wages have gone up, the productivity of their labour has, if anything, declined relatively in the process. (See Plate 26.)

The two chief industrial towns are Lima and Arequipa. But Peru still has to import large quantities of manufactured goods, and in 1960 these accounted for about one-third of the country's total imports. Away from the coast the establishment of industries is again restricted by the lack of power supplies in areas where these are either non-existent or else not yet harnessed.

Transport and commerce. Relief and structure have been serious obstacles to the development of a transport network in Peru (see Plate 27). It might be expected that, on the world's greatest river system, the Amazon, water transport would play an important role, but in reality there is very little freight to transport in this part of Peru. Nor does the coast serve well for water transport; on the 1200 miles of Peru's coastline, the only reasonably good harbours are at Talara, Callao and Mollendo (which also serves Bolivia).

There are three main roads linking the coast with the *sierra*, while only two continue into the Amazon Lowland. Out of a total mileage of 24,000 only about one-eighth of the roads are surfaced by modern standards. The railways, with their 2300 miles of track, do little more than render the *sierra* accessible. However, the engineering of these lines is bold and universally admired, particularly that of the Callao-Oroya line, which reaches an elevation equal to that of Mont Blanc, and they have made possible the export of the area's mineral wealth. In 1950 the railways carried 4·5 million passengers, and the airlines 120,000, but buses and long-distance 'taxis' provide the main means of passenger travel.

Since the foreign trade of Peru depends almost entirely on the export of agricultural and mineral raw materials, it is intimately linked with the fluctuations of world prices. Thus a general increase in the price of manufactured goods—which Peru must import, and which with foodstuffs comprise over 60% of the total imports coupled with unstable and generally weakening prices for her exports—has forced upon the country a most cautious trade and financial policy, designed to reduce indebtedness and balance the trade accounts.

CHAPTER TEN

Ecuador

Landscapes and Regions of Ecuador

As in Peru, so in Ecuador, there are three principal regions whose character is dictated by relief and climate: the coastlands, the mountains and the eastern forest lands beyond the Andes.

THE COASTLANDS

West of the Andes lies a coastal plain which in places attains a width of 40 miles. Out of this plain rises the Coastal Cordillera, to elevations of 2000–2500 feet. Along this coast the Peru Current, which so powerfully affects the Peruvian coastlands, is of less importance, and both temperature and rainfall are high, the latter reaching more than 80 inches p.a. Under these wetter climatic conditions, the vegetation is both varied and luxuriant—mangrove swamps and tropical rain-forest, with open and drier patches of the *campo* type here and there. Only in the extreme south does the desert belt intrude into the coastlands. It is in this humid coastal region that Ecuador's economic centre of gravity lies, thanks in large part to the presence here of numerous plantations. It was the establishment of cacao plantations in the *costa* which marked the beginnings of modern commercial life in Ecuador. Today bananas are the single most important product.

In southern Ecuador, there is a break in the Coastal Cordillera, and the sea has penetrated into the breach to form the Gulf of Guayaquil, affording useful harbour possibilities on a coast not well endowed in this respect.

THE ANDES

The mountain region is formed by two main chains, 10,000–18,000 feet high, between which lies a series of upland basins at 6000–9000 feet, separated from each other by low transverse ranges. The bulk of the country's population is to be found in these basins, where they live below the craters and snows of some thirty volcanoes, of which several are still active. In the more easterly of the Andean chains there are Antisana (18,800 feet) and Cotopaxi (19,400 feet), the highest active volcano in the world, and long renowned for its perfectly-shaped cone. The mountain is usually capped with snow, but Humboldt, who happened to be in the vicinity during an eruption in 1803, described how 'suddenly, in a single night in January, the thick snows lying on the slopes disappeared, and daylight revealed to the astonished on-lookers the grey-black bulk of the mountain absolutely bare. Above it rose a dark red pillar of fire as the volcano threw up its showers of burning lava to a great height above the crater.'

The peak of the extinct Chimborazo (20,498 feet) in the western chain is also snow-capped. There was a time when it was believed to be the highest mountain in the world, and until comparatively recently it was regarded as the highest in the Americas. (There are actually some thirty higher peaks in the Andes.)

Although the climate of the high basins of the Andes is, on the whole, quite healthy, the high *paramos*, which stretch from about 13,000 feet up to the snow-line (15,000–16,000 feet) possess a bad reputation from the point of view of human occupance. The name *paramo* signifies a waste land in Spanish, and these areas are generally treeless (unlike the lower parts of the basins) and covered with tall grass. At these altitudes, the thin air sometimes brings on a well-known mountain sickness (the *siroche*) to the unacclimatised traveller, which manifests itself in such symptoms as fainting, difficulty in breathing, and nose or lung bleeding. As one visitor describes it: 'The traveller becomes tired, and wishes to do nothing but sit down; then his fingers and toes become numb, and exhaustion engulfs him; indeed, unless he is given oxygen very promptly, he may well die.'

The two main Andean chains are interrupted by the deep gorges of a number of rivers which rise in the highlands, and flow either east or west. On the outer flanks of the chains, the mountain vegetation gives way, at lower altitudes, to luxuriant tropical forest.

THE EAST

The forested region of eastern Ecuador, which stretches down from the mountains and out into the immensity of the Amazonian *hylea*, is one of the least-developed areas of the continent. Meagre indeed are the traces that remain of visitors to this region during colonial times—missionaries to the Indians, or the occasional fortune seeker on the look-out for gold; much later on, a handful of prospectors caught up in the rubber boom. It is a region whose remoteness, even within Ecuador, was dramatically demonstrated when, in 1956, five American missionaries were killed on the banks of the Curaray River (2° S, 77° W), by a tribe of Indians, the Aucas, upon whom the Ecuadoran government had never attempted to impose its authority.

This lack of interest in eastern Ecuador is not wholly the result of its remote situation. Quite apart from the question of access, there is the consideration that, whereas Peru uses part of her eastern foothill belt for growing tropical plantation crops, Ecuador has no special need to do so, since she has her humid coastal plains in the west available for this purpose (whereas the Peruvian coast is largely desert).

The charms of this land that lies across the equator have been frequently evoked by artists and writers alike. Here, for example, are the comments of Pahlen:

> Ecuador is certainly scenic; indeed many parts are truly beautiful. There are, in the first place, the mighty ranges of the Cordillera, crowned by the snow cap of Chimborazo, the cone of its extinct volcano rearing its head above the 20,000-foot line. Eternal snows beneath the equatorial sun! Eternal snows amidst a landscape of such tropical luxuriance; so soft and gentle, so filled with tall palms, waving in the warm winds; so full, too, of wonderful fruits and rare animals! The villages, too, are enchanting, especially on feast days when the Indians flock into them from far and near, dressed in bright costumes and curious headgear, and bringing with them all kinds of musical instruments—harps and pipes and drums. Thus gathered, they dance their old folk dances, full of grace and hidden meaning. These gatherings reveal odd differences in physical characteristics among the Indians, for while most of them are small, with somewhat coarse facial features, one occasionally comes across a few tall, finely-featured men, whose faces bear the marks of dignity proper to the old Indian aristocracy, and whose presence in these out-of-the-way valleys comes as a surprise.
>
> Scenic, too, are Ecuador's forests, when the sun sets over some broad, slow-moving river, and the dying rays of light paint the forest with colours which the dweller in temperate latitudes has never seen. Or the coast, with its blues and purples, its millions of sea birds and its brightly-coloured fishing boats. These boats have changed little in form since an earlier generation of fishermen encountered Pizarro's ships sailing southwards, and thereby entered a revolutionary new world of experience.[1]

The territory of Ecuador includes the Galapagos Islands, which

1 Pahlen, K., *Südamerika, eine neue Welt*, Zürich, 1949.

lie some 600 miles off-shore. These islands are famous for their distinctive plant and animal life. The islands are formed by the remains of a number of volcanoes, which today rise in places as much as 5000 feet above sea-level. They support only a sparse population.

Ecuador and Its People

HISTORICAL

Originally the Spanish administrative district of Quito, Ecuador became a part of Colombia in 1809, but parted from the latter on good terms in 1830 to become independent. Then, after General Santa Cruz in 1836 had obtained control of Peru and Bolivia, he laid claim also to Ecuador. His forces were defeated, however, by Chilean troops, and he was obliged to flee to Guayaquil, whereupon he took power in Ecuador and notably made his mark upon the country's future development.

During the first half of the nineteenth century, it was the cocoa plantations in the coastlands which formed the solid base of Ecuador's economy. At this point, however, the highland region began to attain greater significance, and so, simultaneously, did the conservative element in the young nation's political life. The decades that followed were marked by a strong tie between the State and the Roman Catholic Church, and out of this circumstance arose the formation of the Liberal party, which in turn provoked a long period of internal strife. At length, in 1945, the Army took over and set up a military government—a form of administration which persists in 1966 in spite of several attempts to establish and maintain civilian government in the intervening period.

To the present day the country lacks even the basic essential of agreed frontiers. East of the Andes, Ecuador's sovereignty is disputed by her neighbours, and even the settlement negotiated at the Pan-American Congress in Rio de Janeiro has not yet been accepted by all the parties concerned.

POPULATION AND SETTLEMENT

Excluding the 3000-square mile Galapagos Islands, Ecuador comprises 18 provinces, administered under the terms of a constitution framed in 1947—the eighteenth, incidentally, since the republic was founded. The vote is theoretically universal and obligatory for both men and women over eighteen, and the elections are for seats in the National Congress, which consists of two houses. Justice is administered through a linked series of courts culminating in a Supreme Court.

In practice, however, only a very small proportion of the population takes part in the political life of the nation, and this fact in part reflects the wide range of cultural differences present in the population. Pure whites form only a small percentage; more than half are of mixed parentage of various shades—mestizos (Indian and white parentage); cholos (white and mestizo); mulattos (white and Negro), and zambos (Indian and Negro). There are a few true Negroes, and the remainder of the population is Indian. In such a community there is no serious racial problem, perhaps due in part to the pronounced cultural and economic contrast between the thin upper crust of pure whites or wealthy mestizos and the broad mass of the largely illiterate. Education has been promoted by the government, but it will be a long time before the means it sets aside for education rather than for other purposes matches the need. Critical observers have, however, praised unstintedly the pioneer—indeed, sacrificial—work of teachers who, here as in other tropical lands, carry the torch of learning through desert, mountain and forest. To them, more perhaps than to any other group, the State owes its expanding sphere of influence.

The density of population varies considerably from place to place. It is, in any case, still unknown throughout much of the eastern forest. In general, political and economic life is restricted to the towns, among which only Quito (280,000) and Guayaquil (410,000) can be considered as important in terms of population and function.

Quito, founded in 1534 and lying 9300 feet up in the mountains, was once among the finest cities of the Empire. Tragically, earthquakes laid low much of its original splendour, and volcanic ash from the adjacent Pichincha has several times covered the city to a depth of a foot or more. Nevertheless, Quito has retained its distinctive character. Wilhelmy describes it as follows:

> Quito has preserved to this day, in its seclusion, much of the beauty of its colonial past. Laying out the city on the broken slopes of Pichincha, its builders could not adhere quite so closely to the familiar checkerboard pattern of streets as could the founders of other Iberian towns in the Americas. But the basic pattern is discernible all the same. There are a multitude of churches and these, with the 55 monastic foundations that existed at one time or another, occupy almost a quarter of the whole city area.[1]

Pahlen adds:

> A tour of the centre of Quito is a remarkable experience—a glimpse into the past. Here there are narrow alleys, in which stand houses dating from

1   Wilhelmy, H., *Südamerika im Spiegel seiner Städte*, Hamburg, 1952.

colonial times and decorated with a hand both loving and tasteful; gorgeous old churches like San Domino, San Francisco and the cathedral; monasteries, gloomy but somehow at the same time inviting, with their air of calm detachment, their quiet courtyards and pillared cloisters, their towers and cupolas that might be in Spain or even Italy. Spain or Italy—but for the tropical quality of the air and the mountains.

Around this old centre of the city, which is scenic and wonderful, but hardly functional, there lie the modern suburbs of Quito, with their gardens and houses, forming as it were a frame for a picture of unique character. Quito lies on the equator. Day and night are about the same length, and buildings and men throw little shadow. Since the city lies high in the mountains, it possesses a climate which you describe, if you are an optimist, as perpetual spring; or if you are a pessimist you say that life is one long succession of April showers.[1]

The annual rainfall of Quito is in fact 40–45 inches (Fig. 20, page 111), and there is always a possibility of showers, and of showers that turn to snow or hail. The mean temperatures compare with those of Western Europe, but these averages can be very deceptive, as Wilhelmy explains:

> The montane tropical climate of Quito is in no way comparable with the temperate climates of European latitudes, on the one hand because there is no seasonal rhythm and on the other because, in spite of the considerable altitude above sea level, the high humidity of the inner tropical zone is not diminished by height, nor its effect upon human activity lessened.[2]

The second of Ecuador's cities, Guayaquil, is the country's principal port and manufacturing centre, and it has outdone the capital in its population growth. It lies on the gulf of the same name, in an area of savanna-type climate, with a pronounced rainy season, and until comparatively recently it was subject to the ravages of yellow fever and malaria. To check the epidemics of the former and decrease the incidence of the latter has been a long and costly process.

Guayaquil is more cosmopolitan, more up-to-date and more active commercially than Quito. It possesses the usual adjuncts of a modern port-city—flour mills, lumber mills, breweries and even foundries—surrounding its modern harbour with its 3 miles of quays. (The depth of water in the port, however, is not very great, and larger vessels have to load and unload off-shore.) As in most other tropical cities, the European element of the community, and especially the wealthier class, lives in villa-strewn suburbs on the surrounding hills.

Riobamba (39,000), where the road down to the coast branches off from the Pan-American Highway, serves the usual functions of such a

1 Pahlen, K., op. cit.   2 Wilhelmy, H., op. cit.

junction point. Cuenca, with a population of 67,000, is the third city of Ecuador. The town of Ambato (40,000) was overwhelmed by a tragic fate in 1949, when it was destroyed by an earthquake in which 15,000 people lost their lives. Lastly, Esmeraldas (14,000) may be mentioned, as the port of northern Ecuador; it is the port of shipment for a range of tropical products from the coastal plains and has recently gained access to the highland basins by a road running from Quito. However, the port requires continuous dredging and, therefore, San Lorenzo—connected by rail to Quito—is being developed as the alternative port for this part of Ecuador.

Reference has already been made to the extension of the school system to remote areas. Education is free, but not compulsory. All schools, even the private ones, are under state supervision, and there are four universities in the country. Although there is no official religion, the position occupied by the Roman Catholic Church is a dominating one, both in cultural matters and in terms of church property. The small size of the culturally awakened element in the population is shown by the limited circulation of the 24 daily papers. In 1961, it was only 251,000.

The Economy of Ecuador

Up to the present time, Ecuador has been basically an agricultural producer. Out of a total labour force of roughly 800,000, about 50% work on the land, but there are now almost 25% in manufacturing and cottage industries.

Land use. Ecuador's mountain region produces mainly for home consumption. It is also, however, the centre of the livestock raising within the country, and both beef cattle and sheep are reared. The distribution of land use in this region is roughly:

Cultivated	5%
Pasture and meadow	16%
Arable but unused	16%
Mountains and waste	63%

In the east, the forest lands are almost untouched, while even on the coastal hills a number of valuable forest products—rubber, balsa wood, tagua nuts, and tannin from the red mangrove—have only recently come to be exploited. The main obstacles to a more intensive development of the land-use possibilities are poor communications and sparse population. As it is, the principal crop exports in order of importance are bananas, coffee, cacao and rice, all of them produced in the coastal plains. Many of the old cocoa lands are today under rice or cotton, since the witches-broom disease struck a severe blow at cocoa production.

The rise to prominence of bananas and coffee as export crops dates from the Second World War. The expansion of banana production and exports has been the most significant development, and Ecuador, whose bananas are well known for their flavour and find ready markets in the U.S.A., has now overtaken Central America as the world's most important exporter of this fruit. Among the crops grown for the home market, maize, potatoes, wheat, fruits and vegetables have all shown notable production increases in the last ten years. For this some of the credit must go to a special Institute of Production Research which was founded in 1949.

In 1961, the livestock population was reckoned as 1·5 million cattle, 1·7 million sheep, 350,000 goats and 260,000 pigs. In view of the low intensity of land use in the highland region, considerable attention is currently being paid to the possibility of extending the area of sheep farming in the Andes, and technical assistance in this field has been extended by Australia on the basis of its experience in very large-scale sheep raising.

Mining and industry. Ecuador has made strenuous efforts to strengthen the national economy, by developing new industries on a basis of Andean mineral wealth and oil from the fields west of Guayaquil. However, production from the latter is still low. East of the Andes the large international oil companies have long been prospecting, but so far with no success. Renewed interest in north–eastern Ecuador has, however, recently been generated by what appear to be major oil discoveries just across the border in southern Colombia.

The one valuable mineral product exported is gold; a United States firm is currently mining some 2 million grammes a year.

The overall development of industry is at present slight, even although a good deal of capital was invested in existing industries during the Second World War. Most of the industries produce consumer goods. There are a number of sugar factories in the coastlands, while various small plants process other agricultural products. The State possesses a monopoly in salt, matches and tobacco. About one-quarter of the total industrial output is textiles, the oldest and most important branch of Ecuador's industries. A number of rather specialised industries, such as the manufacture of Panama hats (made from the Tonquilla palm) have been losing ground. The government is taking steps to promote consumer and even capital goods industries in an attempt to increase the measure of Ecuador's economic independence, but there is now some concern at the impact of the Latin American Free Trade Area on industrial development in Ecuador such that the government has sought and obtained special conditions to protect domestic industries.

Transport and commerce. In Ecuador, as in several of the other states which we have been considering, the extension of the transport network represents one of the main tasks confronting the State. In anticipation of this the main port, Guayaquil—which handles 75% of Ecuador's exports and 90% of the imports—has recently been enlarged and modernised. In company with Venezuela and Colombia, Ecuador formed the *Flota Mercante Grancolombiana*, which in 1951 possessed a merchant fleet of thirty vessels and had regular sailings to Europe and elsewhere.

The 700 miles or so of railways (nationalised in 1944) are rather in need of both reconstruction and re-equipment. The main line runs from Salinas, through Guayaquil to Quito, and is about 300 miles in length. There is an extension from Quito northward as far as Ibarra. The connecting lines which are to run from the ports of Machala, Manta and Bahía de Caráques to this main north-south line remain, until the present, largely in the planning stage. The road network is generally inadequate; it is some 18,000 miles in length, and although a number of branches are planned from the Pan-American Highway to the coast, there are considerable financial, not to say technical, problems to be overcome. There are various small airlines which handle internal traffic, while the major foreign lines fly to Quito and Guayaquil.

In Ecuador, one can hardly speak of a real circulation of goods within the country. It exports a variety of commodities, however, about 94% of them plants or vegetable products, such as cocoa, rice, coffee and bananas. Ecuador also possesses a virtual world monopoly in the supply of 'plant ivory' (tagua nuts), which is used in button-making. The country also supplies most of the balsa wood that finds its way onto the world market.

The U.S.A. is the chief trade partner of Ecuador; in 1960 it was the source of 48% of the imports, and absorbed 63% of the exports. The principal imports—which have maintained their relative positions, with very little change, since before the war—are machinery, cotton textiles, wheat flour and other necessary foodstuffs, bicycles, metal goods and chemicals. Among the exports, bananas account for 62% by value, coffee for 15%, cocoa for 14% and rice for 3% (1960 statistics).

The government of Ecuador has striven to control trade by dividing imports into essential goods and luxuries, to ensure priorities. Trade and currency controls are strict. As a result of these cautious fiscal policies, the financial position of the State has considerably improved, and the value of the currency unit (the *sucre*) has steadied, such that the cost of living rose by only 15% between 1950 and 1960 after increasing more than sixfold between 1938 and 1950. In 1960, however, the average annual income *per capita* of the population was still less than £70, an average figure held down by the extremely primitive conditions in which many of the Andean Indians live.

CHAPTER ELEVEN

Colombia

Colombia: Structure and Landscapes

The state of Colombia occupies the north-western corner of the continent. Before 1903, when the separate state of Panama was established, it extended also over part of the Central American land bridge. The only country in the South American continent which possesses a coastline on both the Atlantic and Pacific Oceans, Colombia's natural orientation is decisively towards the Caribbean; that is, towards the Atlantic side. The distribution of mountain, valley and high plateau, besides giving Colombia its south-to-north orientation, assures the state of a wide range of climatic conditions. More than 50% of the area of the state, however, lies to the east of the mountains, in the basins of the Orinoco and the Amazon, and suffers the drawbacks of remoteness which it shares with the eastern territories of other Andean states. Colombia can, therefore, be broadly divided into two principal regions: (1) the mountains and uplands of the west, and (2) the eastern lowlands (see Fig. 33).

THE MOUNTAINS AND UPLANDS

The mountain west contains the regions most significant in the life and economy of Colombia. Its structure is clearly defined. North of Pasto, in southern Colombia, the Andes become broader, and break into three prongs, which diverge as they run north across the state, leaving room for two trenches; through the lower and broader of these runs the Rio Magdalena, while the higher and more westerly is occupied by the Rio Cauca (see Fig. 33).

The Central Cordillera, the middle 'prong' which divides the two trenches, bears evidence of both ancient and recent volcanic activity, in such peaks as Tolima (18,438 feet) and Huila (18,701 feet). At its northern end, it merges into the upland of Antioquia, lying at 8000-10,000 feet. Opposite this upland, on the eastern side of the Magdalena, and lying close to the north coast, is a transverse range of mountains of great age—the Sierra Nevada de Santa Marta. These rise as high as 16,000 feet, and are snow-capped. North-eastward again from the Sierra lies the dry peninsula of Guarjira, the most northerly point in South America.

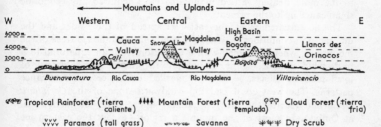

Fig. 33. The Andes: cross-section through Colombia, along the 4th parallel of north latitude.

The Western Cordillera (*Cordillera Occidental*) forms a linear range at a height of about 10,000 feet, and between it and the sea there appear remnants of an old coastal range. Between these and the Cordillera lie the valleys of the Rio San Juan (which opens on to the Pacific) and the Rio Atrato (which runs northward down to the Gulf of Darien). Between these two valleys, the watershed lies at a height of only 360 feet. It was realisation of this fact that prompted Alexander von Humboldt to suggest, early in the nineteenth century, the possibility of joining the Atlantic and Pacific by a canal at this point.

The Eastern Cordillera (*Cordillera Oriental*) broadens as it runs northwards. It contains two upland basins at around 7500 feet which have become important settlement areas, and it was here that the Spanish pioneers found remnants of the empire of the Chibchas. (See Plate 29). Finally, this eastern prong of the Andes divides again, encloses the Maracaibo lowlands and runs out over the Venezuelan border as the snow-capped Sierra Nevada de Mérida.

THE EASTERN LOWLANDS

The lowlands of Colombia are part of the great basins of the Amazon and Orinoco. The main tributaries of the latter are the Rio Meta and the Rio Guaviare, while the Rio Vaupes, the Rio Japura and the Putumayo (which forms the Colombian-Peruvian border) flow into the Amazon.

The southern part of the lowlands—and the area so described comprises at least a quarter of Colombia's territory—is covered with tropical rain-forest. The northern part, on the other hand, is a region of *llanos*, or grasslands, with *galeria* forest (see p. 38) along the river banks. Owing to their remoteness, however, only the grasslands nearest to the more densely settled mountains have acquired any economic significance up to the present.

The accentuated relief, the east-west spread of the Andes and the difference in conditions between the windward and the lee sides of the mountains, when combined with a transition from an equatorial to a trade wind climatic régime, all conspire to produce a wide variety of local climatic effects, leading to marked differences of occupance patterns. The west coast and the windward slope of the *Cordillera Occidental* receive the heaviest rainfall—more than 400 inches p.a. at Quibdo. In most of the mountain region—except the eastern lee slope—there are two rainy periods. North of a line drawn roughly from Buenaventura to Bogotá, there is a rainfall minimum during the northern hemisphere winter, while south of this line it is the southern hemisphere winter which is the driest season.

In general, too, the climate becomes more arid with the approach to the Caribbean. Here, however, relief is important, for with the trade winds blowing off the western Atlantic, a good deal of orographic rain falls on the higher ground all the year round. On the *llanos*, on the other hand, there is a rainy season in the northern summer, while the southern lowlands of Colombia experience the year-long rains of equatorial regions.

In Colombia the altitudinal climatic zones are very marked. The *tierra caliente*, or warm zone, extends up to about 3000 feet. It experiences very slight seasonal ranges of temperature (monthly means between 75° and 85° F) and is the most widespread in terms of the area it covers. Here are to be found a full range of tropical plants and crops. The *tierra templada*, or temperate zone, rises to altitudes of 6000-7000 feet, and shows monthly means in the range 62-75° F. This zone contains dense mountain forest, but it is also the principal coffee region of Colombia.

Still higher up is the *tierra fria*, the cool zone, with mean annual temperatures falling from 60° F at the lower limit of the zone to around 50° F at the upper limits of the main populated areas—for it is in this zone that the bulk of the population is to be found. This is the main cereal-growing region; wheat, barley and potatoes are the principal crops (see Plate 28). In appearance, the lower cultivated part of the *tierra fria* resembles some parts of Europe.

Higher than this, between the tree line and the snow line (which lies between 14,000 and 15,000 feet), barley and potatoes can be grown, but with limited success. Mean annual temperatures are likely to lie between 45° and 54° F. Above the snow-line rise numerous volcanic peaks and these, together with the highest parts of the main Andean chains, lie within the *tierra gelada*.

In all these zones, the annual *range* of temperature is small—seldom more than 15° F. The cycle of the seasons is marked less by temperature change, therefore, than by the régime of the rains. Fig. 33 shows the relationship of altitude to climate and vegetation in Colombia by means of a section drawn (following Troll) along the 4th parallel of north latitude.

Colombia and Its People

HISTORICAL

Before 1819, Colombia was a province of the Spanish Empire. Following the successful fight for independence under the leadership of Simón Bolívar there was formed the state of Gran Colombia, but this in turn broke up, in 1830, into the three modern states of Venezuela, Colombia and Ecuador. A further partition took place in 1903, when that part of Colombia which lay on the Central American isthmus—which on account of its remoteness and its forested and often swampy character had never been closely linked with the remainder of the country—broke away, with U.S. assistance, to become the country of Panama. Colombia's constitution was first promulgated in 1886, but has repeatedly been modified, most recently in 1945. The constitution requires that, to become law, all bills must be passed by both legislative houses by absolute majorities.

The favourable conditions for settlement and agriculture which are found on the high plateaux (particularly in the Eastern Cordillera) made of these areas the earliest centres of power. It was here that the Spaniards on their arrival found the Chibcha Indians, a nation of cultivators whose descendants to this day have a reputation for diligent farming, as well as for a peaceful disposition.

POPULATION AND SETTLEMENT

Over the past centuries the population of Colombia has become thoroughly mixed. For most of this period the exploitation of the country's rich natural resources was frankly destructive, but about the beginning of the present century, there began an economic renaissance. Towns and settlements that were moribund took on a new lease of life, and some of them became important cities. The key to this development was an improvement in communications at this period. The main routeway from the interior runs north to Barranquilla, in spite of the fact that Buenaventura, on the west coast, has made great efforts to exploit the advantage of its proximity to the main production areas of the interior. As a port, it possesses, too, the advantage of location on a fine sheltered harbour, on a coast poorly provided with such harbours, and today it has a population of some 50,000. Buenaventura is Colombia's main Pacific coast port, and handles half of the country's coffee exports. Its equipment—newly constructed quays and cranes—gives it a traffic capacity well beyond the present tonnage which is limited by its less than adequate communications with the interior of Colombia.

From here, a railway runs inland to Cali, a rapidly growing city of more than half a million inhabitants in 1962, which is the centre of the department of Valle. The railway continues southwards for 100 miles to Popayán which lies at an elevation of 5500 feet and is generally acknowledged to be one of the finest historic cities of Colombia and one of the cultural and intellectual centres of the nation's life. At Popayán the west coastline ends, and the traveller must rely on the main road system (which runs from north to south) for further progress.

There is also a main road route from Popayán to Cali and thence to Medellín which is the second largest city in Colombia, with a population of about 733,000. Apart from being the regional centre for the coffee-growing and mining districts which surround it, it is Colombia's industrial capital. Its textile industry dates back to the early 1900's and it now has a growing range of consumer-goods industries.

Bogotá itself lies high up in a mountain basin at 8500 feet, and surrounded by the steep slopes of high mountains. Throughout the centuries since its foundation (in 1538), it has always been jealous of its position as a capital city. In the early days it was known as the Athens of South America. Its modern rise, however, dates from the years after the depression of 1929–33, and by 1963 it had a population of over 1,300,000

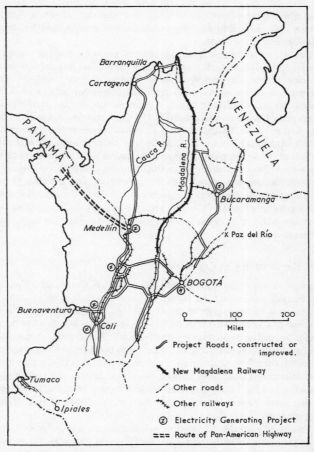

Fig. 34. Colombia: the role of international investment in national development. The map shows the transport and power projects made possible in Colombia by funds advanced by the World Bank and Agency for International Development. These funds had, by 1961, totalled more than $200 million; in addition, funds had been supplied for agricultural projects, such as supply of farm machinery, which are not represented on the map.

In spite of this rapid growth, Bogotá still lacks direct rail connection with the west coast (see Fig. 34), and must depend on road routes for its links with Cali and Buenaventura in the west, and Venezuela (via Cúcuta) in the north.

But an important role is also played in the communication system by the Rio Magdalena, and even passenger traffic has utilised this route, at least before the development of modern airways, and the 1961 completion of the railway linking Bogotá and Medellín with Santa Marta on the Caribbean coast. At the mouth of the north-flowing rivers stand the cities of Barranquilla (500,000) and Cartagena (180,000). The first of these is situated some 15 miles upstream from the mouth of the Magdalena, and a 27-foot dredged channel makes it accessible for ocean-going shipping. Cartagena (founded in 1533) grew up as the main naval base, and even today fortifications of colossal strength can be seen flanking the entrance to its harbour, while its buildings bear the stamp of the great days of Spanish imperialism. From Cartagena, a canal runs through to Calamar, giving access to the Magdalena, but its main trade is in crude oil and oil products from the large local refinery.

The Economy of Colombia

Agriculture and forest products. More than 60% of Colombia is forested, but in spite of this fact the output of forest products is small. Most of the cover is of the evergreen rain-forest type, a feature of which is the absence of compact stands of timber of one species, and this has been a factor retarding exploitation. Furthermore, the means of transport are lacking for the shipment of timber from the felling sites to markets. We find, therefore, that the chief economic activities in the rain-forest are collecting rather than cutting (as, for example, the gathering of nuts for making buttons). At higher elevations, however, in the temperate forest zones, forestry is practised in the stands of oak, walnut and pine.

Two-thirds of the population are supported by agriculture, and yet agriculture accounts for only two-fifths of the national income. Colombia possesses the advantage of a wide variety of environmental conditions, at different altitudes, and so of producing a considerable range of crops with widely differing climatic requirements. The country is an exporter of tropical produce, and especially of coffee, which makes up about 70% of the exports by value. The main coffee-producing regions yield two harvests in the year, of which the first is somewhat better than the second. (See Plate 32.) There is now a national planters' organisation which has campaigned with considerable success for improved methods of cropping and for grading the product. Colombia produces, in the main, the so-called 'washed' coffee, a higher priced variety than most Brazilian types.

The cultivation of another tropical crop, sugar-cane, is usually carried out on large holdings (see Plate 33); in the main sugar area (the Cauca Valley) 80% of the crop is produced on plantations which have been greatly extended in recent years under the impact of rising domestic demand and opportunities for export to the U.S. following the latter's political break with Cuba in 1960. The output of cacao, by contrast, is insufficient to meet the country's own needs.

Other crops which Colombia grows to meet her own requirements are rice and potatoes. There is also a small output of wheat. Besides these food crops the production of fibres is well developed, and the country produces a high-quality cotton in sufficient quantities to meet the demand of the country's important textile industry.

In the savanna region of northern Colombia, on the *llanos* of the Orinoco Basin and in the valleys of the west, there are immense natural grasslands which form the basis for ranching and livestock farming on a potentially very large scale. A recent report on the ranching in Colombia's principal cattle region—where about a third of the country's 15 million cattle are to be found—allows us to form some impression of how this ranching is carried on.

The stock graze alternately on the dry savannas and on water meadows in the valley bottoms, but today increasing use is being made of cultivated pastures seeded with imported grasses. (See Plate 34.) The crossing of pedigree European stock with Creole stock and with the Zebu from India has produced a good breed, with superior resistance to tropical conditions. According to location, the cattlemen concentrate on beef or dairy stock; in general the dairy farms are restricted to the coastlands. Colombia has not, however, been able so far to establish an extensive meat-processing industry, on account of the competitive strength of older-established producers elsewhere in the hemisphere. About half the land in this region is held in huge estates. Only one-fifth of the population are landowners, most of them in the range 12-200 acres. (The big estates may comprise as much as 100,000 acres.) The other four-fifths are tenants on short-term leases; they are known as *colonos*. The *colono* takes over from two to five acres of former grassland, probably now covered with bushes of scrub. This he is under obligation to clear (with the exception of shade trees) within eighteen months. Thereafter, he can farm the land for himself until his lease is up. Under these arrangements there is a good deal of squatting on the large estates, and a recent law—though difficult to enforce—makes it illegal to turn the squatters off.

There is, in consequence of this and other factors, a trend towards increased mechanisation and also towards the formation by the estate owners of their own teams of workers. However, this perpetuates the limited ownership of land and would not survive any radical agrarian reform even though change may initially reduce the productivity of the area. At the moment, however, Colombia's programme of land reform is not being implemented very effectively.

Mining and industry. The full exploitation of Colombia's mineral resources is hindered by lack of capital and by inadequate communications. As it is, foreign capital plays a very prominent part in the mining industry. Among the precious metals, the country is the world's

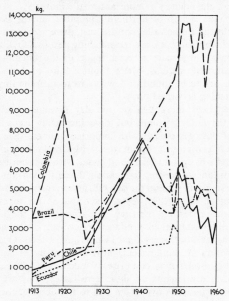

Fig. 35. South America: gold production, by countries, in kilograms, 1913–60.

second largest producer of platinum, and has a considerable output of gold (see Fig. 35), from placer deposits in river alluvium. It supplies, too, most of the emeralds which find their way into the world market. Production of silver, on the other hand, has declined considerably.

As far as the supply of industrial minerals is concerned, there are iron ore deposits and coal reserves (estimated at 2000 million tons) north of Bogotá which are being developed to form the basis of a native heavy industry centred on Paz del Rio. Oil production has steadily increased since 1945, but the government has not effectively encouraged foreign investment in the industry in recent years and thus Colombia's exports of petroleum have not expanded as quickly as they might have, given greater encouragement of development. Even so, oil exports account for about 15% of the country's total exports. The expansion of refining facilities within the country has enabled Colombia to achieve self-sufficiency in refined products which form the basis of the energy economy in most of the country.

In the post-war years, when the great industrial nations were having difficulty in meeting the demand for manufactured goods, Colombia expanded her own consumer-goods industries, with the aid of foreign technicians and capital, beyond the production of textiles and leather goods—industries which had grown up in the Medellín and Bogotá regions since the beginning of the century and which now not only meet local demand but also provide a surplus for export. Shortage of power resources has restricted the speed of industrial advance, particularly in the new industrial area around Cali, but the country is now self-sufficient in a wide variety of products and has recently established a motor vehicle manufacturing industry together with the fabrication of components such as tyres. An example of a small home industry is seen in Plate 35.

Transport and commerce. After the Second World War there was a period when, under the pressure of pent-up demand, Colombia spent very freely for a wide range of import goods. The result was inflation, currency devaluation, and, inevitably, import controls. The balance of trade was unfavourable, the national budget showed a deficit, the cost of living rose steeply and the dominance of foreign capital —most of which was either American or British, in the proportion 3 : 1—increased within the economy.

Between 1950 and 1957, however, the situation improved, largely due to the success of Colombia's coffee on the world market, and partly, also, to strict government direction of trade, particularly of imports.

Since 1957 the situation has deteriorated once again as Colombia has had to struggle to maintain its export income in the face of falling prices for coffee which account for 75% of total exports.

Natural obstacles hamper communications both by land and water. As an inland waterway, however, the Magdalena is very important (see Plate 31); in 1950 it carried 1·6 million tons of cargo, some 200,000 travellers and almost 100,000 head of cattle. Air traffic is also on the increase to an impressive extent; in the first half of 1960, the airlines carried 101,000 tons of freight and 1·5 million passengers. Ocean shipping operates under the *Grancolombiana* merchant fleet, which Colombia has established in conjunction with Ecuador and Venezuela. The principal ports of Colombia, with tonnages of cargo handled, are: Mamonal (1·5 million tons), Covenas (950,000 tons)—both ports shipping oil—Buenaventura (615,000 tons), Barranquilla (412,000 tons) and Cartagena (98,000 tons). Santa Marta (see Plate 30), although important in the transport of banana and cocoa, is at a disadvantage because of its restricted hinterland.

The railway system has a length of some 2000 miles which means that, while its capacity is quite high, it is really only a token network within a country of the size of Colombia. The rail system, however, does provide communications between the most developed parts of the country and the most important parts. There are, in addition, about 12,000 miles of roads, including a stretch of the Pan-American Highway some 1100 miles in length, of which, however, only a part is an all-weather road.

CHAPTER TWELVE

Venezuela

Venezuela and Its Regions

Venezuela, which borders the Caribbean and sends an almost rectangular 'tail' of territory south into the Amazon Basin, is the continent's most northerly state. It might be described as the state of the Orinoco; yet it can be classified equally well with the Andean states. Actually the Apure-Orinoco line forms the central axis of its territory and the Andean section of the country is smaller in extent than the part which lies within the highlands of Guiana. The only reason, in fact, for classifying Venezuela as an Andean state is that, today and in the immediate future, it is the northern part of the country—which represents the easterly extension of the Andes—that will be the region of overwhelming economic pre-eminence within its borders. But it should be added that already development is beginning in the empty lands along and beyond the Orinoco, a development that will progressively increase their importance and that of the river along which the products of the new lands will be transported.

The main regional divisions of Venezuela are: (1) The northern uplands; the Andes, the Maracaibo Basin and the coastal mountains; (2) the *llanos* of the Orinoco; (3) The Guiana Highlands. (See Fig. 36.)

THE NORTHERN UPLANDS

Possessing as it does three-fifths of Venezuela's population, this region is the cultural and economic heartland of the state. In a sense it reproduces on a smaller scale the characteristics of the Andean landscapes we have been considering; the mountains dwindle to the breadth of a single range, which becomes progressively lower and less formidable towards the east. On reaching the coast, it continues out to sea in the form of a scatter of off-shore islands.

The Cordillera de Merida, however, is of impressive height, with its snow-capped peaks of La Columna (16,406 feet) and La Concha (16,144 feet). It is a range of fold mountains, with its crystalline core exposed, and forms a true outlier of the main Andean chains, with its altitudinal zones of climate and vegetation clearly marked. Snowfalls

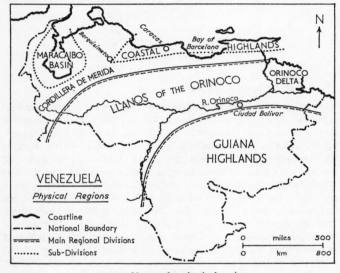

Fig. 36. Venezuela: physical regions

occur quite commonly as low as 11,500 feet. The *tierra fria* is the home of a pure Indian population. In the *tierra templada* lie the towns of Trujillo (19,000) and Merida (40,000).

The north-western slopes of the Cordillera fall away into the tropical rain-forests that cover the southern end of the Maracaibo Basin. North-eastwards, by contrast, the mountains sink to the level of the Coro-Barquisimeto Upland. Among the hills, at heights up to 3000 feet, lie basins which experience severe seasonal drought, a drought that becomes more pronounced towards the coast. Only in the northern winter, with the southerly shift of the trade winds, does this region receive appreciable moisture, which supports a savanna-type vegetation.

The north-western tip of Venezuela's territory is occupied by the Maracaibo Basin. The floor of the Basin holds the pear-shaped lake itself, which is connected by a natural passage with the Caribbean. Here the Andean ranges disappear beneath the coastal deposits. The basin is an area of hot, swampy forest, but towards its northern end, where the rainfall is lighter, this forest cover is replaced by thorn bush, and the pattern of land use reflects this transition. The principal significance of the basin is not, however, agricultural, but derives from the importance of its oilfields. Production increased very rapidly after 1944 and by 1950 the basin was producing from wells both on- and off-shore, three-quarters of Venezuela's oil.

The coastal mountains of Venezuela are divided by the Bay of Barcelona into two parts, a western and an eastern section. The eastern part, which is the smaller of the two, belongs to the little-developed eastern territories (Oriente) of the country. It consists of wooded hills with numerous rivers, but towards the west the vegetation reflects an increasing aridity, with a transition to a poor scrub cover and a coastal fringe of coconut palms.

The western section of the mountains also presents an arid flank to the sea, thanks to the influence of the trade winds, and thorn scrub and cactus characterise its vegetation. Only as altitude increases through the mountains does a forest cover appear, and here, in the *tierra templada*, plantations of cacao and coffee are found.

Within this same zone lies the main longitudinal valley, that runs between the coastal mountains and the interior range. It is actually formed by a series of basins rather than by a single valley, and it is here that the capital of Venezuela, Caracas, is situated. The natural vegetation and the land use potential vary locally with the amount and seasonal distribution of rainfall. In general, the *tierra caliente* zone (mean annual temperature 80–85° F) extends up to about 2000 feet, the *tierra templada* (with means around 75° F) from 2000 feet up to about 6000 feet, and the *tierra fria*, where means are below 60° F, above 6000 feet. (See Fig. 37.)

THE LLANOS

The Llanos of the Orinoco, as the term is usually employed, cover the whole lowland of central Venezuela as far as the edge of the Guiana Highland in the south-east. The Orinoco itself (the name derives from the Indian *orinucu*—a river) is 1500 miles long, and in terms of volume of flow ranks as one of the world's great rivers—this in spite of the

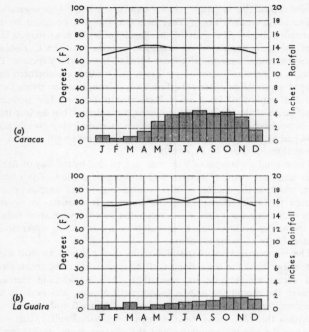

Fig. 37. Venezuela: temperature and rainfall diagrams for (*a*) Caracas and (*b*) La Guaira. Although these two stations are only 10 miles apart, their difference in elevation (3400 feet) and La Guaira's coastal situation make the climates of the two places quite dissimilar; La Guaira is consistently more than 10° F warmer than Caracas throughout the year, and has a much lower rainfall.

fact that one of its headstreams bifurcates and sends a part of its flow southwards to the Amazon (see Fig. 38). At a distance of 850 miles from its mouth, the rapids of Maipures and Atures mark the head of navigation. It possesses a huge delta, covered with swamp forest and mangroves, and a number of the arms of the delta are as much as 150 miles in length.

Above the rapids, navigation is possible on tributaries such as the Meta and Apure right up to the foot of the Andes. However, the flow of the system, and the course of the river itself, are very irregular, and seasonal floods may raise the water-level by 40–50 feet, spreading the water far and wide over the generally low-lying banks of the river. *Galeria* forests mark the course of the river as it winds across the smooth floor of this great alluvial plain.

Although the vegetation of the whole region may be classed as savanna, there are important local differences, as Troll has pointed out. He differentiates between the *llanos* proper—the low-lying plains crossed by river courses—and the *mesas*, which are tablelands between the rivers and which, although the differences in elevation may be only a few feet, act as watersheds. This difference is marked by a change from smooth, uninterrupted grasslands to palm savanna.

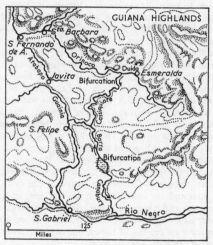

Fig. 38. Venezuela: the bifurcation of the Casiquiare River, showing how it drains into both the Orinoco and the Rio Negro.

In general, rainfall increases from east to west across the region. 'So,' writes Troll, 'we have the characteristic landscape of the *llano* region; the grey-green of the grass-covered plains; here and there a gnarled chaparro tree or a drab palmyra palm, and running through the whole the green ribbons that mark the river courses.' The local differences of relief (noted by Humboldt a century and a half earlier) are of considerable importance, for this is cattle country, and the higher ground secures the livestock against the flood danger on the low-lying plains. Here it may be mentioned that, while the *llanos* are used for ranching, the cattle raised here need finishing on cultivated pastures before they are ready for slaughter. The economic centre of the region is Ciudad Bolivar (56,000) a town for which a great future was once predicted as the 'larder for Europe's meat'.

Humboldt's Description of the Venezuelan Llanos, 1799

Behind lie the leafy valleys of Caracas and the bright green of the sugar cane fields, the deep shade of the cocoa bushes and the cool reflections of Valencia Lake, where the waters mirror the surrounding banana groves. Ahead, to the southward, there extends a barren, treeless steppe, which seems to mount to meet the sky along a horizon infinitely remote. In its very uniformity there is something grandiose, but something sad and depressing too, and it is only slowly that a man can grow accustomed to this landscape, where Nature herself seems to have become benumbed.

We crossed the Llanos in about Latitude 9° N. The sun blazed down on us from almost directly overhead, and wherever the earth was bare of plant life, temperatures of 115–120° F at ground level were common. Where we were, a few feet above the ground on muleback, there was not the faintest breath of air to be felt. But this stillness was illusory, for every so often we saw a small whirlwind raising the dust; they are caused by air currents set up by differences in temperature between patches of bare sand and grass-covered surfaces. These dust storms glide along over the surface of the ground, curling and writhing as they go, and they increase the oppressiveness of the heat. On every side, the plains stretch to the horizon, and the vast and apparently limitless desert seems, to eyes such as ours, like an ocean's surface strewn with seaweed and driftwood. At the horizon, land and sky melt into one another, and in the haze at the sky's edge one can make out the vague shapes of palm trees. By a trick of the air currents rising from the baked earth, they seem to be floating in space. But for their crowns of leaves, one might mistake them for the masts of ships whose hulls were below the horizon.

The Llanos (or Pampas) are true steppes. In the rainy season, they are green with vegetation, but once the dry season sets in, with the sun blazing down day after day from a cloudless sky, they take on the aspect of a desert. The grass cover shrivels up, great cracks appear in the dry surface, and the crocodiles and snakes bury themselves in the mud, to sleep through the heat until the onset of the rains in the New Year rouses them again. Then there is a sudden transformation. No sooner has the first rain fallen than the steppe is carpeted with flowers and grasses, and there is pasture for horses and cattle once more.

The outstanding feature of the Llanos is their absolute flatness. It was for this reason that the Spanish pioneers called them, not desert or prairie, but plains—'los Llanos'. Yet this flatness proves, on closer examination, to be more apparent than real. Careful observation reveals two types of relief. The first consists of the 'bancos', or banks, which are layers of sand or chalky material, 4 or 5 feet high, scattered here and there on the plain. They represent sandbanks and shallows in the sea which once covered the Llanos. The second type can only be detected by careful measurement, or by observing the flow of rivers; it comprises the 'mesas', or tables—small plateaux, or rather, gentle swellings of the surface, which may attain a height of 5 or 6 feet. . . .

And everything conspires to make these steppes seem even broader than they are—the monotony of the surface; the absence of any habitation; the strain of travel under a burning sun and in a dust-laden atmosphere; the way in which the featureless horizon seems to withdraw as one goes on, and the palm trees all look alike, so that there is no sense of progress, for there are always other palm trees ahead, exactly like the ones behind. And ever before the traveller is the torturing mirage, with its false promise of relief, of water.

THE HIGHLANDS

The Guiana Highlands, an old crystalline mass lying between 3000 and 6000 feet, occupy the greater part of this big region. Old quartzite and young intrusives have also created outliers of the highland zone, lying close to the Orinoco and reaching heights up to 5000 feet. Along the borders of Venezuela, Brazil and British Guiana the remnants of an old sandstone cover are responsible for the existence of another feature—flat, table-topped mountains such as Pacaraima and Roraima (which reaches a height of over 9000 feet). This little-known region is largely forested, but possesses wide stretches of savanna, whose character is similar to that of the savannas of central Brazil.

Venezuela: Its Land and People

Venezuela—which means Little Venice—was given its name by the Spaniards who found an Indian village built (for protection) on piles in Lake Maracaibo.

HISTORICAL

In Venezuela there began, about the year 1810 under the leadership of Simón Bolívar, the movement towards Spanish American independence which led to the foundation of the whole series of Latin American republics in succeeding years. Political and social changes took place together, for with the decimation of the old Spanish land-owner-aristocracy, the social order which had underlain the plantation system of colonial days was destroyed.

It was not until 1830, when Venezuela and Colombia finally parted to become separate republics, that something approaching orderly conditions was established in the country. Since 1864, it has consisted of twenty federated states—a union often racked with internal conflicts and economic crises. There have been international crises too, such as the dispute with Britain and the Netherlands over the Guiana boundaries, and with the U.S.A. over shipping on the Orinoco.

A phase of economic expansion began with the *coup d'état* of Gomez in 1910. Venezuela remained neutral in the First World War, and weathered the economic storms of the depression years (1929–33) remarkably well; she was the only country in the continent to remain free of foreign debts. But the price which Venezuela had to pay for this stability was severe repression in internal affairs under the Gomez régime. After the death of the dictatorial President, the parties which came to power took steps to modify the constitution to guard against a repetition of this situation. The steps were not successful, however, for another dictator, Pérez Jiménez, ruled the country from 1952–58, since when freely elected presidents have managed the country's affairs.

POPULATION AND SETTLEMENT

The number of pure Indians in Venezuela—most of whom live in the Orinoco Delta, in the north-west or in the Guiana region—is today very small. Apart from these, the Negroes on the coast and a few white immigrants, the whole population consists of people of mixed descent. Nevertheless, there are, among this population, very wide variations in both ways of life and standard of living, and these contrasts strike the observer at every turn. In particular there is the social gulf which separates the country from the big cities. On the land are the *campesinos*, living lives remote from all progress, in houses made of beaten mud (see Plate 36). In the towns, on the other hand, the last two decades have seen a tremendous rise in the standard of living both enjoyed and expected by the city-dweller. There are few colour problems in these cities, where workers of every nationality work their eight-hour day side by side, although even in the cities there are wide social differences between the classes reflected in contrasting living conditions between wealthy suburbs and large areas of slum dwellings.

Caracas lies at the western edge of the Chacao Plain, at an elevation of 3200 feet. Beyond it rise the Silla Mountains, which reach to over 8500 feet. The city was originally laid out in colonial style, with a gridiron street pattern, and this layout was retained even after the city was destroyed by an earthquake in 1812. It has, however, been submerged beneath the development of Caracas as a 'motor-car city'. In this development urban motorways have slashed their way across the city and have engendered the spread of suburbs throughout much of the basin in which Caracas lies. The metropolitan area has a present population of some 1,336,000.

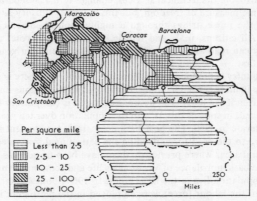

Fig. 39. Venezuela: density of population, by states and territories, 1950.

Across the coastal hills from Caracas, and situated on a small coastal flat beneath the steep slopes, is the important port of La Guaira (40,000). The site is not naturally suitable, and only the construction of huge breakwaters has made possible the creation of safe harbour facilities. La Guaira possesses the unenviable distinction of being one of the hottest coastal cities in the whole of South America.

Much more favoured naturally, and the second port of Venezuela, is Puerto Cabello (32,000). An old port-city with communications with the interior which are in the process of being improved, Puerto Cabello possesses both a developed agricultural hinterland and also the industrial centre of Valencia (161,000) to provide it with through traffic. However, because of the dominance of Caracas in the economic life of the nation it has not so far been able to compete with La Guaira very successfully.

Maracaibo (455,000), the second city of Venezuela, is also the capital of the state of Zulia. It was the capital for the oil region of Lake Maracaibo, but has recently suffered from setbacks as the large oil companies have concentrated their administration in Caracas.

Venezuela is a federal republic, with twenty states, a federal district and two federal territories. Administration is hampered, however, by the lack of a professional Civil Service, so that when, as has all too frequently happened, the government changes, the entire administration, apart from the technical services, changes too. The separate states enjoy some measure of freedom, but this is largely illusory as Caracas controls the purse-strings through a highly centralised tax-collection system. All citizens, male and female, are entitled to vote, provided that they can read and write; immigrants must spend ten years in the country first.

The country is predominantly Roman Catholic, but there is religious tolerance in all spheres, including education, where religious instruction is only given if the parents so desire. Education is compulsory from the age of seven; in spite of this 51% of the population over ten years of age were illiterate in 1950. The post-1958 democratic government has been fully alive to the need for expanding the educational system especially in the rural areas where previously there have been no schools—underlining the basic unbalance of Venezuela's life and economy. About 32% of the population live in the large cities. In 1960 about 43,000 workers (or 3% of the labour force) were employed in the petroleum industry. Modern economic development thus affects about one-third of the population; the remainder are virtually untouched by it, except for the high prices they must pay for goods purchased through commercial outlets.

The Economy of Venezuela

In spite of its recent progress, Venezuela must still be classified among the nations with meagre industrial development, and 40% of the population depend upon agriculture for their livelihood. In 1930 the percentage was much greater, but since then there has been a drift from the land which has brought about structural changes in the economy. Indeed, the output of foodstuffs fell off so markedly that food imports became necessary, and the country had reason to regret its concentration in agriculture on coffee production. Only recently have realistic efforts been made to encourage the domestic production of foodstuffs.

LAND USE

Present estimates place the area of potential farmland at 8·6 million acres, but of these only some 3·7 million are in agricultural use at present. Natural conditions are suited to the production of a wide range of crops belonging to different climatic zones, but in spite of this natural advantage production is by no means at a satisfactory level due in part to the system of landownership prevailing until very recently. For this fact the predominant position occupied by oil production is in part responsible. The basic diet of the population consists of maize, black beans and other legumes. European immigrants, however, have introduced such crops as potatoes, wheat and rice. The acreage under cotton has declined for many years but is now increasing again as efforts are made to ensure self-sufficiency for the highly protected textile industry, while the output of coffee and cocoa has increased. Efforts are being made to introduce more European crops, especially vegetables, and these efforts form a part of a government-sponsored and, in part, oil industry financed programme of scientific farming, the encouragement of food crop production, and the cultivation of industrial raw materials. (See Plate 37.)

In the hills, centuries of ruthless forest exploitation have made it necessary to introduce a national forestry service. Elsewhere, agriculture and livestock raising are usually carried on separately. The raising of stall cattle is not common; it is replaced by ranching on the wide grasslands of the *llanos*, and fattening on cultivated pastures on the coast. At the 1960 count, numbers of livestock were as follows:

Cattle	9,200,000
Pigs	3,200,000

The cross-breeding of cattle with pedigree stock from mid-latitude countries has, as in Colombia, proved highly successful. Present policy aims at increasing production of both meat and milk to the level necessary to supply the country's needs. Along the interior rivers, fish form an important item of diet.

The agricultural processing industries are carried on by numerous small concerns. Their production, however, does not nearly meet internal demand (in 1951, for example, a quarter of Venezuela's imports were products of agriculture). Thus there are thirty establishments registered as 'shoe factories' working with local leather, but in such contexts the term 'factory' is liable to be misleading.

MINING AND INDUSTRY

The development of the Venezuelan economy is only comprehensible when it is related to the growth of world markets for petroleum products. In 1920, Venezuela produced only 0·1% of the world output. By 1930, her share had already increased to 10·3%. In the post-war period production increased rapidly, rising to a peak of more than 15% of the world total in 1957 when Venezuela was second only to the United States. Since then Venezuela's position has become less strong and she has now been overtaken by the U.S.S.R. She now produces about 160 million tons a year, but the rate of growth has fallen to under 3% per annum. (See Plate 38.)

Petroleum in Venezuela's Economy

Petroleum is the axis of Venezuela's economy. It buoys up Government, industry, and commerce. Although the petroleum industry employs under 3% of the labour force (about 43,000) it accounts for one-third of the gross national product. Oil taxes provide the Government with 60% of its revenues. In addition, the petroleum industry contributes an equal amount to Venezuelan labour, industry, and commerce as a result of domestic expenditures incurred in the conduct of its operations. Oil company purchases of bolivars to pay taxes and to purchase domestic goods and services provide over 95% of the country's foreign-exchange requirements.

Petroleum thus explains Venezuela's prosperity, her high national income, her financial solvency, her large volume of foreign trade. Revenues from oil have enabled the Government virtually to eliminate foreign and domestic debts and to invest heavily in development. Petroleum has made Venezuela's currency strong and provided the nation with substantial quantities of foreign exchange, thus enabling her to import large volumes of foodstuffs, machinery, and manufactures.

Petroleum has also made the Venezuelan economy lopsided, dangerously dependent upon foreign markets, extremely sensitive to events abroad. Moreover, the industry's demands for limited domestic goods and services have tended to raise domestic prices, and its payments to the Government, which have had the result of greatly increasing the state's demands, have also helped to raise prices. Thus dollars have become cheap and bolivars dear, so that it is cheap to import and expensive to export. As a result Venezuelan industry and agriculture cannot compete with foreign suppliers in the domestic market without substantial tariff protection, which also raises consumer price-levels, and cannot compete in foreign markets without government subsidies.[1]

1   Lieuwen, E., *Venezuela*, R.I.I.A., London, 1961, pp. 112-13.

Yet in the colonial era Venezuela had already proved to be a valuable source of mineral products. Copper has been mined ever since the early days of the Spanish régime. In the eighteenth century, Capucin monks were prospecting for the gold of 'Bolivar', beyond the Orinoco. But it was the Second World War which produced the decisive impulse towards exploitation of these varied resources. Raw materials were in short supply, and demand soared for oil. On the other hand manufactured goods to pay for the oil were scarce, and as a result credits were built up. Mineral prospecting also went ahead rapidly, and the results were encouraging. Development began in exploiting the iron-ore deposits of Manua which had been discovered in 1912–13 by English interests. A subsidiary of the Bethlehem Steel Corporation from the U.S.A. has recently opened iron mines at El Pao, and production aims at an eventual output of 10 million tons p.a. Plate 40 shows the older Cerro Bolivar operations.

For the present, most of this iron ore is shipped to the U.S.A., but a local steel industry has been initiated, with a big plant at Santo Tomé de Guayana, at the junction of the Orinoco with its tributary, the Caroni. High-grade manganese ores have been discovered in the states of Carabobo and Bolivar, while uranium deposits are suspected in the region of the Orinoco headwaters. The country's meagre supplies of bituminous coal, however, are unsuitable for the iron and steel industry and coke has thus to be imported, whilst new processes for reducing iron-ore are also being employed in the Venezuelan steel works.

Efforts to create local consumer-goods industries have already resulted in the construction of numerous factories. The country already supplies its own requirements of textiles, and of chemical and pharmaceutical products. But in other sectors of manufacturing imports are still necessary, even including such basic requirements as cement. There is a motor vehicle assembly plant at Caracas, and new plant has now been developed such that imports—formerly mainly from the U.S.A.—are essentially prohibited.

TRANSPORT AND COMMERCE

If further development of Venezuela's resources is to take place, and if, in particular, the great unused interior is to be integrated into the economy of the nation, then the first prerequisites are the improvement of existing communications and the creation of new ones. (See Plate 39.) Such projects would involve the enlargement of port facilities and the establishment of links between the line of cities on or near the coast. La

Guaira may serve as a case in point. A description of that port published in 1930 described in detail a new motor road linking La Guaira with Caracas. It was 25 miles in length and wound in innumerable curves through the 8000-foot high coastal mountains. But modern construction has completely eclipsed this effort. Since 1953 it has been possible to make the trip from port to capital, along a motorway (which cost U.S. \$7 million per mile), in little more than fifteen minutes. Such are the changes that can be wrought. With the extension of the motorway beyond Caracas to Valencia along the line of the country's main belt of industrialisation, La Guaira seems destined to become one of the continent's greatest ports.

One of the major obstacles facing the road engineers is the need to construct an immense number of bridges in this mountainous terrain, and the problem is complicated by the fact that the seasonal character of the rainfall involves the extra cost of building for flood peaks rather than steady flow. However, the *Transandina* (a branch of the Pan-American Highway) is complete, linking Venezuela with Colombia. To the east the main road to the mouth of the Orinoco is now complete, thus linking Caracas with the new heavy industrial area that is being developed to the east of Ciudad Bolivar at the confluence of the Caroni River and the Orinoco. The juxtaposition of iron-ore, other minerals, hydro-electricity potential, oil and natural gas, gives this area great potential for development and a new city of 250,000 people—Santo Tomé de Guayana—is planned for 1980.

The role which the railways have played in opening up Venezuela has been relatively unimportant, and although there are plans for extending the system, it is doubtful whether these will ever be fulfilled in an era when other forms of transport are being developed so rapidly. Air transport is already well developed, at least for passenger traffic. There are more than thirty airfields capable of handling four-engined planes. Traffic is in the hands of national airlines, while numerous major lines, such as Pan-American, B.O.A.C. and Varig of Brazil, provide international links to North America, Europe and the rest of Latin America (see Fig. 40).

The backbone of Venezuela's foreign trade is provided by the export of oil and is likely to remain so for the foreseeable future in spite of efforts at diversification. However, the prospects for large increases in oil exports are now much less favourable, and Venezuela is likely to face relative stagnation in her export income thus joining most of the other Latin American countries which have faced this problem for many years. It may possibly be Venezuela's realisation of this fact which helped to persuade her to consider membership of the Latin American Free Trade Area.

A system of import licences—which act, in effect, as protective tariffs—has been introduced in order to make the country's own infant industries viable. Venezuela is such a prolific dollar-earner that import restrictions have not generally been necessary on any other grounds. Indeed, it might be true to say that oil production has had the effect of throttling a number of other branches of the economy which might otherwise have developed.

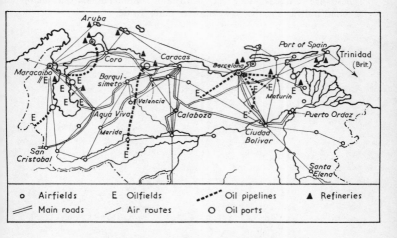

Fig. 40. Venezuela: communications and oilfield development.

Local trade and traffic is mainly concerned either with the distribution of the consumer goods which oil buys, or with the movement of agricultural products to market. These goods move by both road and air. Petrol is cheap, and Venezuela has a better national road network than any other country of Latin America.

It is the purpose of every Venezuelan government to put the national economy on a sounder and more rational basis. The main stumbling-blocks in such projects are human ones, however; agricultural production must be increased, for example, but efforts to draw back to the land some of those who have left it for the towns founder because of the differential in standard of living between town and country. In order to develop new agricultural areas, to attract labour, and to make reasonable use of agriculturally qualified immigrants, the living and working conditions on the land must be greatly improved and the structure of landownership radically altered from the present situation of relatively few very large holders and millions of landless labourers. This problem is now being tackled by the governments which have followed the dictatorship of Pérez Jiménez.

As industrial development continues, it seems as if it is crystallising at certain points, which are becoming major manufacturing centres. These are Caracas, Valencia, Maracaibo, Cumaná, Barquisimeto, Ciudad Bolivar and the new centre of Santo Tomé.

CHAPTER THIRTEEN

The Guianas

Guiana and Its Natural Features

The three territories of Guiana lie on the north-eastern flank of the Guiana Highland, whose western and southern sides belong to Venezuela and Brazil respectively. Here three European powers—Britain, France and the Netherlands—carved out for themselves colonial footholds in South America; the only colonies, incidentally, that have existed within the continent since the revolt against Spain in the early nineteenth century. In spite of their association with highly developed European states, however, these three territories are neither fully opened up nor economically developed to any appreciable degree. Rather is the contrary the case, and for this state of affairs a combination of physical, cultural and historical factors is very largely to blame. Whether the increasing measure of self-government granted to these territories will lead to a more rapid development of their resources remains to be seen.

All three territories extend inland from the Atlantic across a coastal plain which, although narrow in the east, attains a breadth of some 60 miles farther to the west. Beyond lie the old, highly folded remnants of the Guiana Highland, with granitic and gneissic intrusions thrusting up above its surface to form ridges and mountain ranges. The Highland culminates in the sandstone tableland of Cretaceous age which forms the watershed and which includes Mt. Roraima (9219 feet), the highest peak in the region. This is a landscape of precipitous walls of grey or red sandstones, flat-topped mountains with elevations around 6000 feet, and immense waterfalls, of which the most impressive is to be found on a tributary of the Essequibo—the Kaieteur Falls, with a height of 741 feet. Over the Highland as a whole, the average elevation is between 1200 and 2000 feet.

The rivers flowing down from the tableland have innumerable rapids, both in the mountains and also at the point where they enter the coastal plain, and these rapids render them useless for navigation. They are, in fact, used for water transport only over that part of the courses of the north-flowing rivers which lie within the coastal plain. Only the larger rivers are able to keep their own mouths clear of the sediments which they bring down to the sea. Owing to the action of the Guiana Current, alluvial material is transported rapidly westwards along the coast, blocking the mouths of the smaller rivers and forming a shoreline of bars and lagoons where the local structure and geological features are masked by the deposition of alluvial materials.

Both the coastlands and the mountains receive abundant rainfall, but frequency and seasonal character vary slightly from place to place. For the most part, however, the climate closely resembles the classic type of warm, humid conditions often found at low elevation in low latitudes. The coast is bordered by mangrove swamps, while the plain behind it is cultivated in parts. Over the whole region, however, rain-forest forms the principal original vegetation, with stretches of savanna here and there where local soil conditions are appropriate and the dry season is sufficiently long to affect conditions—notably in southern British Guiana. The highest rainfall figure is that of Cayenne, which receives 128 inches p.a.

History and Development

In many tropical areas, early penetration has been made by way of the river systems. In Guiana, however, as we have seen, the head of navigation is quickly reached, and penetration beyond this point is very difficult, even at the present day. Even the coastal settlements of the European colonisers were not founded until relatively late in the colonial era. After the Treaty of Tordesillas (see p. 10), this area appears to have attracted the attention of neither Spain nor Portugal, and it lay open to seizure by other powers. Holland, England and France all secured a holding. The Dutch had the greatest initial success, and when in 1667 the Peace of Breda brought to an end the Anglo-Dutch wars, the Dutch ceded New York (or New Amsterdam) to the British, and built up, by exchange, the colony of Surinam around their already flourishing settlements of Essequibo, Berbice and Corantyne.

During the Napoleonic Wars, the Dutch overseas territories were all occupied by the British, and when they were handed back the latter retained a part of the former Dutch territories. In Guiana, in fact, the boundary between the British and Dutch territories was not finally fixed until the beginning of the twentieth century.

Meanwhile, the French had strengthened their claim to their Guiana foothold. During the Napoleonic Wars they had to withstand, for a time, the attacks of the Brazilians, who were operating under the protection of the British fleet.

During this same period at the beginning of the nineteenth century, the importation of slaves, as a vital necessity to the sugar plantation economy, reached its peak. With the abolition of slavery (which took place in British possessions in 1834, in French territories in 1848, and in Dutch Guiana in 1853), many of the erstwhile Negro slaves moved inland into the forest, where they settled as the so-called Bush Negroes, and where their descendants remain to the present day.

Today the population of the Guianas is compounded from an extraordinary mixture of races. The forests and savannas of the interior are inhabited by Amerindian tribes, the forests of the coastal plain by Bush Negroes, and the coast itself by Asiatics—Indians, Javanese, Malayans, Annamese, Chinese and their descendants—who originally came in as indentured labourers, to supply the need for labour after the abolition of slavery. By contrast, the actual administration of these territories has, until recently, been under the control of a handful of white officials.

Guiana Today

BRITISH GUIANA

The British territory is the largest of the three, in terms of both area and population. Some 560,700 people inhabit its 83,000 square miles, and in 1961 about half of these were of South-East Asian origin. Georgetown, which lies just upstream from the mouth of the Demerara River, has almost passed the 150,000 mark.

The centres of agricultural production are found on the 30-mile wide coastal plain, while the foothill zone at its inland edge is a source of forest products and minerals. Farther south lies the savanna belt.

The political status of the territory has undergone a number of changes. In July 1928, a constitution was brought into force which has since been amended several times, most recently in 1962. The legislative power was placed in the hands of a council of state of 9 members, and a chamber of deputies with 28 members. The executive is an 11-member cabinet. Men and women have equal rights before the law, and British civil and criminal law apply. After the elections of 1957 and 1961, a left-wing government took office, and complete independence had not been achieved by 1966 because of continuing political and racial strife.

Education is compulsory between the ages of six and fourteen years. There are a number of State schools, but most of them are run, with State support, by religious groups.

As in most other South American countries, there is a close correlation between economic development and the spread of communications. Up to the present, a little over 150 miles of railways and some 300 miles of roads have been built. Navigation—for anything more than canoes or rafts—is restricted to the lower courses of the rivers and a few canals —about 300 miles in all.

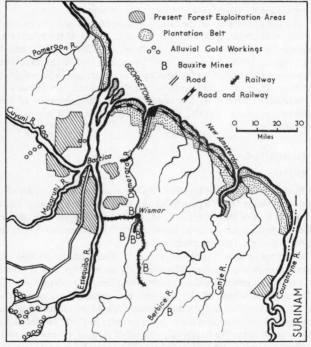

Fig. 41. British Guiana: economic development. (Based, by permission, on a map prepared by the Department of Lands and Mines, George-town, 1958.)

Sugar-cane was for long the principal product of British Guiana. In the 1930's sugar accounted for two-thirds of the colony's exports by weight. After 1945, however, this proportion declined to a half, while rice gained in importance and mineral products assumed a leading role. Of the minerals, gold and diamonds are now overshadowed by the greatly increased bauxite production. Huge deposits of bauxite are awaiting exploitation, while in 1960 the year's output amounted to some 2·5 million long tons. The situation regarding the exploitation of the colony's forests is similar to that in other tropical lands—great resources (some 60,000 square miles of forest) but little development. In addition, there are 12,000 square miles of wholly untouched land, which give promise of valuable resources for the future.

SURINAM (formerly Dutch Guiana)

By an amendment of September 1948 to the Netherlands' constitution, Surinam became an autonomous part of the Kingdom of the Netherlands, and received full self-government under an agreement of January 1950. There is a governor, appointed by the Crown, who is the head of the administration and who appoints ministers and a council. There is also an assembly, elected for a four-year term. The ultimate objective is to accord Surinam dominion status.

The population of the territory is racially mixed and socially diverse—so much so that there are real obstacles in the way of democratic progress towards self-government in such a community. The racial mixture —with its divergent religious associations—is extraordinary; out of a population estimated at 294,800 in 1960, there was some 38,000 Bush Negroes, 5000 Guiana Indians, 115,000 Creoles, 93,500 Hindus or Asian Indians, 43,100 Indonesians, 4500 Europeans and 4400 Chinese, with smaller groups besides. Four continents have thus contributed to Surinam's population, each providing different living standards, attitudes, interests and skills in agriculture or mining. Some 85% of the inhabitants at present earn their livelihood through agriculture.

Surinam is well suited to the production of tropical crops, thanks in part to the type of polderland agriculture imported by the Dutch, and in part to favourable conditions of soil and climate. In the past twenty years, however, great changes have taken place here, and there has been a drift of population away from cultivation of the land and into bauxite mining. As a result of this shift of interest, the output of sugar-cane has declined considerably, and that of rice, coffee and citrus fruit has also done so, though to a lesser extent. This decline has taken place in spite of the increase in Dutch interest in Surinam which has followed the loss of her East Indian empire. The Netherlands has sought replacements here for tropical products no longer available from the East.

In the last two decades bauxite mining has offered a more promising field for investment than the agricultural projects, such as dyking, draining, and crop cultivation which have been carried out in the past along the coast. Bauxite production, backed principally by United States capital, has been rising steadily since 1937. By 1960 it had reached a level of over 3·6 million metric tons p.a., so that Surinam and British Guiana together supplied more than half the total world output of this mineral. The U.S.A. buys the greater part of this output, and during the Second World War, Surinam alone supplied over 50% of the U.S.A.'s bauxite requirements. Fresh sources, brought to light since 1952, permit of mining by open-cast methods, and form the basis of future plans—for electricity generation, and the building of plants that will produce aluminium within the country, and thus enable Surinam to benefit from the development of the processing industry. In 1959, bauxite represented 80% of the total of exports by value, and has thus taken over the dominant role played by sugar-cane previously.

FRENCH GUIANA

The French section of Guiana was for long the best known of the three territories, partly for its pepper, but more especially because of its unsavoury reputation as a penal colony, in the years between 1798 and the Second World War, when the prisons were finally closed.

French Guiana, with an area of roughly 35,135 square miles and a population of some 31,000, is the smallest of these European footholds in South America. The term 'colony' can no longer be applied. Since March 1946, the territory has the status of a *département d'outre mer* in the French Union. It has an elected council and a Prefect who heads the administration, while as is the case with other overseas departments of France, it also sends representatives to Paris. Cayenne, a city of 15,300 inhabitants, acts as capital; the remainder of the territory contains less than 20,000 people.

French Guiana is almost entirely covered by rain-forest, and agriculture is limited to small coastal areas where rice, maize, cocoa, sugarcane, bananas and coffee are grown. There are valuable mineral resources, such as gold and bauxite, but these are virtually untouched. A small quantity of forest products—principally rosewood—finds its way down the rivers to the coast.

MIDDLE AMERICA

CHAPTER FOURTEEN

Central America and Mexico: Introduction

Structure

As Europe is separated from Africa by a great down-faulted and folded depression, so North and South America are divided by what might be called the American Mediterranean. Throughout this zone of separation the land areas are scattered. These are (1) the projection into the area of Mexico, a continuation of the northern land mass, (2) the land bridge of Central America, comprising Guatemala, British Honduras, Honduras, Nicaragua, Costa Rica and Panama, and (3) the islands of the Caribbean, which can be grouped as follows: (a) the Bahamas, (b) the Greater Antilles—Cuba, Jamaica, Hispaniola and Puerto Rico, (c) the Lesser Antilles, including the Windward and Leeward Islands, (d) the continental off-shore islands including Trinidad.

The structural basis of the Central American isthmus is formed by two great mountain systems. In Tertiary times, these were separated from each other by a broad area of the sea stretching between them where Lake Nicaragua lies today. This Tertiary sea was sufficiently wide to hinder the diffusion of both flora and fauna between the northern and southern continents.

The northern, or Antillean, mountain system curves round through Guatemala and Honduras, and thence out towards the Greater Antilles (see Fig. 42). In parts of Guatemala and El Salvador, young intrusive rocks such as andesites and basalt have been forced up, but most of the mountain blocks owe their present elevation to upthrust along east-west fault lines at the close of the period of Miocene folding. With the coming of the Tertiary and Quaternary periods, volcanic activity became widespread, and has resulted in the creation of cones which rise above 12,000 feet in Guatemala and El Salvador as well as farther north in Mexico.

In Honduras, Nicaragua and southern Mexico are to be found wide-spread lava flows and other erupted materials covering great areas, beneath which the pre-existing relief has been buried.

The central sea between the continents was partially filled in, and somewhat narrowed, by volcanic materials, but it was not until the up-lift of the Upper Pliocene period that the Nicaraguan depression finally emerged from the sea. Even as late as the beginning of the Quaternary, Lake Nicaragua was linked with the Pacific Ocean. Further volcanic outpourings finally blocked the arm of the sea, and allowed the present fresh-water lake to form. Thereupon the San Juan River cut back its head to the lake and now drains it into the Caribbean.

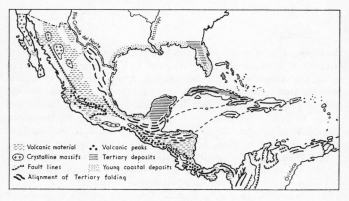

Fig. 42. Central America and Mexico: structure.

The southern mountain system begins south of the Nicaraguan depression and forms what appears as an S-shaped prolongation of the main Andean chain although the rock structures and types north and south of the Atrato River basin are distinctly different. Like western Colombia, Costa Rica and Panama consist of a main mountain range, paralleled by a longitudinal valley and then by a coastal chain. The latter however, is discontinuous in the Isthmus, and only appears in the Peninsulas of Nicoya, Osa, Burica and Azuero.

On the map, the 'land bridge' of Central America appears to link the two American continents. In reality, it divides them. Structure and erosional forces have conspired to impede the building of both railways and roads. In terms of modern transport, Central America is a great road-block between north and south, with no through route yet completed. Before the long-planned *Carretera Inter-Americana* can be completed as an all-weather road, as part of the great Pan-American Highway, there are still obstacles to be overcome in the rugged relief and forest-choked depressions of the isthmus—particularly in the Darien area to the south of the Panama Canal.

Climate and Vegetation

The mainland of Central America and Mexico can be divided into three very broad climatic regions, the Caribbean, the Pacific and the desert of the north. On the Caribbean side, there is a heavy winter rainfall due to the prevailing easterly winds. With both high humidity and high temperatures, conditions favour the growth of tropical rain-forest; at higher altitudes, the character of the forest changes but the cover persists right up to the drier plateaux of Mexico, where its outliers are the remnants of coniferous woodland.

The ancient cultures developed mainly on the plateaux, especially the Mexican; that is, beyond the dense forest belt. For the Spaniards, too, the rain-forest represented a barrier, seldom pierced, and then only to afford passage to the settlements of the well-populated highlands where the labour force of the Indians and their objects of silver and gold attracted the Conquistadors. Even today, Europeans have not settled in any numbers in the forest belt; the sparse population is composed largely of Indians and Negroes.

Caribbean Central America lies under the influence of warm seas. The north-east trades carry oceanic influences far inland. Relative humidity is very high, and the annual temperature range is small. The amount of cloud cover is greater than on the Pacific side. Summer rains often occur as thunder showers, while winter rains tend to occur as a result of intrusions of cold air from the north. In any case the north-east trade wind is the main source of precipitation on the Atlantic side; as it crosses to the Pacific, or leeward, side it arrives as a dry wind, descending from the mountains under clear skies.

North of the Nicaraguan depression, the eastern slopes of the mountains receive over 120 inches of rain per annum, and, to the south, at Colon, the Atlantic terminus of the Panama Canal, the figure is 130 inches. At higher altitudes—above about 5000 feet—the amount of rainfall decreases, and it also falls off northward along the Mexican coast, but the duration of the rains is longer. As a result of the various influences mentioned—convectional rain, the intrusion of cold air from the north, and the trade winds encountering the Central American mountains—the Atlantic coast of this region does not experience the pronounced dry season which is so charactertistic of the sub-tropical zone elsewhere.

The Pacific region of Central America is also bordered by warm seas, at least as far north as the Tropic of Cancer. Along the north-west coast

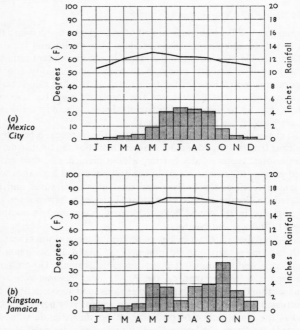

Fig. 43. Middle America: mainland and island climates. Temperature and rainfall diagrams for (*a*) Mexico City and (*b*) Kingston, Jamaica.

of Mexico, the prevailing winds tend to blow parallel to the coast, and therefore do not bring rain to that area. Rain-bearing winds blow from the west as one progresses southward, and deposit their moisture on the windward slopes of the mountains. As a result, there are small dry zones in the basins of the interior, where the mountains exclude the effects of these westerly winds. One area, however, which does not conform to this general pattern is the shore of the Gulf of Panama, where there is an upwelling of cold water which may keep the sea temperature as much as 18–20° F below the air temperature.

The north-east trades, which are rain-bearing on the Atlantic side, are *foehn* type winds on the west coast, so that the trade-wind season is a dry season here. Thus most of the Pacific side has a savanna-type rainfall régime, with a dry winter, which passes northwards along the west coast of Mexico into desert and then into semi-desert. This winter dry period is known locally as *verano* (that is, summer) and the rainy, high-sun season as *invierno* (or winter). The Pacific coast receives less than half as much rain as the Atlantic side. Panama City, for example, at the Pacific end of the Canal, receives only 57 inches compared with 130 inches at Colon—merely 30 miles away across the isthmus. The only parts of this west side which receive as much as 120 inches of rain are the peninsulas of Nicoya and Azuero, where the mountains project out of the sea and force the south-west winds to rise.

In winter, there are regular intrusions of cold air southwards across Mexico and Guatemala from the U.S.A. These bring a rapid fall of temperature and rainfall to the plateau lands, while they later arrive on the coastlands of Guatemala and El Salvador in the form of *foehn* winds, warm and dry. Temperatures on the Pacific side are governed in the main by relief. In the densely populated upland areas they are generally moderate, but insolation is very strong.

The vegetation cover reflects the contrasts between the two sides of

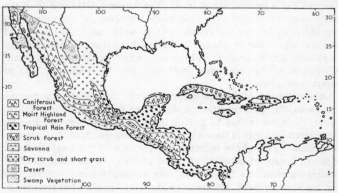

Fig. 44. Middle America: the generalised pattern of natural vegetation.

the mainland. On the Caribbean coast, there is a narrow belt of man-groves, and then behind this the evergreen tropical rain-forest. A pro-fusion of undergrowth and of epiphytes and parasites makes this Atlantic forest almost impenetrable. Surface travel through the area is usually accomplished only by river except in those areas cleared for banana plantations by intensive use of both labour and machinery.

On the Pacific side, such tropical and sub-tropical forest is found only in the north, and then only between about 5000 and 7000 feet. It stretches from southern Mexico into Guatemala and El Salvador. Towards the upper edge of this forest zone the evergreen oak appears, and above 6000 feet there are the deciduous and coniferous trees of the *tierra fria*. In the interior, dry forests of oak and pine predominate. Similarly, on the coast itself, conditions are drier and favour a mixture of dry forest, chaparral and savanna which is to be found everywhere from Guate-mala to Panama. On the Pacific side with its denser population, how-ever, the vegetation has been modified by man far more than on the thinly settled Atlantic coast.

Discovery

On his fourth voyage Columbus sailed along the Caribbean coast from Honduras to what is now eastern Panama, but it was only in the Panama area that subsequent efforts at founding settlements were successful. It was here, too, that the first crossing was made to the Pacific, then called the Mar del Sur, in 1513. In 1517, the city of Panama was founded on the shores of this newly reached ocean. The forested Atlantic side of the isthmus provided little of interest to the Spaniards; it was only thinly populated by Indians, and furthermore, those Indians had a low level of cultural attainment in relation to the sedentary Aztecs of the Mexican highlands. There was also very little in the way of precious metals found. Consequently, the Spaniards never attempted to establish a base of operations there.

About the end of the sixteenth century the Caribbean coast became the haunt of English privateers, and many an illicit base was established, from which the raiding of trading ships was carried on. The English were interested, too, in the mahogany and other woods of the forests on this eastern side of the isthmus. The presence of the English in this Spanish sphere of influence attracted runaway slaves from the West Indies and elsewhere, and in 1711 there was established a separate state on the Atlantic coast. The British withdrew after 1783, but returned in 1840 to assume control of this Negro state of Mosquitia, and the newly formed Central American republics were unable to dislodge Great Britain from her Caribbean foothold. In 1850, however, she renounced, together with the U.S.A., all claims to occupy the Atlantic coast of Nicaragua and Costa Rica, and retained control only of British Honduras. English-speaking groups of Negroes, however, remain along parts of the coast and on some of the off-shore islands.

With the gold rush to California in 1849, the land route across the Central American isthmus suddenly achieved importance, for most of the early movement between the eastern parts of the United States and the goldfields was along this route. For a short time (prior to the completion of the transcontinental railway across the U.S.A. in 1869), the lowland passage to the Pacific via Lake Nicaragua was a much-frequented route.

Population

The long succession of Amerindian cultures in Central America is as yet imperfectly understood. However, it seems that one stream of cultural influence spread with the movement of population southwards from Mexico, keeping to the mountain belt on the Pacific side. Another, of South American origin, seems to have spread north into the forest lands of the Atlantic coast.

The most important of these Indian groups were the Aztecs and the Mayas. The Aztecs will be discussed in the section on Mexico. The Mayas developed their first civilisation in the highlands of Guatemala, but later migrated north into the forest lands and there they lived out their heyday and their decline. Their basic food crop was maize. At the time when the Spaniards arrived, the Mayas did not form a political entity. On the contrary, internal conflicts had led them to choose defensive locations for, and to fortify, their settlements. Their settlements were subsequently abandoned to the forest, which soon overwhelmed them. The bases of the Mayan economy and the structure of its urban civilisation remain subjects of archaeological controversy.

In 1513 the Spaniards under Balboa reached the Pacific, and soon afterwards the city of Panama was founded. This was the signal for the exploration and conquest of the Pacific coast of Central America. The Spaniards were motivated by a desire for gold and for slaves, whom they sold in the West Indies. They set up a system of *encomiendas*, under which the Indians living within a specified territory were 'entrusted' to the care of a Spanish *encomendero*, who obtained the right to their labour in exchange for his tutelage.

The Encomienda

As developed in the Indies, the *encomienda* was the patronage conferred by royal favour over a portion of the natives concentrated in settlements near those of the Spaniards; the obligation to instruct them in the Christian religion and the elements of civilised life, and to defend them in their persons and property; coupled with the right to demand tribute or labour in return for these privileges. So far as we know, no grant of land was involved, although references in some of the early documents are ambiguous. The recipients of *encomiendas* were to be *conquistadores* and meritorious settlers so rewarded for their contribution to the founding of new colonies. It was an attempt to reconcile the crown's determination to deal kindly with the natives and the need for a stable and continuous labour supply, and it became the basis for Spanish-Indian relations over a period of two and a half centuries.[1]

Between 1519 and 1521, the Spaniards under Cortes conquered the Empire of the Aztecs in Mexico. Cortes and his small band thrust inland from the Gulf coast, and fought and bluffed their way to the heart of the empire, at Mexico City.

To reach Mexico they had to cross a pass 12,000 feet high between the volcanoes of Popocatepetl (the Mountain that Smokes) and Ixtaccihuatl (the White Woman), an extinct volcano, both snow mountains of over 17,000 feet which lay twenty miles due west of Cholula. Popocatepetl had become active after a long quiescence shortly before the Spaniards' arrival, an added portent of calamity in Mexican opinion. 'A great volume of smoke came from it day and night, rising to the clouds as straight as a pillar,' wrote Cortes. As they approached they could hear it roaring. With its cap of snow it was a marvellous sight. That night camp was pitched about six miles below the top of the pass. On reaching the top next day they saw the city of their dreams 5000 feet below. . . . They were some twenty miles from the southern shore of the lake, which at that time filled the greater part of the valley. Near its centre was the island on which Mexico itself stood. As they were the best part of forty-five miles from the city, the causeways which connected it with the mainland can hardly have been visible. The lake, which was fifty miles long, was in six compartments, opening out of each other. Round the shores were ten large towns and twenty smaller ones. This secluded valley at the end of the world, surrounded on all sides by high ranges, was densely populated. Though the people all spoke the Nauatl tongue, they were not all Mexicans. Only the inhabitants of Mexico City were of that race. The rest were descendants of the several North American tribes which settled in the valley before

1 Haring, C. H., *The Spanish Empire in America*, New York, 1963, p. 40.

Plate 28. Colombia: on the Paramo of Santurban, between Pamplona and Bucaramanga, Indian farmers hoe in unison as they plant potatoes at 12,000 feet. The forerunner of our Irish potato was first domesticated in the central Andean area in Pre-Columbian times.

(Courtesy: Standard Oil Co. (N.J.))

Plate 29. Colombia: in the Cordillera Oriental between Pamplona and Bucaramanga. Although all directions here are reduced to two—up and down—cultivation of the steep mountain slopes is standard practice. *(Courtesy: Standard Oil Co. (N.J.))*

Plate 30. Colombia: docks
at Santa Marta
(*Courtesy: Thames and
Hudson Ltd., from South
America' by Hans Mann*)

Plate 31. Colombia: river traffic on the Magdalena. The steamer, seen at Barrancabermeja, hauls petroleum products and other cargo on charter. (*Courtesy: Standard Oil Co. (N.J.)*)

Plate 32. Colombia: a coffee plantation near Armenia, in the state of Caldas. Shade trees are always planted to protect the coffee from noon-day heat.   *(Courtesy: Standard Oil Co. (N.J.))*

Plate 33. Colombia: on the Mannelita sugar plantation near Cali in the Cauca Valley. The picture shows the cane passing into a press which removes all the liquid from the cane, for further refining in another part of the plant. *(Courtesy: Standard Oil Co. (N.J.))*

Plate 34. Colombia: drying hides on a ranch near Cali, in the Cauca Valley.
(Courtesy: Standard Oil Co. (N.J.))

Plate 35. Colombia: making cigars. This is an activity in which the whole family shares, from planting and picking to rolling the cigars. The family earns about 2s. 6d. (or 35 cents) for every fifty cigars.
(Courtesy: Standard Oil Co. (N.J.))

Plate 36. Venezuela: planting dry-land rice on a newly-cleared farm on the margin of settlement near San Felipe. (*Courtesy: Standard Oil Co. (N.J.)*)

Plate 37. Venezuela: the role of rural credit facilities. Operating a hand tractor cultivator purchased with a Rural Welfare loan. (*Courtesy: Standard Oil Co. (N.J.)*)

Plate 38. Venezuela : watching drilling operations in the Jusepin oilfield, in eastern Venezuela. The distended abdomen of the boy in the foreground is a reflection of the poor health and nutrition standards in the backlands.   *(Courtesy: Standard Oil Co. (N.J.))*

Plate 39. Venezuela: a river-front scene on the San Juan
river in eastern Venezuela, showing river boats unloading and the
market place on the opposite bank.

(*Courtesy: Standard Oil Co. (N.J.)*)

Plate 40. Venezuela: Cerro Bolivar, the mountain of iron-ore, from where a 90-mile standard gauge railway carries the ore to the port and steel town of Puerto Ordaz on the Orinoco River (see Fig. 40).

(Courtesy: Aerofilms for Ewing Galloway)

Plate 41. Central America: clearance and construction work on a light,
narrow-gauge railway being built to serve the banana plantations.
(Courtesy: United Fruit Co.)

Plate 42 (*top*). Guatemala: in the foreground, the fishermen of Lake Atitlan laze away an hour, while in the background rises the volcano of the same name, its slopes partly cleared for crops and pasture.

(*Courtesy: Pan American Airways*)

Plate 43 (*bottom*). Guatemala: a lively regional market at Chichicastenango. The people of the Guatemalan highlands are mainly Indians, the descendants of the ancient Mayans. (*Courtesy: Pan American Airways*)

Plate 44. The Panama Canal: the Miraflores locks.

(*Courtesy: Pan American Airways*)

Plate 45 (*opposite, top*). Mexico: the legacy of Spain. The church of San Francisco, Acatepec, which has been recently restored with fresh white plaster and dazzling gold leaf applied to its intricate baroque interior. (*Courtesy: Canadian Pacific Railway*)

Plate 46 (*opposite, bottom*). Mexico: the legacy of the Aztecs. While the shape and structure of the University Library, Mexico City, are undeniably modern, the decoration motifs clearly recall Mexico's past.

(*Courtesy: Braniff Airways*)

Plate 47. Mexico: the Latin American Building, in the heart of
Mexico City.   (*Courtesy: Canadian Pacific Railway*)

Plate 48. Mexico: a scene in an island fishing village on Lake Patzcuaro. Note the unusual butterfly shape of the nets.

(*Courtesy: Canadian Pacific Railway*)

Plate 49 (*top*). Mexico: a village street, where time has wrought
little change.   (*Courtesy: Canadian Pacific Railway*)

Plate 50 (*bottom*). Mexico: near Puebla, peasants weave straw
hats as a form of home industry. (*Courtesy: Canadian Pacific Railway*)

Plate 51. A travelling rural nurse makes a house visit in El Salvador under the sponsorship of the World Health Organisation.

(Courtesy: United Nations)

Plates 52 and 53. Jamaica: bananas are wrapped in specially ventilated 'Diothene' tubing and delivered via lighters to the banana boats. New methods of boxing in Jamaica are now being experimented with. (*Courtesy: Fyffes' 'Blue Label' Bananas*)

the Mexicans arrived. But all of them were now subject to Montezuma, and the lords who governed them were related to him.[1]

The arrival of the Spaniards brought smallpox and cholera in its train, and disease decimated the native population. So, too, did recurrent famines and Spanish methods of conquest. It is all the more remarkable, in fact, that enough Indians survived this tragic period for 60% of the population of Guatemala, for example, to be composed at the present day of pure-blooded Indians. By contrast, the populations of El Salvador and Honduras are highly mixed racially. Then in Costa Rica, where the sparse Indian population fiercely resisted conquest, and where, as a result, it was virtually eliminated, whites comprise a majority of the population today.

The effects of the Spanish conquest on the Indians were probably greatest in those areas where the native population had been scattered in single dwellings and isolated homesteads. The Indians were concentrated by the Spaniards in villages, to facilitate the tasks of both the missionary and the tax collector. This policy was not always successful, and in some cases it was necessary to re-establish scattered settlements, away from the village churches and from central control.

The Spaniards also founded new towns in the well-settled interior uplands. In 1527, in the Captaincy-General of Guatemala, a capital city was founded at the foot of the volcano Antigua. However, earthquakes and eruptions have made it necessary to change the site of the city no less than four times, after successive devastations. It was from these Spanish cities in the New World that European ideas were disseminated, and European control was exercised, while on the other hand the Indians living in the vicinity of the city had the duty of supplying agricultural produce to it as well as the manpower to perform the menial tasks for the Spanish masters. The Spanish culture as it was developed in Central America was the urban culture of Mediterranean Europe, transposed into the New World.

The homelands of the Central American Indians stretched from the Pacific across to the Atlantic. The Mayas and the Lencas, for example, pressed out from the highlands of the interior into the forest zone of the Caribbean coast. But the cultural heartland of the region was situated, long before the Spaniards appeared on the scene, on the Pacific side of Central America and in the dry interior. The tribes of the Atlantic coast continued to lead a primitive way of life, closely adapted to their habitat by virtue of their low level of subsistence and cultural elaboration. At the time of the European explorations, the population on this

1 Collis, M., *Cortes and Montezuma*, London, 1954, pp. 116-7.

forested coast was very sparse, and subsistence was obtained by hunting, fishing and a little 'slash and burn' cultivation. The Misquitos[1] lived in stilt dwellings. Shortly after the settlement of the Spanish colonies, there began a steady trickle of runaway Negroes to this coast from the West Indies, and these intermarried with the Indians. Then in the seventeenth century there followed numerous Englishmen attracted by the timber supplies of the area, and to supply the English with labour, the racially mixed Misquitos carried on slave raiding into the surrounding forest lands. A very sharp decline in the numbers of the forest Indians resulted. These slave-gathering expeditions continued well into the eighteenth century, and many hundreds of captured forest Indians were traded by the Misquitos for arms and ammunition in Jamaica.

Fig. 45. Central America: distribution of population.

In 1795, the English banished the last remaining 5000 Caribs from the Windward Islands to the islands off the coast of northern Honduras. These Caribs had already acquired much Negro blood by intermarriage, and in due course they spread from the islands to the adjacent mainland coast. Today, their descendants speak an Indian dialect.

Finally, late nineteenth- and early twentieth-century immigration of Negroes from the West Indies to provide labour for the banana plantations of the Caribbean coastlands and for the construction of the Panama Canal added yet another element to the population of this region.

1 The name Misquito is an Indian word, and was transformed into Mosquito or Mosquitia by the English. Thus the name Mosquito Coast which appears on modern maps has nothing to do with the presence of insects.

The Economy of Central America

As in the rest of Latin America, Spanish interest in Central America lay mainly in the production of precious metals which, in this area, were found scattered in the highland zone. Along with this went control of the land but, except in Costa Rica, little effort was made to develop its potentialities. Natural dyestuffs, such as indigo and cochineal, provided export crops, but soon after independence in the 1820's the market was undermined by the introduction of synthetic dyes. About the year 1850, however, coffee was introduced and rapidly achieved economic importance as the volcanic soils of the west side of Guatemala and El Salvador proved to be particularly well suited to the coffee crop because of their porosity and good drainage characteristics.

In this coffee-producing region, the decisive natural factor is the existence of a humus layer which is commonly found on land newly cleared of forest. Thus each coffee *finca* possesses a large reserve of forest land. The soil must be provided with plenty of moisture, but also be well drained. The best locations in this region are in the westward-flowing river valleys, which are protected from the north wind. The development of coffee was mainly financed by local entrepreneurs, but in Guatemala the industry has been expanded by German planters, and by the Second World War 30–40% of the coffee estates in Guatemala were owned by Germans. In 1942, however, Guatemala declared war on Germany, and these estates were taken over by the government and placed under the control of the national bank. The coffee industry contributes significantly to the economy of these small countries since production and processing of this crop creates a large demand for labour, including that of the poorer Indians who live in the highlands, and thus provide a migrant labour force for the *fincas* at harvest time, and so depend on the coffee crop for some part of their livelihood. Moreover, coffee exports provide much of the export income of these countries and the basis of government revenues.

The cultivation of bananas provides a marked contrast with that of coffee, for in this case capital investment is usually foreign. Most of the bananas are grown in private groves, particularly in those of the United Fruit Company which is one of the largest agricultural organisations in the world. The company's contribution to the economic and cultural development of Central America has been considerable (see Fig. 46) in spite of the fact that large profits have been paid to the American shareholders.

Bananas grow throughout the *tierra caliente* (see Plate 41), and also in the lower part of the *tierra templada*, where they provide both a food crop and also shade in the coffee-growing zone. In terms of world trade, however, commercial banana cultivation is limited to areas with particularly favourable transport facilities, since the fruit spoils easily if delayed or damaged in transit. Bananas which are to be exported to mid-latitude lands are picked while still unripe, and are then brought up to the

Fig. 46. Central America: location and character of the activities of the United Fruit Company, 1952.

desired state of ripeness under carefully regulated conditions of heat and humidity, either during their journey to market or while in storage.

Thus the time of harvest is fixed in relation to market conditions. Boesch describes the operation:

> Work on the plantations has begun early. About midday, then, the railway trucks into which the bananas are loaded will be marshalled into trains, and in the course of the afternoon these will be run down to the dockside station. The United Fruit Company has its own refrigerated banana ships, which are known as the Great White Fleet. On the quays, two conveyor belts will be mounted, one on the foredeck of the banana ship, and one aft. The stevedores will lift the great bunches of bananas out of the railway waggons, one by one, and carry them to the conveyor belts.

Here there stands a man with a razor-sharp machete. Aiming a single, well-directed blow which skims past the porter's head, he will sever the main stalk. At the same time he inspects the fruit, and any that is imperfect will be flung into the sea, while the good fruit will be laid carefully on the belts and be stowed in the ships' holds. In the course of the evening and the night hours, seven or eight long trains will arrive and be unloaded, and so the work will go on, without a break, hour after hour. Gradually the heat and the work wear down the sweating porters, and the tempo slows as the ship fills. It holds anything from 45,000 to 85,000 bunches.

By next morning, the ship will be far away on the high seas.[1]

In the course of the last few years, it has proved necessary to replace many of the banana plantations on the Caribbean coast of Central America by new producing areas on the Pacific coast. The latter is, of course, less accessible to the markets of the Eastern United States, and involves the extra expense of transport through the Panama Canal. But the bananas on the Atlantic side have been suffering both from plant diseases and from damage done by hurricanes, and since the Second World War the stricken plantations have been abandoned. (In this connection, it may be noted that, since 1952, the chief source of banana imports into the U.S.A. has been Ecuador—the world's major banana exporting country.)

New lands must continually be brought into production by forest clearance and the large banana companies have allowed for this by securing concessions over very extensive areas of suitable land. In some cases, it has simply been a matter of felling the trees, selling off the valuable timber, and leaving the rest to rot quickly away in the hot, humid climate of the tropical lowlands. In other cases, however, a different method of clearance has been adopted—in northern Honduras, for example, and the Ulua Lowland: the sediment-rich rivers are simply diverted from their courses to flood the forest land. This has the twofold effect of enriching the soil with a layer of alluvium and of destroying the vegetation. Leafless and grey, enlivened only by a few parasites still flowering on the upper branches, these sump forests present the dreariest spectacle imaginable, until eventually they are brought under cultivation.

In the new lands the labour problem is serious, since both Europeans and Indians have avoided the forested coastlands in the past. But as a result of advances in medical science the position has today improved to the point where the danger of disease and epidemics is greatly reduced, and where labour can work in the region without damage to health.

1 Boesch, H., *Zentralamerika heute*, Zürich, 1952.

When the new banana plantations are established, the labour force must often be recruited at a considerable distance. On the Pacific side of Costa Rica, the plantation workers are migrants from the north-western part of the country. In northern Honduras many of the workers represent an overflow from densely populated areas of El Salvador. When, during the Second World War, new areas were being opened up in Panama, the agricultural labour force was recruited in northern Honduras. On the older banana plantations, the labourers are predominantly Negroes: this is especially the case in eastern Costa Rica. The Negroes came originally from Jamaica and Barbados, the sugar islands, which have become seriously overpopulated. Such immigration is no longer permitted by the Central American countries in all of which unemployment is a serious problem.

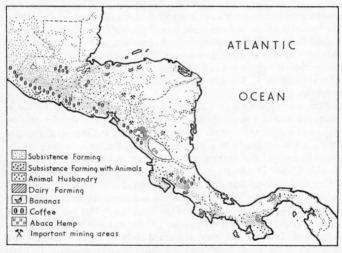

ATLANTIC

OCEAN

Subsistence Farming
Subsistence Farming with Animals
Animal Husbandry
Dairy Farming
Bananas
Coffee
Abaca Hemp
Important mining areas

Fig. 47. Central America: distribution of primary economic activities, 1952.

When the banana plantations are given up, many of the workers do not move away but simply change to some form of subsistence agriculture. They have little difficulty in supporting themselves, and while secondary forest quickly overwhelms much of the cleared land, food crops grown in limited areas provide a means of subsistence. Experiments have been made with cocoa, oil palms and rubber plantations on the former banana lands—well provided, of course, with transport facilities—but these have not been very successful. Other forest products of the region are chicle, the base for chewing-gum, which is obtained from the sapodilla tree, and several types of timber, such as teak, balsa and mahogany, whose particular properties of light weight or weather resistance afford them a world market.

The importance of coffee and bananas, both to the individual states of the Central American isthmus and to world trade in these products, is shown in the following table:

Coffee and Banana Exports of Central American States, as a Percentage of Total Exports and of World Trade in these Commodities

State	% of Total Exports represented by						% of World Exports			
	Coffee			Bananas			1947		1963	
	1946	1950	1960	1947	1950	1960	Coffee	Bananas	Coffee	Bananas
Guatemala	61	78	70	22	11	12	2·8	3·2	3·2	4·6
El Salvador	80	85	80	–	–	–	2·9	–	3·2	–
Honduras	6	–	19	35	35	45	0·6	21·6	0·6	12·0
Nicaragua	25	50	31	2	–	–	0·9	0·5	0·6	2·3
Costa Rica	43	60	49	20	25	28	0·7	1·6	1·6	7·4
Panama	–	–	5	50	40	55	0·2	1·2	0·1	10·0
							8·1	28·1	9·3	36·3

The purely agricultural basis of the economy of Central America, however, is now recognised as being inadequate to ensure rising living standards for a rapidly increasing population. The possibilities of diversification of economic activities within the narrow bounds of the separate states are severely limited, particularly because of the very small national markets for locally produced industrial products. Out of the difficulties of such a situation has arisen a move towards economic integration within Central America. In 1960 the Treaty of Central American Economic Integration was signed by Guatemala, Honduras, El Salvador, Nicaragua and Costa Rica. By this the five countries decided to form a Common Market with the eventual free interchange of all products manufactured within the region and the establishment of industries designed to produce sufficient quantities of goods to meet the needs of the whole area and thus to eliminate the need for imports. Under the stimulus of this new approach to the economic needs of Central America new industries are being established and trade between the countries is being increased. The success of the venture depends in part on the improvement of communications, and increased expenditure on roads—particularly those joining the capitals of the five countries—is producing a more effective network. Successful economic diversification, however, will only be possible over a relatively long period and, in the meantime, coffee, cotton and bananas will maintain their position both as dominant export products and as the bases on which government revenue depends.

CHAPTER FIFTEEN

The Countries of Central America

Guatemala

Guatemala, the Land of the Indians, bears little resemblance to those North American Indian territories where, according to popular fancy, the Indian braves lived in wigwams, hunted the buffalo and collected the scalps of white men. These Indians live in permanent mud dwellings, and lead the placid lives of maize and bean cultivators, with the hoe as their principal implement. They are the descendants of the Mayas, of whom a sixteenth-century Spanish chronicle—the *Chronica de la Santa Provincia del Santissimo Nombre de Jesus de Guattemala*—had the following to say: 'When one looks into the matter closely, one finds that all that they do and say is bound up with *maize*. In fact, they have almost made of it their god. And so great is the joy and satisfaction which they derive from their maize fields that they seem to forget all about their wives and families, as if the cultivation of maize was their life's work and highest good.' They had, in fact, a maize god, and their religion was centred upon a series of deities who were held to control maize cultivation: the sun, the rain and the wind gods.

In Guatemala, most of the population is concentrated in the zone between 5000 and 8000 feet above sea-level. Above this zone rise the cones of volcanoes which extend above the limit of cultivation, and are used in places for pasturing flocks (see Plate 42.) Tropical export crops cannot be grown in the densely populated highlands where the Indians are concentrated, and consequently this region has hardly been developed by the Spaniards, or by later white settlers (see Plate 43.) People of European descent are to be found mainly in the big towns, and the same is generally true also of the ladinos, or mestizos, who are of mixed white and Indian descent.

Below the 5000-foot contour there begins the zone of coffee cultivation, focused mainly on the central highlands in the vicinity of Guatemala City. Both foreigners and Guatemalans are involved in coffee-growing.

The ports of the Pacific coast (which handle 80% of all foreign trade) and the Atlantic coast port of Puerto Barrios are all linked to each other by road and rail. The country is crossed by two main international highways, the Pacific Highway which runs along the west coast, and the Inter-American Highway, which forms a link for road traffic between the U.S.A. and Costa Rica, via Mexico, Guatemala, El Salvador and Honduras. The Guatemalan railways are narrow-gauge lines. There is a considerable network of air routes.

In the Pacific coast lowlands, besides the banana plantations already described, there are cultivated grasslands where livestock raising is carried on, and plantations for the production of essential oils.

Indian customs and traditions have been preserved in the northern highlands of Guatemala to a greater extent than anywhere else in Central America. In this area, as much as four-fifths of the population are pure-blooded Indians speaking no Spanish, raising only subsistence crops for local use, ignoring the wheel as a means of improving transport facilities and playing no part in the national life of the country except that the area in which they live has become an area of considerable attraction for anthropologists and tourists.

In the towns of the rest of Guatemala there is to be found a somewhat mixed population, which includes not only Spaniards but also Turks and Levantines. If we exclude the pure Indians, the remainder of the population comprises 55% Spaniards, and the rest is made up of ladinos, Turks and Levantines. The non-Indians predominate not only in the towns, but also in the plantation areas.

The most important commodities produced are coffee and bananas; in 1960, the former accounted for 70% of the country's exports and the latter for 12%. However, the output of bananas on the original plantations on the Caribbean coastlands has been seriously reduced by hazards of climate and disease, and much of this area is now given over to cotton production while the production of bananas has been developed on the Pacific coastlands—a previously largely unused area. The economy has suffered as a result of political instability. In 1953, for example, the government then in power—which was strongly left-wing —nationalised and expropriated the plantations of the United Fruit Company (which owned 95% of the banana land, and was the largest employer in Guatemala, providing the livelihood of some 20% of the labour force together with their dependants) as part of a programme of radical social reform. This upset the United States which then encouraged the overthrow of the régime and secured the return of a government which re-established the status quo.

The leading exports are coffee, bananas, chicle, cotton, timber and essential oils. The leading imports are manufactured goods, foodstuffs and yarn for the production of textiles.

British Honduras

Physically it is, like northern Guatemala, a part of the peninsula of Yucatan, and by its position it bars Guatemala access to the Caribbean, except for the short stretch of coastline in the neighbourhood of Puerto Barrios. It is not surprising, therefore, that on this and other grounds Guatemala has repeatedly made claims to the territory of British Honduras—claims denied by Britain and by the political parties in the colony which will soon achieve independent status.

In the seventeenth century, the coast of the territory was a thriving area under English influence. Timber merchants and other traders settled here. During this period, British Honduras was administered by the Governor of Jamaica. When, however, Great Britain renounced her previous claims to most of the coast of Central America in favour of the newly established republics of Nicaragua and Honduras, the territory was reorganised as a Crown colony.

This is a sparsely populated area, with a total population of less than 100,000 of which one-third live in the capital, Belize. Economic development has been limited mainly to the exploitation of forest products as most of the colony is under natural forest cover. The large banana companies, which had done so much to open up the coastlands of the Caribbean, have no foothold here. In addition to timber some other products—coconuts, grapefruit and sugar—are grown for export but, on the other hand, British Honduras is not self-sufficient in foodstuffs and there are large imports of rice—one of the staple items in the diet.

El Salvador

This, the smallest state in the region with the highest population density, is sometimes called 'the Switzerland of Central America'. As far as its location is concerned, it is at something of a disadvantage in relation to its neighbours, since it only has a Pacific coastline and has to carry on its considerable export trade with Atlantic ports either by way of its railway connections with Guatemala or the Panama Canal.

By contrast, however, with its neighbours Guatemala and Honduras, what strikes the eye in El Salvador is the transformation of the familiar natural landscape of Central America into a genuine cultural landscape; the forest gives way to a densely settled agricultural region—cropped so as to maximise the output of foodstuffs, particularly with beans and maize, the dietary staples—covered by a network of good roads.

Apart from the supply of foodstuffs for the home market, the main emphasis of El Salvador's agriculture is on coffee production which flourishes on the volcanic soils of the highlands. Its coffee output is the largest in Central America and it is the world's third most important exporter (after Brazil and Colombia). The producing areas are located conveniently close to the Pacific coast. The country also enjoys the advantage of possessing a labour force of skilled and hard-working craftsmen and workers. Owing to the pressure of population in El Salvador, these workers readily migrate—when permitted to do so—to adjacent areas in order to find work, so that they are found in large numbers in Guatemala and Nicaragua, and on the banana plantations of Honduras.

As an exporter of coffee El Salvador has in recent years suffered from increased competition from new producing countries in Africa, but coffee still accounts for about 70% of its export income in spite of the increasing importance of raw cotton. The sacks in which coffee and sugar are packed are made inside the country. Peru balsam, which has a wide variety of uses both in medicine and in cosmetics, is produced nowhere else in the world but here. (Its name has nothing to do with Peru, but is a mispronunciation by the Spaniards of an Indian word, *piru*.) The country's growing population, increasing pressure on the land which is now fully used with consequent dangers of rural over-population and soil erosion, and the unfavourable outlook for coffee on world markets provide the background to El Salvador's efforts to industrialise (private foreign investment in manufacturing industry has been encouraged) and, as a corollary of these efforts, explain the initiative shown in trying to secure freer trade between the Central American countries. El Salvador's initial relative advantage in industrial development, combined with better communications and the greater availability of electric power should enable the country to make economic progress within the framework of an economically integrated Central America.

Honduras

Honduras is the land of the banana *par excellence*. It suffers from the severe drawback of an inadequate transport network. The capital, Tegucigalpa, with 125,000 inhabitants, for example, has no railway connection with other parts of the country. Only air communications, in fact, are at all well developed, with the exception of a very few trunk roads.

Honduras does not possess a central upland area, as does Guatemala. Rather, the interior consists of a series of basins, surrounded by high, forested mountains which effectively cut the basins off from one another. This combination of isolated basin lands—whose development was based initially on local mineral wealth—and undeveloped communications has seriously hindered economic progress. In the limited basin areas agriculture for the most part takes place on 'islands', cleared in the forest by burning, and it is purely subsistence in character, but in the more accessible areas coffee is grown commercially and now accounts for about 20% of total exports.

From Tegucigalpa in the highlands the valley of the Ulua leads down to the Caribbean coast of Puerto Cortes. It is followed by the only effective road linking the two main areas of settlement in the country. In the lower part of the valley and in parts of the coastal plain farther east there has been large-scale development of plantation agriculture with much capital invested in flood control and land reclamation projects. About 60% of Honduran exports—mainly bananas—originate from this area. It is one of the main banana growing areas of the world, but large areas are now devoted to other crops owing to the onset of disease, etc., in the banana plantations. In addition, however, much former banana land has reverted to use for subsistence agriculture, but this land in general is not being maintained as an effective producer of food crops. In the northern coastal area, Negro elements are dominant, but elsewhere in the country the population of a little under two million is essentially Mestizo.

Nicaragua

This is the largest, but also the most sparsely populated of the small Central American states with an estimated 90% of the land unutilised. Its unpopulated frontier with Honduras has frequently been under dispute, but a settlement, which has been accepted by both countries, has now been reached.

Although Nicaragua is bordered by both the Atlantic and Pacific

Oceans, in economic terms it is orientated decisively towards the Pacific, since all the important centres in the country lie within 30 or 40 miles of the western coast. The largest towns and the areas of population concentration are to be found in a lowland area in the west, lying between the Gulf of Fonseca and the southern boundary of the state, and which is interrupted here and there by the presence of volcanoes. In this lowland live over two-thirds of the population, and here are the most important areas of farmland. Cultivated land and stock pastures occupy the valley bottoms and extend a short distance up the foothills and the slopes of the volcanoes.

The Caribbean coastlands, here at their widest in Central America, are linked with the centres of the west only by air and by water communication along Lake Nicaragua and down the river San Juan, and are quite different in character. This so-called Mosquito Coast (see p. 216) is an area of year-long heavy rains, and is covered by dense forests which, as might be expected, are only thinly populated. Banana plantations were of some importance but have been generally abandoned because of disease.

The central highlands of Nicaragua possess a healthy climate but are, nevertheless, only sparsely settled and indeed are still partially unexplored. Coffee output in Nicaragua has fallen off somewhat in contrast with that of other Central American states as a result of its having been replaced in the lower areas by cotton which has been developed as an important alternative export crop. Agricultural production, moreover, is varied and includes sugar-cane, cocoa, maize and beans as well as coffee and cotton.

The population of the Pacific side consists mainly of Spanish strains mixed with Indian, with a few pure Spaniards and a large number of pure Indians. On the Caribbean side, on the other hand, there are zambos (people of mixed Indian and Negro descent) and Mosquito Indians, together with Negroes from Jamaica and other islands. The immigration of Chinese, Turks, Arabs, Negroes and Jews, which was formerly considerable until 1930, has been almost eliminated.

Since 1916 there has been in existence a treaty between Nicaragua and the U.S.A., under the terms of which the latter secured, by payment of £3 million, the first refusal of land to construct a ship canal across Nicaragua as well as naval bases on the Bay of Fonseca to the west, and on Corn Island to the east. Shortly before the Second World War a canal was surveyed, with the object of relieving the pressure on the Panama Canal, and although a project would certainly encounter immense obstacles in the form of earthquake dangers and volcanic eruptions it is now being seriously considered as a supplement to the Panama Canal.

Costa Rica

Known as the Rich Coast of the Spaniards, it has never lived up to its name, at least in the way in which the Spaniards were interested, for neither gold nor silver nor large numbers of Indians for a labour force were found here.

Just as Guatemala is essentially the Indian country of Central America, so Costa Rica is the land of the whites. There are very few people here of mixed race, for the few Indians were quickly exterminated by disease and warfare and the Spanish settlers were obliged to work their own land—a most unusual phenomenon in Spanish Latin America. During the eighteenth century the descendants of the Spanish settlers began to increase rapidly in numbers, and as they did so they expanded their settlement over the small, healthy upland area of the Central Meseta, which lies between 3000 and 4000 feet. It is here that about 70% of the country's total population now lives with the capital San José in the centre of the area.

From the uplands, however, settlement has now been forced to spread outwards to the slopes of the Atlantic and Pacific coasts as a result of a rapidly growing population which, by using only the limited central part of the country, has become too large for the maintenance of living standards. There is also a movement afoot towards the settlement of the northern lowlands along the Costa Rica–Nicaragua border. Indeed, the example of Costa Rica serves to show that it is possible for a white population to thrive in a tropical region, given the right conditions.

The population as a whole live in simple and far from wealthy circumstances, but are proud of the fact that the country possesses more school-teachers than soldiers. The social structure is based on the small-holding, and the bulk of the population is composed of hard-working and educated farmers and small businessmen. The middle and lower slopes of the Meseta provide ideal coffee land, while the slopes of the volcanoes provide pasture which supports dairy farming. Well-developed fruit and vegetable cultivation helps to support the relatively dense population. In the Caribbean coastal lowlands, the cycle of banana planting, decline and abandonment has run its course, and the plantations—the first in Central America—have been replaced by the secondary vegetation which is so typical of this area. In the lowlands of the Pacific coast, however, where the seasonal character of the rainfall produces a grassland cover, there is a livestock industry producing both meat and breeding animals, and new banana plantations have been established in the extreme south of the country on the border with Panama.

The economy of Costa Rica depends upon its exports, of which coffee and bananas account for 77% of the total. Other exports include sugar-cane, cocoa, abaca (see p. 220), timber and beans. 50 to 60% of these exports are sent to the U.S.A. The leading import is machinery. However, the rate of population increase (3·5% per annum) is one of the highest in the world and future economic growth will have to be based on the diversification of the economy so as to reduce the country's dependence on coffee and bananas. An economic development plan has been adopted and a law passed designed to attract foreign capital for the expansion of industry.

Panama

In Panama, the Cordillera which extends south-eastward across Costa Rica sinks to the lowland forming the narrow isthmus. Beyond the Canal Zone, to the east, the chain continues in a narrow discontinuous form, but the most populated part of Panama is essentially a lowland area. East of the canal lies a lowland which is one of the least developed —and indeed, least explored—areas of Central America. West of the canal, the warm, humid coastlands of the Pacific and the Caribbean virtually meet across the isthmus, although there is still preserved a distinctly more humid aspect to the landscape on the Caribbean side of the isthmus. On the Caribbean side, banana plantations have been developed by the United Fruit Company, while on the Pacific side are natural grasslands which form the basis for dairying. The milk is sold in the cities of the Canal Zone, Colón (62,000) and Panama City (270,000).

Panama has a permanently adverse trade balance, but this is more than offset by receipts in the form of payments to the Canal Zone staffs by the United States, and of income from tourists. Panama's economic position is indeed peculiar. The natural environment offers real possibilities for economic development. But instead Panama lives on its canal; it imports rather than produces. As one writer has remarked, 'The herds of cattle on Panama's grasslands dwindle away, while the townsfolk eat corned beef from Chicago. Panama is a fisherman's paradise, but no one fishes there; they import sardines from Norway.' In 1950, 60% of the foodstuffs required by the country had to be imported. Of the exports, most of which consist of bananas and cocoa, 90% is shipped to the U.S.A.

> The old city of Panama is full of delightful corners, of narrow alleys that lead to out-of-the-way squares lined with palm trees, and of baroque façades on its churches. The city once stood on the sea shore, where the single tower of the cathedral still stands today. But it was plundered and destroyed by freebooters at the end of the seventeenth century. The new city was built in a better position, on a peninsula, and protected on the seaward side by sandbanks. Then in the nineteenth century the French company which was attempting to build the canal constructed a line of grand, well-shaded palaces. Less than fifteen minutes' walk away, there is another, utterly contrasting world—a world of Negro children playing round the wooden shelters which are their homes. Sometimes, of course, it is not a Negro but a Chinese or Indian face that grins up from beneath the curly hair, for here we are in the world of what might be called the homeless proletariat—the labourers drawn from all over the world to work on the canal.
>
> Beyond lies the Canal Zone. It is under United States administration. Over the Canal headquarters buildings, and over the barracks and airfields in the zone, flutters the Stars and Stripes. In 1960, in response to Panamanian nationalist demonstrations, the flag of Panama was placed beside the United States flag. (Schmid.)

The Canal Zone

The Canal Zone has an area of 553 square miles, and a population (including U.S. military personnel) of roughly 50,000.

HISTORICAL

The Isthmus of Panama is only 30 miles wide at its narrowest point, and 210 feet above sea-level. It was the Spaniard, Balboa, who, in 1513, succeeded in forcing his way through the forests to the Pacific. Trade between Spain and its Empire in South America was restricted to this routeway until the eighteenth century and it is no wonder that, as early as 1551, the Spaniards produced a plan for a canal across this tantalisingly narrow strip of land in order to avoid the trans-shipment of goods from ship to land and then back to ship again on the other side of the isthmus. The idea was not allowed to lapse in the following centuries, but was revived from time to time by such diverse advocates as Alexander von Humboldt and the poet Goethe.

The first modern plan for the canal was worked out in the U.S.A. between 1870 and 1874 following the immediate success of the Suez

Canal, opened in 1869. Then in 1885 the Panama Railway was opened, as an alternative solution to the problem. It soon became clear, however, that this railway was no real substitute for the through route that a canal alone could provide—if only because double trans-shipment was still involved.

Eventually the French Panama Company was founded under the same man, De Lesseps, who had built the Suez Canal. The work was begun in 1881, but in 1889 it came to a standstill. The stoppage was due in part to financial mismanagement—the so-called 'Panama Scandal'—and in part to the effect upon costs of unforeseen difficulties in construction. The builders found, for example, that they had underestimated by a half the amount of earth-moving necessary, and much of this excess proved to be hard rock. When the work was abandoned, only one-third of the task was complete. Little but the tragedy of Panama remained. Stefan Zweig has thus described it:

Twenty thousand men had perished while working on the canal. A mountain of money had been swallowed up, almost without trace, in the white sands and the muddy swamps of Panama. Only abandoned houses and rusty machinery remained to tell the story. For nature fought against man here in Panama; fought as if warned by some heavenly instinct. It was not only that she had placed, between the Atlantic and the Pacific Oceans, a whole range of hills that had to be removed, inch by inch and stone by stone. She had also ranged against the workers a whole armoury of tropical weapons, a witch's brew of poisons with which to arm the tip of the arrows of death. There was the fever that rose like a dank breath out of the lowland swamps, and there were the mosquitos and other insects that seemed to be everywhere, bearers of death upon the wing. Unnoticed but inescapable was their attack, as day by day they poisoned the blood of men weakened by the heat with the hundred poisons of the forest swamps. One by one the workers deserted and the engineers broke down, until at length the machines were left idle, for they alone were unaffected by heat and sickness, and stood there abandoned, like corpses after the battle.

During the Spanish-American War of 1898, the U.S. Navy ship *Oregon* was ordered to move from her station on the Californian coast to the Atlantic coast. The 15,000-mile journey took sixty-nine days. This event focused the attention of the U.S.A. on the immediate need for an inter-ocean canal. In order to achieve this objective the United States, in 1903, persuaded the Panamanian province of Colombia to declare its independence. Panama's independence was immediately recognised by the U.S.A. and a treaty signed between the two countries gave the U.S.A. the right to build and operate a canal in perpetuity within a zone over which the U.S.A. exercised control as if it were the sovereign power. This alienation of Panamanian territory forms the underlying basis to the present difficulties between the two countries. As Zweig says:

> In place of the French, there now came the Americans, with their tremendous powers of concentrating efforts on the task in hand, with their resilient optimism and their splendid boldness. Learning from the fate of their predecessors, they had the foresight to begin by sending to Panama not engineers but doctors. The first task was to drain the swamps, or in some cases to cover them with oil, in order to eliminate the breeding grounds of the insect pests which rose from them in clouds. Then they built hospitals, and made provision for healthy living quarters. Not until they had mastered the health problem did they begin to bring in workers—workers well equipped with machines.

The work was many-sided. Mountain torrents were dammed, for instance, and these included the Rio Chagres, whose rainy season flow is up to 300 times as great as that of the dry season. In order to check flooding, a sluice was built into the Gatun Dam, near Colón, and this not merely regulates the flow of water, but also generates enough hydro-electricity to supply the whole Canal Zone and the cities of Panama and Colon. Deep cuttings had also to be made, most of them through solid rock. One of these, the Culebra, cuts as much as 450 feet below the land surface. Earth tremors repeatedly caused landslides which blocked the canal; such landslides still occur from time to time with the result that the engineering works along the canal have had to be very strongly constructed. A view of one of the locks on the Pacific end of the canal is seen in Plate 44.

THE CANAL AND ITS VALUE

The capital cost of the canal was finally assessed at $U.S. 546 million, or five times as much as Suez. Passage through it generally takes about eight hours. The toll costs average several thousand dollars per ship, yet still represent a fraction of what the total cost of rounding South America would be for the same ship.

The opening of the canal immensely aided movement by sea between the two coasts of the U.S.A. One result of this was to stimulate economic development on the Pacific coast, with San Francisco now only 6000 sea miles from New York, instead of 15,000-16,000 miles. The U.S.A. also acquired a route from its east coast to the Far East which was not dominated, as was the Suez route, by Great Britain. For eastern North

America and Europe alike, a new and shorter route was opened to western South America and to New Zealand, although for Europe the Suez route still represented the shortest way to South-East Asia and Australia.

The canal is now used by about 12,000 ships a year and is approaching the limits of its capacity, so that various schemes for expanding the facilities are under consideration. These schemes, however, involve difficult political as well as economic considerations.

Fig. 48. The Panama Canal traffic: proportion of the traffic using the canal which is headed for selected destinations.

CHAPTER SIXTEEN

Mexico

Mexico: The Land and Its Character

GENERAL

To understand the physical character of Mexico we must, in the first instance, look not south but northwards from this country, focusing upon its plateau lands of ancient culture. It lies at the southern edge of the dry belt of the northern hemisphere, separated from the well-watered grasslands of the Mississippi Lowlands and the Pacific Coast by desert and steppe. Rainfall increases the farther south we go.

Then again, the Rio Grande marks the boundary between a rich and technically developed land to the north—the U.S.A.—and a poorer, under-developed land to the south—Mexico. The Rio Grande is a divide, too, between areas of Anglo-Saxon and Spanish culture. If we may take the skyscraper to symbolise the former, then the latter is represented by the baroque cathedrals of Spanish colonial days, and only now are skyscrapers beginning to appear, alongside and over-shadowing them in the large cities.

Physically, northern and central Mexico represent the triangular southward extension of the Cordilleran system of North America; that is, the continuation of the south-western U.S.A.—Texas, New Mexico, Arizona and California. This great wedge-shaped highland mass stretches south and east to the Gulf of Tehuantepec. On the west, the deep, recent trench occupied by the Gulf of California (which is, of course, a continuation of the line of the Pacific Coast troughs in the U.S.A.) separates the long peninsula of Lower California from the mainland. On the east, the projection of Yucatan separates the Gulf of Mexico (here known as the Gulf of Campeche) from the western Caribbean, the Gulf of Honduras.

STRUCTURE

The Mexican Highland is a continuation of the Great Basin of Utah-Nevada, of the Colorado Plateaux with their deeply entrenched rivers and bordering ranges, and of the basin and range structures of Arizona and New Mexico. Characteristically, it forms a tableland with scarp-like outer edges. In the north its surface lies mainly between 4000 and 5000 feet, but rises southward to elevations of 7000–8000 feet. The mountains which border the tableland in the area just south of the line of latitude 20° N contain numerous volcanoes, and frequently act as barriers to rain-bearing winds. Seen from the interior plateau, however, they do not form prominent features. It is only from the coast, especially the east coast, that they appear as a great wall barring the way inland.

The southern edge of the highland is marked by a great fissure, or line of weakness, along which are to be found (see Fig. 42) a row of gigantic young volcanoes with snow-covered summits.[1] These include the highest mountain in Mexico, Orizaba or Citlaltepetl (18,700 feet), the 'mountain of the stars'; Popocatepetl (17,887 feet), the 'burning mountain'; and Ixtaccihuatl (17,343 feet), the 'white woman'. On all three of these peaks evidence of Pleistocene glaciation has been found, although the amount of present ice action is very small. Some of the volcanoes are still active.

South of the line of volcanoes, the plateau surface falls away steeply

1 The most recent volcano in Mexico is Paricutin, which lies 150 miles west of Mexico City, near Uruapan. In February 1943 a peasant in the village of Paricutin noticed a small cloud of smoke rising from the middle of his maize field.

The Indians in the area sent a message to Mexico City: 'We are having an earthquake every afternoon at 5 o'clock, and fissures and puffs of smoke are beginning to appear.' A team of geologists appeared with their equipment, and for the first time in history the birth of a volcano was actually recorded by a group of scientists. During the night the earth's surface cracked to the accompaniment of thunderous detonations, and a dark pillar of cloud and smoke rose into the air. By morning there was a cone-shaped hill, about 150 feet high, already in existence.

After this, growth was astonishingly rapid; at the end of ten days the cone was over 1000 feet high. Then it broke apart into two, but the lava streams quickly filled in the rupture. By night, it presented the spectacle of an uninterrupted series of explosions, with fiery clouds of vapour and debris roaring skyward, only to fall back, like shooting stars, upon the growing pile.

Paricutin, the Indian village, disappeared, submerged beneath a mass of dark red, glowing lava. As the lava spread it levelled a cemetery, dried up streams, suffocated birds and made trees ignite like torches. On the wastes it left behind it, no animal could find pasture. This little Indian village, hitherto unknown, had given its name to a brand-new volcano.

Today Paricutin's cone rises 1050 feet above the plateau surface. The floor of the crater is 500 feet wide; the rim is 1000 feet across, and from it one can see roughly 175 feet down into the crater. By 1953, however, signs of activity had become slight.

into a deep east-west trough some 50 miles wide and occupied by the Balsas River and its tributaries. Beyond to the east lies the Isthmus of Tehuantepec, 120 miles across but only 600 feet above sea level at its highest elevation. Across this runs the oldest and the shortest of all the 'transcontinental' railways of North America.

The Mexican Highland is formed by a horst with a crystalline base which is overlain by Mesozoic sediments and lava sheets. Volcanic activity is still continuing, and is accompanied by frequent earthquakes. The mountains belong to the young fold ranges of America. The Sierra Madre Occidental and Oriental are southward extensions of the Basin and Range province of North America and of the Rocky Mountains. They are formed, for the most part, of Mesozoics and these disappear, in turn, toward the south beneath recent volcanic materials. In its present form, this is essentially a landscape of erosion. Rivers cut through the whole breadth of the ranges and tap the interior basins. Even the plateau has a folded surface, broken by upthrusts and basins, and crossed by higher ranges. Where the surface of the interior is smooth, this is generally only because of infill by recent alluvia and lavas. This is particularly true in the south, where the solid surface is concave in form, but where volcanic materials have partially filled and levelled the basin. Along the southern edge of the highland there is a zone of tectonic disturbance some 40–60 miles wide, in which there are numerous volcanoes. They rise above the surface of the plateau to the 10,000-foot line. Elsewhere, the flat tops of mesas (= tables) rise above the general surface, especially in the drier regions of northern Mexico. These mesas are often formed by a protective intrusive layer, such as basalt, overlying older sedimentaries which have elsewhere been eroded away.

At the southern end of the plateau, a line of lakes lies at the northern foot of the bordering volcanoes. These lakes have no outlet, and are salt lakes. At the eastern end of the line is Mexico City, the capital, with its 5 million inhabitants. It lies in a well-cultivated upland basin, some 7400 feet above sea-level.

COASTS

The western coast of Mexico is a shoreline of submergence; it is for the most part rocky and only here and there, in the shelter of some projection, is there a natural harbour such as that found at Acapulco. On the low-lying eastern coast, which is a shoreline of emergence and under the influence of the dominant easterly trades, there are lines of high sand dunes, and lagoons cut off from the sea by sand bars. Sand banks block the mouths of the few rivers of any size. Along the whole length of this coast, therefore, there is not a single natural harbour suitable for modern shipping. The two main ports are Veracruz (101,000) and farther north Tampico, (100,000), both of them man-made. Tampico lies close to the oil-fields, and its fortunes have fluc-tuated with the quantity of oil exported from Mexico. Only about one-twentieth of Mexico's foreign trade passes through the ports on the west coast whose hinterlands are severely limited by the little-crossed Sierra Madre Occidental.

CLIMATE AND VEGETATION

Much of this section is based on the work of Carl Troll, who has carried out extensive research into the relations of climate and vegetation in Mexico, and who, in 'Forschungen Zentralmexiko', writes as follows:

The commonly-accepted division of the tropical American mountain lands into four altitudinal zones—*tierra caliente, templada, fria* and *gelada*—does not apply precisely in Mexico, as it does in South America. In the latter, the pattern is fairly uniform everywhere between the Caribbean and about 18° S. There the humid forests retain their tropical character right up to the forest line at 11,500 or 12,000 feet, and the highest belt consists of luxuriant mist-zone forest with a wide variety of species, beyond which lie the tropical Andean humid grasslands, the *paramos*. In Mexico, on the other hand, there is an intermediate belt at the upper limit of the forest which consists of evergreen oak. Thus the altitudinal vegetation profile is rather more complicated than in South America.

The *tierra caliente* can be identified here in eastern and southern Mexico; it is a zone in which cocoa, vanilla, coconut palms and cotton are grown. Above it lies the *tierra templada*, a zone of coffee, banana, sugar cane and rice cultivation. In climate, and also in appearance, it corresponds exactly to the *tierra templada* of Colombia, or the so-called *medio yungas* of Peru and Bolivia. Then too, the mixed evergreen mist-zone forests of the *tierra fria*, with their numerous epiphytes, can be recognised on the humid outward-facing slopes of the Mexican mountains, and in the east they extend as far north as 20° N. As elevations increase, however, so too does the proportion of oak, pine and fir, and above about 11,000 feet we find pure coniferous stands, especially pine, silver fir and juniper, existing up to the tree line at 13,000 feet, where the chief species is *Pinus Hartwegii*.

At the same time we must recall that in Mexico and Central America, as well as in the Antilles, some types of oak and pine are found in lowland areas; indeed, in places in Cuba and on the Mosquito Coast of Honduras and Nicaragua where the soil is particularly acid and light, there are extensive areas of a kind of pine savanna right down at sea level. These lowland forests are, however, quite distinct in character from the mixed and coniferous forests of the *tierra fria*.

The full altitudinal zoning of the vegetation belts in central Mexico is as follows:

(Snow line)	
Alpine grasses and shrubs	up to 15,000–16,000 feet
Pure coniferous forest	up to 12,500 feet
Mixed forest, conifers or oaks, with little cultivation	up to 11,000 feet
Upland forest, etc. (*Tierra fria*), and cultivation of subtropical crops	up to 10,000 feet
Tropical upland forest (*Tierra templada*)	2500 to 5000 or 5500 feet
Tropical lowland forest and savanna (*Tierra caliente*)	0–2500 feet

Troll investigated the problem of climatic transition as it appears 'three-dimensionally, between the tropical lands of Central America and southern Mexico and the sub-tropical latitudes of northern Mexico'.

He came to the following conclusions:

In the mountains of Mexico are found plants characteristic of both boreal and tropical montane zones. On the whole, however, the boreal forms are the dominants while the plants of southern origin play a subsidiary part. A study of the climatic data shows very clearly that there is practically no difference between the climate of the Mexican Meseta and that of the mountain basins of southern Peru and Bolivia. North and south of the equator, the climatic régimes of these two regions form virtual mirror images of one another.

In view of this climatic similarity, one would expect identical vegetation also. But this is a case where we are reminded of the fact that, in the sphere of biology, it is not merely the local environment which is important. The decisive influence here has been the proximity of Mexico to the great land mass of North America. It is from there that the plant life of present-day Mexico has spread; from there that the species of conifer and oak have migrated, have adapted themselves to a tropical environment and have developed—owing to the seasonal change in the tropical montane climate —the wider variety of types.

The Gulf Coast of Mexico lies in the path of the trade winds, which are here forced to rise, and consequently the southern part receives a very heavy rainfall. Behind the mangrove swamps that line the coast, and along the edges of the Meseta, where the rainfall is plentiful, spread thick forests. Gaily coloured birds flit among the trees, and a tangle of orchids of every kind weaves a sort of web over all, with flowers of enthralling beauty. In the shadows beneath the trees grow giant ferns. The twelve-hour train journey from the hot Gulf Coast, over the mountain rim and on to the plateau with its snow-capped volcanoes must surely rank as one of the most fascinating and varied on earth.

The forest yields a variety of useful products: Brasil wood, Pernambuco wood (which is a source of yellow and red dyes for cloth and leather), Campeche or blue wood (for red and blue dyes), mahogany and iron wood. The use of synthetic dyestuffs, however, has reduced considerably the demand for vegetable dyes such as these.

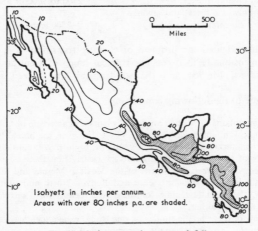

Fig. 49. Mexico: annual average rainfall.

The soils are moderately fertile and where the forest has been cleared a wide range of tropical crops is grown, such as sugar-cane, cotton, coffee, rubber, cacao, tobacco, vanilla and bananas, while grapefruits are comparative newcomers.

On the high plateau the air is thin but pure, and the climate is generally invigorating. From early times the central plateau has formed the heartland of Mexican culture, and the focus of population, possessing as it does both a healthy climate and ample fertile land in the innumerable basins on its surface, highly suitable for agriculture given the availability of water. The meagre rainfall on the plateau falls mostly in summer, when the atmospheric circulation is characterised by more variable winds and calms which encourage convection. The daily range of temperature is large at higher elevations in the south, particularly during May when the sky is cloudless; the *annual* temperature range, on the other hand, is smaller as one moves equator-ward. Because of the refreshingly cool nights experienced here on the plateau (night frost sometimes occurs), the climate is often described, at least in the south, as one of 'eternal spring'. In the north, the mountains are sometimes snow-covered, especially when the north wind is blowing. In general, the climate of interior Mexico compares favourably for mildness with that of, say, Florence in Italy, but highland Mexico never experiences the blistering heat of summer in the Mediterranean nor in the American mid-west.

Because of several factors, including the meagre rainfall, there is practically no tree cover on the plateau; the only exceptions are oak woods at intermediate elevations and coniferous forests at higher elevations along the mountain slopes. Of course the pressure that man has exerted upon the vegetation cover due to his repeated clearings and burnings over hundreds of years has intensified the marginal character of the habitat. In the south the vegetation varies between grassland and steppe, while it grades northwards into desert. The introduction of horses and cattle by the Spaniards and the practice of overgrazing has left scars of erosion in the areas of former grassland. During the long dry season in winter the interior, burned by the sun, looks barren and desolate. But where water is available there is an immediate and vivid contrast, and this is especially noticeable at the foot of the wooded mountain spurs. Where irrigation agriculture is practised on these mineral-rich, volcanic soils, high yields of maize, wheat and fruit can be obtained. Maize is the principal subsistence food crop of the Indian population, and an important staple of diet of all Mexicans. In fact, the crop which occupies the greatest cultivated area in all Mexico, as indeed in most Latin American countries, is maize.

A Journey from Mexico City to the U.S.A. Border

The journey by rail takes two days. When I woke up, I looked out on a barren dusty land that became a little more friendly as we approached the mining town and industrial centre of Aguascalientes (or Hot Springs). Near the gold—and silver—mining town of Zacatecas, which lies amidst bare hills, the railway line reached its highest elevation, some 8000 feet above sea-level. Around the town are innumerable spoil heaps from the mines. The landscape of the high steppes presents a dreary picture; sand and stones for mile upon mile, with a low hill breaking the surface here and there, and for vegetation nothing but willows, cactus, agave plants and shrubs. Soon the inside of the railway coach was covered with dust and grit, and waves of heat seem to well over me. In the evening, the dust clouds stood out in shimmering relief against the dark hillsides that formed a background. All the windows had to be kept tightly shut, in spite of the appalling heat, although I tried to get some relief by keeping my window open a crack—until the influx of dust and grit threatened to bury me before the heat killed me.

On the second day, the same depressingly barren landscape as before! Cattle roamed over the almost grassless steppe, seeming to wade through the sand. An occasional ribbon of green along a watercourse merely threw into relief the barrenness of sand dunes beyond. Here and there a sandstorm whirled its way overhead, blotting out the sun, and when it passed by it set up an unpleasant tingling feeling in our finger tips.

We were relieved to reach the frontier at last. As we rolled slowly across the Rio Grande into the U.S.A., I looked down at the great river. There was practically no water in it, for there had not been a drop of rain for nine months.[1]

The vegetation of the high steppes reflects the aridity of the region and the effects of overgrazing. There are numerous forms of cactus, and several types of agave, plants which may grow to tree height (35–40 feet), whose leaves are used to provide a form of sisal, and whose sap (in the case of the *Agave atrovirens*) is sweet and makes a kind of beer which is quite nutritious as well as being very popular in Mexico. All these plants are xerophytic, and are equipped to withstand the long dry season.

Much of the area is without regular drainage throughout the year, and there are no really large rivers at all. In the north, a few streams flow to the Rio Grande; the rest either flow into basins of interior drainage (*bolsons*) or simply disappear in the sand of the stream bed. In the south, where the interior upland is narrower, more rain falls since rain-bearing winds from the sea can penetrate farther inland and the orographic barriers are higher. During the rainy season in summer, however, the streams flow as torrents, cutting themselves deep ravine courses which make overland movement extraordinarily difficult across the area. Only a few of the most powerful streams have succeeded in cutting headward and back through the low mountain fringe of the plateau to drain part of the Mexican plateau.

TYPES OF LAND USE (after Troll)

The contrast between the peripheral mountains and dissected plateau

1 Johannes Wilda.

edges of Mexico, with their plentiful rainfall and their deep-cut valleys, and the drier basins and ranges of the interior upland finds expression in the patterns of land use. The peripheral areas are, even today, generally areas of shifting cultivation, where a process of clearing and burning the forest is carried on, and the chief implements are the axe and the digging stick. The cleared land, which receives no fertiliser apart from the ashes of the burning, soon loses its natural fertility, and when yields begin to drop the clearing is abandoned to a slow process of natural reafforestation, and the whole cycle is begun again in forested areas elsewhere.

This form of cultivation is often practised on the mountain slopes, where its effects are especially deleterious; in the course of time larger and larger areas of forest are replaced by a secondary cover of bushes, and the soil surface lies exposed and abandoned to the forces of erosion. This cycle of cultivation, fallow, secondary growth and forest is highly characteristic of the humid areas of the Mexican mountain rim, as well as of similar regions in the countries lying to the south. As they see the way in which the cultivated clearings climb the steep mountain slopes, some observers are alarmed by the dangers of a practice so destructive of the soil and so seriously affecting run-off while others can only marvel at the perseverance and the energy of the cultivators, who contrive, by this method, to occupy a rugged mountain area in such numbers. The Mexican word for a maize field is *milpa*, and on this basis the term 'milpa system' has been applied by geographers to the whole process of burning, clearing and cultivating. Other names are given in other parts of the tropical world to identify the same basic activity of shifting cultivation. By contrast the farmers of the plateau practise permanent cultivation, for which the corresponding name 'tillage system' has been suggested. This latter is carried on today with the aid of the plough, but it is safe to say that the system originated long before the Spaniards introduced the plough. The Indians had a spadelike digging-board known as *uictli*, although they definitely lacked any beast of burden which might pull a cultivating tool.

When the Spaniards reached the Mexican 'meseta' in 1520, they found conditions very similar in some ways to those with which they were acquainted on their own Meseta in Spain—apart, of course, from differences in the climatic sequence throughout the year. This similarity persists in the cultural landscape to the present day, in particular in the contrast, existing in both areas, between dry farming (*secano*) with fallow years and irrigation agriculture with annual cropping (*regadío*).

The forms of irrigation vary from the collection of flood water in shallow buckets, through the use of diversion canals on streams, to the raising of ground water by means of water wheels. Perhaps the most interesting method is that of the *galerias filtrantes*. Apparently these have only recently been studied by outside observers. They form an underground canal system, and are designed to bring the ground-water to the surface. They correspond to the *kanats* of Persia and Afghanistan and the *foggaras* of the Sahara, and they are obviously of pre-Spanish origin. Because of the tell-tale white mounds of earth which mark the position of the air shafts (*lumbreras*), they can be readily traced by the trained observer and also show up clearly on air photographs. Where the slope of the ground brings the canals to the surface, use is at once made of branching channels to irrigate surrounding land. The same system can be seen in the province of Tarapaca in Northern Chile and in the coastlands of Peru, and in each case it is clear that the system is of great antiquity.

In the Sierra Madre Oriental, the dividing line between sedentary agriculture and shifting cultivation for the most part follows the natural boundary between the two regions—the plateau and the peripheral mountains including the dissected scarp of the central plateau. Thus the climatic and vegetational boundary is carried over into, and emphasized by, the cultural landscape.

In Central Asia, Richthofen made the observation that the peripheral lowlands have become the homes of a dense mass of sedentary agriculturalists and the cradles of advanced cultures, while the steppes and desert of the interior are occupied by nomadic pastoralists lacking such cultures. It is interesting to note that in Mexico, as in the tropical Andes, the exact reverse is the case. The central highlands have become the home of sedentary agriculturalists, while the peripheral regions have lagged behind, culturally, as areas of shifting agriculture.

Mexico and Its People

HISTORICAL

Mexico's history can be divided into four sections: the pre-Colonial Indian period (before 1519); the Spanish Colonial period (1519–1810); the post-colonial period (1810–1910); and the Revolution (1911 to date).

Recent dating experiments utilizing radioactive Carbon 14 at the archaeological site of La Venta in Mexico throw some light on the cultural origins of the area. La Venta, 10 miles from the Gulf of Mexico, on the borders of Tabasco and Veracruz states, developed as a cultural centre between 800 BC and 400 BC. Thus the Olmec culture of La Venta corresponds chronologically to the heyday of the Etruscan and Grecian cultures. The La Venta site is a great mound, 4 miles long and a mile wide, which rises like an island in the middle of an impassable swamp. Its culture seems to have died in about the tenth century AD, by which time the Olmec people had a knowledge of mathematics, a calendar and a pictograph form of writing. La Venta seems to have been both religious centre—the likeness of a jaguar god has been preserved in mosaics—and political capital. The unearthing of the Olmec culture throws light on a long period of man's development in the American continent.

The much better-known Indian cultures—Toltec, Aztec, and Maya —which blossomed in the period AD 600–1300, were already familiar with written pictograph language, irrigation and a highly-developed sedentary subsistence agriculture based on maize. Their crafts were well advanced and they built cities with remarkable temples.

The Toltec and the Mayan cultures passed away before the Spaniards arrived in the New World, while the Aztec was destroyed by Cortes in 1519–21. Spanish rule, which lasted for 300 years, gave Mexico its language and its Roman Catholic religion. New domesticated animals (cattle, horses, sheep, pigs, poultry and practically all other common European farmyard animals) were imported; so too were new crops, such as wheat, oats, barley, and rye, cultivated with the aid of the plough. In the towns there sprang up Baroque churches whose decoration was a mixture of Spanish, Moorish and Aztec *motifs*. The Indians intermarried with the Spaniards (who were known as Creoles from the Spanish *criollo* = the new generation), so that a mixed population (mestizos) was formed. Mestizos now comprise some 60% of the Mexican population, and persons of European origin 9%; the remainder are mostly Indians. The Spaniards exploited Mexican resources of silver and lead, and also worked other minerals such as gold, zinc, copper, iron and antimony.

The post-colonial period began with the War of Independence, 1810–21. But serious territorial losses soon followed. In 1836 Texas seceded from Mexico, joining the federation of the U.S.A. in 1845. Then the war with the United States in 1846–8 led to the loss of New Mexico, Arizona and California. Half the nation's territory had thus been lost. It was only under President Porfirio Diaz (1876–80; 1884–1911), and only by dint of brutal enforcement, that the Mexican nation as such emerged, and even then the price paid was social convulsion and economic subjection to foreign business interests. The revolution of 1910 was a reaction to the Porfirian era—particularly to the large-scale alienation of peasant land that had taken place in the period. Although the Spaniards introduced the feudal system with its concept of individual ownership of land and the great estates (*haciendas*), the village community of both Indians and mestizos had persisted and it was this communal land which was alienated under Porfirio such that by 1910 Mexico was a country of landless labourers. At this time 80% of all Mexicans depended for their livelihood on agriculture, but of these 95% possessed not a scrap of land of their own. The great masses of the Mexican people thus struggled against sickness and undernourishment.

Reform of land-ownership and a general rise in educational opportunity were the two primary demands of the masses in the Revolution of 1910; the watchword of those revolutionary years was 'Land and Books'. In reality, it was a revolt of the Indians and mestizos against the Spaniards, Europeans and Americans who played so dominant a role in the economy. In 1917 a new constitution was drawn up, by which land, minerals and water were declared to be the property of the nation. The nation, in turn, was authorised to grant title to these national possessions to individuals; that is, to create private property. Common land was returned to the villages, and the size of large landholdings was restricted by law. A democratic programme of reform was drawn up, including universal education, agrarian reform, organisation of labour and limitation of the power of the Church.

In spite of these changes, however, Mexico in 1930 was still a land of *haciendas*. Alongside these there existed the original communal farming and small individual landholdings. In 1934, Lazaro Cardenas became president. He stressed the need for a peaceful, but rapid, reform of the system. He brought about reorganisation of land tenure, nationalisation of minerals, a labour law, industrial reform and educational improvements. When he retired from the presidency in 1940, some 40 million acres of land had been distributed to a million farmers, under the agrarian reform programme, while in the previous twenty years only 20 million acres had been distributed. In 1938 the foreign oil companies had been expropriated (but the companies received compensation for their loss). By these programmes, the social structure of the nation was altered to the advantage of the worker and the peasant. By 1945, at least one-third of the population had benefited as a result of the land reform; 2 million farmers owned land, and some 20,000 *ejido* farm community groups existed. These figures become somewhat less impressive, however, when it is added that less than 4% of the land distributed was supplied with water, and that more than one-third was unsuitable for cultivation.

The poverty of the average farm labourer still drives many thousands of them each year to cross the Rio Grande into Texas, to seek seasonal work on the cotton or truck farms, for in spite of agricultural improvements, such as the rapid expansion of irrigated agriculture since 1948, it is still true that only 10% of the total land area is farmed. This farm-land is located (a) in the hot and relatively humid regions on either coast and in the extreme south; (b) in the basins and on the plateau among the mountains of central and southern Mexico; (c) in the irrigated areas of the north and north-west.

THE POPULATION

Of Mexico's 38 million inhabitants, some 60% are mestizos. Roman Catholicism is the dominant religion, but traces of the former Indian beliefs have by no means disappeared; indeed, there has been a curious blending and merging of elements of both pagan and Christian back-grounds. In remote areas of the country indigenous rites still hold sway.

The Roman Church gained attention in the sixteenth century by its championship of the Indians and their rights as human beings. —the name of Bartolome de Las Casas will always be associated with that humanitarian endeavour. In subsequent years, however, the Church became more closely associated with the feudalism and mercantilism of the Spanish conquerors. By the end of the colonial period, it had become the largest landowner in Mexico. The priesthood was divided socially just as secular society was; the higher dignitaries of the Church had to be Spaniards by birth, and Creoles (people of European blood born in the New World) and mestizos were limited to the lower clerical ranks. The Church maintained its social position and large landholdings during the nineteenth century and the revolution of 1910 was anti-clerical in character, although the original extreme antipathy to the Church has moderated in the last fifty years. (See Plate 45).

In colonial times the status of the individual before the law depended on his racial origin and social and economic stature. The assertion of equality in the sight of the law, which dates from the republican constitution of 1821, was a factor in encouraging racial mixture. Immigration from Europe has been insignificant compared to that of some other Latin American countries.

The official language of Mexico is Spanish, with numerous additions of Indian origin. Among the Indians themselves, there are almost 100 languages or dialects, and in Yucatan, for example, over 50%

of the population speak Indian tongues. In other areas, however, Indian dialects are dying out.

The mestizos live mainly in the towns where the Creoles have gradually lost their superior social standing. Europeans and North Americans are generally to be found in wholesale businesses or mining, industry or plantation agriculture. Arabs and Syrians concentrate in retail trade, and Jews in textile and leather businesses and in the industries supplying them. The Chinese, who used to dominate wholesaling and retailing on the Pacific coast, suffered considerable persecution in the 1930's and their influence has subsequently declined.

Foreigners, especially North Americans, have invested large amounts of capital in the Mexican economy. Even though Mexico's minerals have been nationalised and many of the plantations have been split up under the land reform laws, their influence still makes itself felt, for the mineral prospecting concessions are still 97% in their hands.

SETTLEMENT

Mexico City, the capital, lies at the densely populated southern and higher end of the plateau and was located at the site of the former Aztec capital where the climate is pleasantly cool.

Spanish as to its origins, American as to its present form; skyscrapers now tower above the ancient palaces. Shining limousines on wide avenues glide past cypress hedges and splashing fountains glimpsed behind ruined gateways. Smart residential districts are bordered by slums. The price of land is atrociously high. The city contains the largest cathedral in America, but the interior smells musty, and earthquakes have shattered the arches. The foundation of the apse rests on filled-in canals; the floor is sinking and the walls threaten to collapse. The only building with a solid foundation was the pagan temple; the city is built on a drained and, therefore, unstable lake bed. As long as the lakebed surface was moist, it was firm enough to support buildings. But as it dried it shrank, and some parts of the city today are sinking at a rate of as much as two feet per annum. With the great drain of a modern city on water supplies, the shrinkage continues; the only way to remedy it would be to replenish the underground supply. Newly-built skyscrapers are in fact 'watered' in this way to secure their foundations, but there is simply not enough water available to maintain a whole city in this way.[1]

Puebla (285,000), lying to the south-east of Mexico City (see Plate 50), and Guadalajara (750,000) in the west are both flourishing industrial cities which have developed from colonial days, and which still exhibit

1 Peter Schmid, *Nachbarn des Himmels*, Stuttgart, 1953.

some outstanding examples of colonial architecture. Then there are smaller centres such as Orizaba, on the railway linking Mexico City and Veracruz. On the line which runs north to Texas lies the silver mining town of San Luis Potosí (174,000), while farther on is Monterrey (600,000), an important industrial centre producing iron and steel.

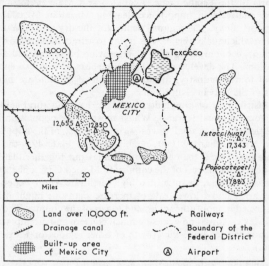

Fig. 50. Mexico: the site of Mexico City. The present Lake Texcoco represents only a remnant of the five lakes which occupied the floor of this basin in the mountains at the time of the Spaniards' arrival. These lakes have been gradually drained away to make room for cultivation and settlement; the most notable effort in this drainage development was the construction in the seventeenth century of the canal shown running north-wards from the city, which passes through a long tunnel and drains into the headwaters of the Moctezuma River beyond the water-parting.

At the point where access from the east coast to the interior is most direct lies the port of Veracruz (101,000), a city which was once renowned for yellow fever epidemics and bore the ominous title 'Cemetery of the Tropics'. From 1900 onwards, however, the danger of epidemics has been progressively reduced. Part of the town is situated on a coral reef, part of it on the flat coastal plain, and the newest section is on land which has been artificially built up above the general level of the coastal plain.

The leading port of Mexico was for a long time, however, not Veracruz but Tampico (100,000), which lies farther to the north. Tampico is close to productive oilfields, but it has suffered a decline in recent years. The ports of the Pacific coast, Acapulco and Manzanillo, have also declined relatively in importance, leaving Mazatlán (42,000) as the leading port today. The regional centre for the dry area of Yucatan is Mérida to which the government is trying to attract industry to diversify the region's economy by means of improving both land and air communications. The development of air transport should also encourage the local tourist industry, for to the south of Mérida are numerous remains of the Mayan civilisation.

The distribution of population among urban and rural settlements reveals some unusual features. Whilst most of the population lives in rural settlements or in small towns—with only 20% of the population in cities with more than 100,000 inhabitants (see Plate 49)—the capital has more people in it than all the other cities put together. This arises from a drift from the rest of the country to Mexico City, a phenomenon which has produced, in spite of a high birth-rate, rural depopulation in many areas and a lower rate of increase than one might otherwise have expected in most other cities and towns of the country. The dominance of Mexico City is now causing much concern and attempts are now being made to encourage the growth of other regions of Mexico. (See Plate 46.)

This rapid increase in population aggravated the flight of Mexicans from the country to the cities—a tendency which alarmed Mexican leaders. Those who know rural Mexico can readily understand why Mexicans leave the farms: lack of sanitation, poor communications, few social advantages, low pay. The results, in the case of Mexico City, were striking. In 1910 the Federal District (Mexico City and its suburbs) had a population of less than 500,000; in 1930 it passed the one million mark; and in 1960, the figure was four million. [See Plate 47.] The influx of country people created grave problems for the capital city: the newcomers could not find employment in industry, for there were never jobs enough, and the strong labour unions erected barriers against them; the result was the increase in great slum areas in and around the city. By 1955 the Federal District housed about 13% of the national population, but its economic monopoly was even more striking: 37% of the automobiles were licensed there; 40% of the cinema tickets were sold there; it accounted for 22% of the national industrial product and collected 70% of the taxes on industry. . . .

This burgeoning population also provoked the flow of Mexican labour abroad, chiefly to the United States. Migrants left in such numbers as seriously to deplete the labour force in Mexico. This caused dislocation of the farming industry in Mexico: for example, so many able-bodied men left southern Chiapas during recent years that there were not enough harvest hands to handle the coffee crop, and as a result workers were imported from Guatemala.[1]

As far as rural settlement is concerned, the density of population in Mexico increases with altitude—up to a height of about 8000 feet. The Central Mesa, the heartland of the interior, comprises only one-tenth of the land area of Mexico, but supports a half of the population.

The Economy of Mexico

Agriculture. About 55% of Mexico's working population is still employed in agriculture which has always formed the basis of the economy. Although the country includes a wide range of climatic and other physical attributes which makes possible the production of all types of cereals and a wide variety of fruits and vegetables as well as many agriculture raw materials from cotton to wool and henequen, most of the agriculturalists continue to follow the traditional methods of subsistence farming particularly in the densely populated inter-montane basins of the central plateau (see Plate 48). Here all the suitable land is used—and, over large areas, over-used with consequent problems of soil erosion—and the principal crop is maize which, however, is not well suited to the cool and often very dry summers of the region. The strength of dietary and farming tradition inhibits a change to crops which are more suited to the physical environment. This factor, coupled with primitive agricultural practices and the use of poor seed and little fertiliser means that this land is being used less efficiently than it might be although the government is trying to encourage better farming practices and the use of strains of maize and other crops more suited to the environment through a number of experimental farms, training centres for farmers and an agricultural extension service. In part, of course, these problems are the problems of the agrarian reform whereby the haciendas (large estates) have been split up and distributed to the peasants. The measures that the government is able to take to improve agriculture on the central plateau do not seem likely to produce much more than a slight amelioration in the situation, at least over the medium term, as the opportunities for change are minimised by the existing social conditions in an area which in any case has a higher density of rural population

1 Herring, H., *A History of Latin America*, New York, 1955, pp. 392–3.

than is justified by the opportunities provided by the environment.

Contrasting with this situation is the intensification of agricultural activities in parts of the warm coastal lowlands where plantation crops such as cacao, coffee, rubber, rice, cotton, sugar and tobacco, etc., can be grown. The problems of development in these areas arise from the used for extensive and expensive drainage, irrigation and clearance schemes and from the need for additional settlers to work the land. Such schemes of development and resettlement have been initiated as, for example, in the valleys of the Yaqui, Mayo and Fuerte Rivers on the

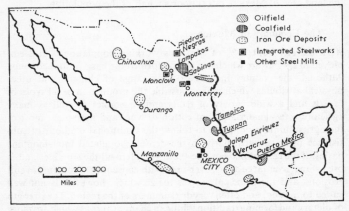

Fig. 51. Mexico: oil, coal and iron. The map shows the three types of field, and the location of steel-making plants. Output of coal in 1961 was 1·05 million tons, and of iron ore 1·68 million. The names of the Caribbean oil ports are underlined.

Pacific coast and in the Papaloapan basin to the south of Veracruz on the Gulf of Mexico. Of greatest importance, however, in the development of agricultural production in the last fifteen to twenty years has been the post-1934 break-up of the vast cattle haciendas of the north of Mexico into communally worked *ejidos* and large commercial farms. With irrigation and the use of modern agricultural techniques and methods large increases in output—particularly of cotton and wheat—have been obtained.

Industry. Pressure of population on the land will not, however, be lessened by extending agricultural areas or by improvements in agricultural practices. These can barely keep pace with the high rate of population growth (now over 3% per annum) and are thus unlikely to bring much higher living standards. In light of this, the major objective of the government's economic policy has therefore been the promotion of industrialisation. Since 1940 there has been a rapid expansion of industry within Mexico which is now one of the most industrialised nations of Latin America. From producing only a limited range of consumer goods—particularly of textiles—Mexico has now advanced to the stage at which it is self-sufficient not only in most consumer goods but also in industrial equipment such as that required in the petroleum industry. The development of industry has been particularly important in Mexico City and other neighbouring cities and towns. The second most important industrial centre is Monterrey which has a growing iron and steel complex based on iron-ore from Cerro de Mercado, coal from Sabinas and oil and natural gas from the fields of the Gulf Coast.

Mining. The well-being of the Mexican economy was long based on the country's rich mineral resources. Tectonic disturbances in the forms of geological folding and vulcanism have resulted in a very large variety of minerals, precious metals and non-metallic ores, especially along the western side of Mexico, from the northern border roughly to the Gulf of Tehuantepec, and on the central plateau. The mining industry—concentrated on the northern plateau whose mineral wealth has attracted settlement for four centuries and which contains a profusion and variety of mineral resources unequalled in Latin America—has, however, declined in importance relative to the rest of the economy in the last twenty years although it does still provide over 20% of total exports. A new source of mineral wealth which has been developed in recent years is sulphur. The exploitation of large reserves—mainly in the Isthmus of Tehuantepec—by United States companies has led to sulphur becoming one of the main exports of the country.

Of particular importance is the role of the petroleum industry. Oil was first discovered just before the First World War. The resources were rapidly developed with American and British capital such that in the early 1920's Mexico was second only to the United States in the world petroleum industry. Production fluctuated in the 1920's and the 1930's owing to continuing difficulties between the foreign companies and the government. Finally, in 1938 the whole industry was nationalised. After nationalisation, production fell off for a time as a result of a lack of capital and a sufficient number of trained personnel, but subsequently the industry entered a period of steady expansion such that production increased from some 10 million tons in 1950 to almost 15 million tons in 1960, thus ensuring an adequate supply of low-cost petroleum products for the country's rapid economic development which has also been helped by the growth of the associated natural gas industry.

Transport. In contrast with most of the other countries of Latin America, Mexico has a fairly extensive railway system—at least in the area of the central and northern plateau and to the Gulf Coast. The rail network, however, is deficient in the south and the west and in these areas the construction of modern roads has enabled economic development to go ahead. In recent years the Mexican government has placed great emphasis on the improvement and extension of the road system. There are now almost 100,000 miles of roads, over one-third of which are all-weather roads suitable for modern motor traffic such that regular road passenger and freight services link most parts of the country.

CHAPTER SEVENTEEN

The Islands of the Caribbean: Introduction

Geo-political Considerations

The hundreds of islands in the Caribbean extend in a great chain from the peninsulas of Florida and Yucatan through to the north coast of South America. They are mainly strung along the Antilles Arc which resembles the Sunda Arc with its chain of the East Indian islands. Both sets of islands lie in the great region of earth movement that is represented by the American and Asiatic 'Mediterranean' and the two resemble each other somewhat in climate and vegetation, in beauty of natural landscape and in richness of resources. Their position between two continents and two oceans makes them natural focus points of routeways, and at different times in history both have served in turn as land bridges, or thoroughfares, or terminal points for human movement.

In a political-geographical sense, the West Indies today lie largely within the sphere of influence of their northern neighbour, the U.S.A., astride the route to Panama. This follows a period of four and a half centuries in the hands of European countries in which they served as testing grounds for colonial policies and economic exploitation. They have experienced both rapid rise to prosperity and long declines following the failure of previously successful methods of exploitation.

On mainland Central America economic relations between adjacent states are getting closer, and movements of people and resources are possible between them. Surface communication between the islands of the Caribbean, however, is more tenuous and there is little contact between them. Another problem in the West Indies is that many of the islands have become seriously over-populated. Given the present levels of economic development this is particularly true of Haiti, Jamaica and some of the smaller islands. The rate of population increase would be tolerable if only a sufficient proportion of the labour force could be diverted into industry or mining, and if the yields of the islands' agriculture could be raised. The British Colonial Office—which handed over control to the short-lived Federation of the West Indies in 1957— formulated a plan for transferring the workless surplus from Trinidad and Jamaica to British Honduras, with the object of settling them in what is still largely virgin territory. But the plan foundered on the lack

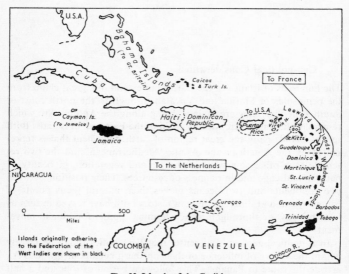

Fig. 52. Islands of the Caribbean.

of political cohesion within the region. Regional movements in any case presuppose regional planning, into which the annual migration of West Indian workers to Florida and Texas must be integrated as much as the industrialisation of Venezuela, the exploitation of iron-ore in the Orinoco area or bauxite in Jamaica and Surinam, and the development of water power and natural gas supplies. There are yet no signs that such regional planning will be possible in the foreseeable future and in the meantime population increases continue at accelerating rates.

The only effective attempt at political integration in the Caribbean was Britain's efforts to secure a Federation of its former colonial territories, and early in 1958 the first parliament of the Federation of the West Indies met in Trinidad. This event represented a real step forward towards that goal of regional integration which we have already considered. By 1962, however, there were insuperable obstacles to the continuation of the arrangement, and the dissolution of the West Indies Federation took place in 1962.

Geological Structure

In plan, the Antilles Arc comprises several elements. It is convex towards the north-east, and on the other side of the curve there is a belt of generally flat limestone platforms. This belt is best developed in the Bahamas and in northern Cuba. The formations are similar to those of Yucatan and Mexico. Inwards from this, there is the belt of the Greater Antilles, more disturbed in formation and varied in character, and this belt is a continuation, as we have seen, of the mountain system of Honduras and Guatemala and southern Mexico. Lastly, there is the inner Antilles belt, comprised of young volcanic materials—including some active volcanoes. The Lesser Antilles are, in fact, mainly the volcanic peaks of a submerged mountain chain.

Owing to the curvature of the arc, the same succession is found in Cuba as in Trinidad, but in the reverse order. Thus in Cuba there is a belt of granite and schists in the south, followed by one of chert with diabase and serpentine, and in the north a flat limestone surface of Tertiary age, dotted with inselbergs and almost devoid of surface drainage, similar to those found in Jamaica and Yucatan. In the Tertiary marls, oil is found. In Trinidad, on the other hand, the crystalline rocks are in the north, with chalk and Tertiary limestones succeeding them to the south. This latter area represents the termination of the adjacent oil region of Venezuela. The Bahamas, like Barbados and Curaçao, are composed of coral limestone. In places, the deposition of guano over the centuries has converted the chalk into calcium phosphate, a valuable fertiliser.

The outer edge of the Lesser Antilles is lined by a series of ocean deeps, one of which, north of Puerto Rico, reaches a depth of over 30,000 feet. Similar troughs separate Cuba from the Cayman Islands and the latter from Jamaica.

The inner edge of the Lesser Antilles is the zone of volcanic activity; it is here alone that recent eruptions have taken place. Earthquakes are infrequent, but Jamaica experienced a devastating one in 1906 which was followed by widespread landslides. The most famous and destructive event in West Indian recorded volcanic history was, however, the eruption of Mont Pelée in Martinique in 1902. Floods of viscous lava were thrown up, hardening at once to form a jagged peak 2000 feet high. Meanwhile, a fiery cloud of incandescent poisonous gases rolled down the mountain-side, following the folds of the slope, and by the time it reached the coast it had killed the 30,000 inhabitants of the town of St Pierre in a few short minutes. The sole survivor was a prisoner, locked in his cell beneath the earth's surface. There are six vents on Martinique, all stemming from the same volcanic throat. (See p. 278.)

Climate and Vegetation

Diverse structural and human features in the islands contrast with climatic similarities. Surrounded by warm seas, all the Caribbean islands enjoy all the advantages of a tropical maritime climate, with average monthly temperatures between 70° and 80° F and an annual range of only 4–8° F. Conditions are often sultry on the coastal flats and in valleys not exposed to the prevailing north-easterly winds, but over most of the area the sea breeze moderates the heat. In winter, the north-easterly trades bring abundant rainfall to all the windward coasts which present an obstruction to their passage. As a result, there are marked contrasts in rainfall between the windward and leeward shores of the islands. The summer is a period of convectional rainfall and is the true rainy season. The transitional periods, especially the autumn, are times when destructive hurricanes sweep over the islands. In view of the danger that hurricanes cause to shipping and the persistent breakers on the windward shores, most of the islands' harbours are located on western shores.

The mountainous relief and the contrast between windward and leeward sides together create a wide variety of vegetation covers. Rainforest with palm trees comprises some 45% of the forest land, which was formerly very extensive but much of which has now been transformed, by man's presence, into palm savanna. Some 35% of the forest was of a dry deciduous type which has been transformed into grass savanna.

Population

The original inhabitants of these islands were agriculturalists, such as the Arawaks, who suffered from constant raids by the warlike Caribs. The latter succeeded in resisting the Spaniards up until the eighteenth century, but the Arawaks succumbed in a very few decades to the Spanish system of forced labour and, more important, to the effects of newly introduced diseases, and as early as 1505 the first Negro slaves were brought in from Africa to replace them as plantation labourers. In Jamaica and Haiti, Negroes today form the majority of the population. The remainder is composed mainly of mulattos and mestizos.

Only in Cuba and Puerto Rico was the influx of whites sufficiently large for them to comprise a dominant strain of the population at the present time. After the abolition of slavery in the nineteenth century a new element was introduced into the population, to replace the Negro slaves—Chinese and Indian labourers from Asia. Today, Asiatics comprise a third of the population of Trinidad.

Owing to the different political histories of islands often adjacent to one another, the social development of the islands has been extremely varied, and a wide field of anthropological research is offered by these contrasts between island and island and between coast and interior. Up to 1623, the Spaniards were spreading their language, religion and general culture through the islands. Then with the decline of Spanish power, other seafaring nations took Spain's place—England, France and the Netherlands. Haiti became a French colony, and possesses to this day a *patois créole*. In Martinique and Guadeloupe, also, French is commonly spoken, while Jamaica and the other British islands are English-speaking, and Curaçao is Dutch.

The last vestiges of Spanish political power in the West Indies disappeared in 1898, when Spain was defeated by the U.S.A. and was forced to give up its colonies of Cuba and Puerto Rico. The United States has since exercised the dominant strategic and economic influence upon the area. The U.S.A. is today the chief market for produce from the West Indies. Jamaica owes much of its economic development to the extraction of bauxite by American companies; the Bahamas export early vegetables to the United States; Cuba found markets there for her sugar and tobacco before trade relations were broken off following the success of the Cuban revolution in 1960.

The large landholdings that characterised the Spanish era are gradually being replaced by independent small holdings. In Jamaica this has produced a wide variety in cropping and in methods, some good, and some destructive of the land. In Cuba, on the other hand, monoculture remained—tobacco in the west, sugar in the centre and cattle raising in the east—until the basic land reform initiated in 1960 after the revolution led by Fidel Castro. In the mountains of southern Cuba and in

Haiti coffee is also grown, but in Jamaica its production declined significantly under the force of competition from other crops.

In Puerto Rico there is virtual monoculture of sugar-cane in suitable areas. The government is attempting to solve the land problem by encouraging diversification as well as the establishment of new industries. In the more humid areas of the Dominican Republic and the Lesser Antilles cacao is grown; in the drier regions, cotton; while the British and French islands produce sugar for the European countries. Agriculture is the principal activity of all the islands, and rural over-population is a serious problem. In Barbados in 1962 the average density of population was 1400 per square mile. Where, as in the larger islands, there has been a real measure of economic development, it seems merely to have accelerated the increase of population without markedly increasing the productivity per person of the total population. Real improvements in living standards must stem ultimately from rising productivity per person, and where population is growing by 2% or 3% per year, most of any increment in total productivity is absorbed by the added increment of population. In such a situation it is hardly surprising that there has been a large outward migration of population—most notably from Puerto Rico to the United States and from Jamaica and other British islands to the United Kingdom.

CHAPTER EIGHTEEN

The Islands of the Caribbean

The Bahamas

The Bahamas were the first land reached by Columbus in the West. On 12 October 1492, he sighted an island which he called San Salvador (probably the modern Watling Island). The group lies generally no more than 100–200 feet above sea-level; the highest point in the islands is at 400 feet. If the smallest islands and protruding reefs are counted, the group comprises 3000 separate areas of land, but only 30 are inhabited. The submarine platform which underlies them is an extension of the Florida Shelf. Coral reefs surround the islands. There is no running water on the Bahamas, which are composed of limestone formations on which a karst landscape has developed.

The climate of the Bahamas is tropical, but under the influence of the persistent easterly winds the heat is hardly oppressive. The annual rainfall is about 52 inches, and the mean monthly temperatures vary from 77° F for the coolest month to 82° F for the warmest. The tree cover consists of sparse pine forest alternating with tropical rain-forest. Around the sheltered coastal inlets are found tidal marshes and mangrove swamps, and in the interior are some stretches of savanna.

A sailor's handbook[1] contains the following description:

A gnarled undergrowth flourishes wherever a little soil has collected in the cracks of the rocks. The rocks are honeycombed with caves. Some of them lie above the highwater mark, but most of them below it, and the sea pours into them on the rising tide. In other places it flows over low-lying land and fills the hollows with deep pools. Some of these pools are deep enough to give anchorage for a ship. These were, indeed, the hiding-places of the

1 *The Pirate's Own Book*, London, 1837.

pirates. They hid their booty in the dry caves until they could dispose of it to a receiver.

The original inhabitants of the islands were the peaceful Arawaks, but they were shipped away to the island of Hispaniola in the first half of the sixteenth century by the Spanish slave-traders. European settlement began with the coming of Englishmen from Bermuda in the early years of the seventeenth century, and the islands have been under British rule continuously since the early eighteenth century. Today, the majority of the population are Negroes or mulattos—the descendants of African slaves.

On account of their pleasant climate the islands attract many tourists, particularly from the United States—only half an hour's air journey away. Tourists, in fact, form the basis of the economy of the main islands and even the out-islands have been developed in recent years. A favourite occupation for the tourists is to go for a sail in the glass-bottomed boats which the sponge-gatherers use, and be introduced to the underwater life of these warm seas—coral gardens and fishes, sea urchins and starfish—all visible through the clear water.

Cuba

Cuba has a dominant role in the Caribbean. It is bigger than all the other islands combined; it has one-third of the Caribbean islands' total population; it is strategically located to control the entrance to the Gulf of Mexico and the route to the Panama Canal; and it is the first country of the western hemisphere to ally itself with the Communist world.

The greater part of the island is composed of plains, rising gently to seldom more than 300 feet elevation on the inland side. Above these plains rise isolated horst mountains, in particular the Sierra Maestra in the south-east which rise to a height of 7872 feet. Limestone formations underlie much of the island, and these have led to the development of widespread karst features. However, the karst form of the tropics is not the solution hollow or fissure but the limestone cone—a steep-sided hemispherical hill resembling a beehive or sugar-loaf. In Cuba, these are called *mogotes*. In the northern part of the island, where these cones are numerous, a range of hills bears the name Sierra de los Organos, since they resemble organ pipes.

The climate of Cuba is influenced by its location on the edge of the tropics. In Havana the mean temperature of the warmest month is 82° F; that of the coolest month is 70° F. For the greater part of the year the island lies under the influence of prevailing easterly winds, but it is also subject to occasional invasions of cold air from the north.

Cuba was originally covered far more extensively with tropical forest than at present. A visitor to the island in the early days of the Spanish Empire reported that it was possible to cross the island from one side to the other without leaving the shade of the trees. The coasts are bordered by mangroves and swamp forests. Today the interior is either given over to cropland and pasture or else it has, under the influence of man, been transformed from forest land to savanna.

The Spaniards came to Cuba early in their campaign of conquest, and evinced little interest in the island. Indeed, with the conquest of Mexico and Peru many of those who had settled in the island moved on to the mainland, where prospects of mineral wealth and large numbers of Indian labourers seemed brighter. After the Spaniards introduced cattle and horses into the New World, the remaining settlers developed extensive cattle raising.

Sugar-cane was being grown in Cuba as early as 1523, but it was only after 1655, when Jamaica was taken by the English, and Spanish *émigrés* from there carried their experience of sugar planting to Cuba, that production of both sugar and tobacco began to increase. Sugar-cane is exacting in its requirements of soil and climate; it thrives on a mean annual temperature of 68° F allied to a tropical régime of temperature changes, and a rainfall minimum of 40 inches p.a. Sugar-cane takes a correspondingly longer or shorter time to ripen, depending upon the suitability of the climate. Stating the same fact in another way, and in a more practical sense, in areas like Louisiana, on the margins of the zone in which sugar-cane can be grown, each stalk yields only one harvest a year. In Cuba, however, and other ideal tropical areas, it is possible to obtain seven, or even more, harvests from the same stalk. Sugar dominates the agricultural economy throughout the lowland parts of the island and the only other crop of importance in Cuba is tobacco. It is grown especially in the world-famous tobacco region, *vuelta abajo*, in the province of Pinar del Rio.

Havana started out upon a great career as the principal port of Cuba, and a main Spanish naval base in the New World. The city became the most splendid and up-to-date in the West Indies with much wealth in the twentieth century flowing in with increasing numbers of American tourists. Today, Havana with its suburbs has more than 1 million inhabitants—in part dependent upon industrial employment arising from the growth of demand for consumer goods and development in large part by U.S. capital.

When, at the end of the eighteenth century, revolution broke out among the Negroes in Haiti, many French planters fled to Cuba, much as the Spaniards had done from Jamaica a century before. This in turn involved an increase in the number of slaves on the island, and these were imported until, by 1817, Negroes and mulattos comprised 65% of the total population. Since, however, land remained in the hands of the whites, and there has been recent immigration from Europe together with a virtual ban on permanent settlers from other more overcrowded islands of the Caribbean, the proportion of Negro people in the population has declined from this peak, and the present figure is approximately 27%.

The rural landscape of Cuba in the twentieth century has been moulded by the influence of the U.S.A. From 1898 onwards—when Spain was defeated in the Spanish-American War and Cuba became independent—United States private corporations have been investing money in sugar plantations and sugar refineries. In a short time, the cattle ranches and under-used haciendas of eastern and central Cuba had given way to fields of sugar-cane, and communications had been greatly improved. Monoculture became increasingly evident, and with the depression years of the 1930's, its implications were made apparent. New industries and new activities were introduced, to try to diversify the economy and thereby insulate it against a recurrence of the crisis. The dominance of sugar as an export earner was not, however, reduced.

Among the food crops which Cuba produces for the home market are maize, beans, coffee, potatoes, tropical fruits and vegetables, but even so this extremely well favoured island was not self-sufficient in even basic foodstuffs. As for the all-important sugar crop, the old Spanish plantations in the north of the island combined processing with production but, in areas of more recent exploitation, the big sugar factories left the actual cultivation of the crop to native tenant farmers (*colonos*). As this system proved to be more economical than the old Spanish system of private mills, the number of sugar factories declined while the output increased through consolidation and economies of large-scale operations. The trend, of course, reduced the employment opportunities in the industry and added to Cuba's difficulties in keeping down unemployment in a period of rapidly growing population.

Since 1898, the U.S.A. has purchased the bulk of Cuba's sugar, and by way of payment has exported foodstuffs and manufactured goods to Cuba under specially favourable arrangements whereby its goods were given preference over those of every other country. Free entry for U.S. goods also hindered the development of industry in Cuba itself. New lands have been added to the area in plantations, and the necessary labour has been provided by temporary immigrants from other islands. New ports, too, were built to handle the sugar trade and the road system was developed. The technology of the twentieth century also helped to stamp out yellow fever.

While sugar cultivation has come to dominate the whole centre and east of the island, the western province of Pinar del Rio has seen the cultivation of high-grade tobacco expand greatly on medium-sized and small holdings. The processing of the tobacco for the manufacture of cigarettes is usually carried out in small rural plants. Thus Cuba's two main crops are sugar and tobacco; besides these, coffee, cocoa, fruits and potatoes are grown. Cuba has the largest area under cane sugar of any country in the world. The processing capacity before 1959 was owned mostly by Americans (54%) and Cubans (34%). The U.S.A. had bought 90% of the crop at fixed prices and imported the sugar under preferential tariff rates. In 1960 sugar and its products accounted for 82% of all Cuba's exports. Among the fruit crops the island produces are pineapples, citrus fruits and tomatoes, and its forests yield several valuable types of wood, such as mahogany and cedar.

Cuba's other main resource is iron-ore. The rich deposits have not, as yet, been fully exploited; it is estimated that some 3500 million tons exist on the island for future use. There are also manganese and nickel deposits which have so far been little used.

The political, social and economic character of Cuba underwent a complete transformation when, in 1959, the dictatorial régime of Fulgencia Batista was overthrown by revolutionaries under the leadership of Fidel Castro. The increasingly close relationship of the new régime with the countries of the Communist world brought it, after a short interval, into collision with the interests and influence of the U.S.A. in the island, and this political divergence has led to the complete severance of those economic ties with the U.S.A. Expropriation of American property in Cuba has been met by economic sanctions against the Castro government, and Cuba has, in consequence, lost both the market for its sugar and the supplies of manufactured goods which the U.S.A. formerly provided for it. The new régime is having a significant impact on the human geography of the island. Whilst attempting (not, apparently, very successfully until 1965) to maintain sugar production—now under state control and exported mainly to the Communist world—greater efforts are being made to achieve self-sufficiency in food production, and hence the pattern of land use seems likely to undergo radical alteration. Industrialisation has also been accelerated and, in contrast with earlier development, it is to include the establishment of basic industries.

Jamaica

The backbone of Jamaica, the third largest island of the Caribbean, is formed by the fold mountains of the Antilles Cordillera which cross the island in a north-west–south-east direction. They rise gradually from a low range in the west, eastwards towards the Blue Mountains behind Kingston, which attain a height of over 7000 feet above sea-level.

> The approach to Jamaica is impressive : the Blue Mountains with their peak, the highest point on the island, tower apparently straight out of the sea for their foothills, the Port Royal Mountains, are here very steep, and the coastal plain so narrow as it nears Kingston as to leave room for little more than the road. These hills are exceedingly dry and infertile, quite unpeopled on the sea side, and hiding from view the thickly populated nooks and crannies of the Blue Mountains proper. The face Jamaica turns to the sea is thus a stony one; brilliantly clear in the sunrise the curiously perpendicular valleys and creases in the hills stood out as if sculptured, folds of drapery on a Greek statue. There is little sign of the work of man; it might be Circe's island, beautiful, inhuman.[1]

Most of the rest of the island is composed of limestone which lies, horizontally bedded and unconformably, on the flanks of the mountains, and which seldom rises above 2000 feet. This level limestone surface reveals the tropical karst formations in classic development, especially in the Cockpit Country. Within the highly dissected limestone plateau are found solution hollows filled with rich *terra rosa* soil giving rise to some of the island's richest agricultural land and accompanying dense rural population.

The climate of the island is characterised by consistently high temperatures. The windward (north-east) side of the island receives up to 100 inches of rain annually, while the southern coast lies in the rain shadow and Kingston, for example, has less than 40 inches p.a. West of Kingston, therefore, irrigation is necessary on the farms. Hurricanes are an annual menace between August and October.

The vegetation cover consists of a mangrove belt along much of the coast; savanna and chaparral in the south-west (at least before clearing for pasture land), with *galeria* forests along the watercourses, merging gradually into the rain-forest of the wetter east. The north side of the

1 Macmillan, M., *The Land of Look Behind*, London, 1957, p. 16.

island and the mountain slopes are covered with evergreen rain-forest, with mountain forest at the higher elevations.

Columbus spent a year on the island, after he had been shipwrecked during his voyage of 1502–4. The original Indian population did not long survive the Spanish conquest and settlement mainly because of fatalities which they suffered from diseases introduced from Spain. The Spanish, however, required labour for their colonial system and this requirement was met by bringing in Negro slaves. Under the influence of the Spanish landowners and their slaves, the island was given over to a fairly diversified agriculture which included livestock raising and the growing of sugar-cane and tobacco, while the forests produced various dyewoods.

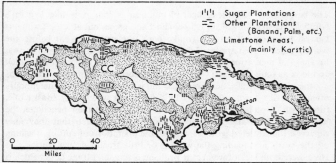

Fig. 53. Jamaica: landforms and plantation agriculture. The shaded areas represent limestone formations, on most of which a hummocky surface of tropical karst forms has developed. This surface is most fully developed in the Cockpit Country (CC on the map). (Landforms based, by permission, on a map in E. Paget's 'Land Use and Settlement in Jamaica', in *Geographical Essays on British Tropical Lands*, ed. R. W. Steel and C. A. Fisher, Philip, London, 1956.)

With the coming of the English in 1655, most of the Spaniards fled to Cuba, while their slaves escaped into the many limestone caves of the karst areas. The English newcomers developed the livestock farming of the Spanish period, but pushed ahead most rapidly with the production of sugar-cane, to such an extent that by the eighteenth century Jamaica was one of Britain's main sources of sugar. The expansion of Jamaica's sugar economy was made possible by a large inflow of Negro slaves—the slave population rose from 3000 in 1655 to 320,000 in 1807. With the abolition of slavery, however, sugar production declined; this was partly because the Negro slaves, once freed, preferred to leave the sugar plantations and set up as independent farmers; partly, too, it was because of growing competition from other producers—Cuba and the East Indies—whose sugar was of higher quality. Before the Second World War, commercial sugar production in Jamaica was small and confined to a few plantations. Its place in the economy had been taken by the banana trade which began in the 1870's and was traditionally a peasant crop. Until 1939, Jamaica was the world's leading producer. The war led to a revival of sugar growing, and since then the production of sugar on plantations has been maintained as a result of the protected market which it enjoys under the Commonwealth Sugar Agreement.

A Jamaican Sugar Plantation

The best way to describe a sugar planatation is that it is like a giant's cornfield, like a cornfield sometimes short and green, but at 'crop', which is harvest time, golden brown. Unlike corn, the canes are cut before the white plumes of seed appear. The cutting is still done in the primitive way, by gangs of men armed with *machetes;* the stalks are several inches thick and look as tough as wood. There are no fences, but each field—known as a 'cane-piece'—forms a neat rectangle and is separated from its neighbours often by a dirt road, and always by a fire-break which may consist of a furrow with water for irrigation. The overseers, and their henchmen the 'timekeepers', are still mounted on horses or mules so that they may supervise the scattered workers, and all the operations of cutting, slashing off the 'trash' and loading the wagons or little tractor-drawn trucks. . . . Here there is no lack of water; the problem is to get it off the land, which is unusually good alluvial clay. A great deal of swamp land is being reclaimed; new acres are added to cultivation every year from the river delta and the coastal border; this drainage work is a major operation in itself, and a permanent contribution to the country. Here and there islands of rough rising ground stood up out of the cane; they were uneconomic to plant but were sown instead with grass leys for the cattle of which Frome [at the western tip of the island] can justly boast. These cattle, a strong sideline in themselves, also make their contribution to sugar production; cane may be allowed to bear for several seasons on the old roots (ratoons), but to get the best results it must then be replanted. Before replanting, the land at Frome is rested; the trash is piled on it and the cattle are penned there to trample it in and to add manure. Then 'bagasse' and filter-mud, waste products from the factory, are ploughed in and by these means the utmost return of fertility is made.[1]

The banana industry suffered from the dislocation of trade with

1   Macmillan, M., op. cit., pp. 131–2.

Britain during the war and has also been affected by disease. Post-war attempts to re-establish banana production have been hindered by hurricanes which have severely damaged the young plantations. Production, however, is now going ahead rapidly, but the success of the industry is at present threatened by difficulties in loading the crop at the Jamaican ports where, owing to chronic unemployment, the introduction of mechanisation has been resisted by the employees. Frequent labour disputes and high costs put the Jamaican fruit at a disadvantage compared with that from other countries. (See Plates 52 and 53.)

Since the decline of the sugar plantations in the nineteenth century, agriculture in Jamaica has become more diversified. Besides sugar and bananas, the small landholders produce coconuts, coffee, cacao, tobacco and cotton as cash crops, and fruits and vegetables for their own use, but even so only about 10% of the island is given over to crops. Most of the interior is given over to cattle-raising. In all, however, although about half of Jamaica's population is still dependent on agriculture, the island no longer has a predominantly agricultural economy. Agriculture now accounts for only 15% of the gross national product. Mining, manufacturing industry and tourism now account for the bulk of the country's income. Industries, such as margarine and soap manufactures, the distilling of rum, and of molasses for cattle food, have developed and the government is now sponsoring a much more ambitious programme of industrial development—the Caribbean's first steel plant is shortly to be built in Jamaica. As a tourist centre of increasing popularity—due, in part, to political unrest in other parts of the Caribbean—the island offers abundant sunshine, sandy beaches, clear water and excellent fishing. Almost all the north coast has been developed into a resort area and tourism is now a major foreign exchange area. This is likely to grow in importance as Europeans supplement the still increasing number of North American visitors. Bauxite deposits, which were discovered during the Second World War and which have a 50% aluminium content, are being exploited by three companies—two American and one Canadian—which have been at work since 1952. The ore is shipped for reduction to Corpus Christi in Texas, Baton Rouge in Louisiana, or Kitimat in British Columbia. Bauxite now provides over 50% of total exports. Gypsum has also been quarried in substantial quantity and there are prospects of iron-ore, copper, lead, zinc and manganese production.

Expansion and diversification of the economy has not, however, been sufficient to absorb the rapidly growing population and thus there remains both pressure on the land and large-scale unemployment.

Jamaica has long provided migrants for other countries—to work on the banana plantations of Central America in the nineteenth century, to help in the contruction of the Panama Canal in the early years of this century, to assist in the growth of the Cuban sugar industry and most recently to take jobs in labour-short Britain. Emigration to the U.K. in the 1950's ameliorated the problems of unemployment for a time, but this flow has now been curbed and Jamaica has to look to longer-term solutions to ensure rising living standards in the future.

Hispaniola

The island of Hispaniola was the starting point for European settlement in the West Indies and Central America. It proved an excellent location for sugar-cane production, but at the moment of history when it was first settled, sugar prices were low and overproduction was occurring. It was not until 1517, when Egypt was conquered by the Turks and eliminated as a sugar producer, that the price of sugar began to rise again and so its cultivation in the West Indies became worth while. In Hispaniola, however, the Spaniards left agriculture to the Indians, and also pressed them into service in the southern part of the island, where gold had been discovered, and thus the agricultural potentialities of the island were not effectively developed. Then with the news of the conquests of Cortes in Mexico and Pizarro in Peru, many of the Spaniards left altogether for the more promising lands of South and Central America.

The net result of these changes was that the island's development was brought virtually to a standstill, and the native population was decimated. A new era of prosperity opened with the arrival of the Negro slaves. The next arrivals were the Dutch, French and English pirates and smugglers who preyed on the Spaniards, and the buccaneers (see p. 276). Then in the middle of the seventeenth century began the French Huguenot colonisation of western Hispaniola, which had never come under effective Spanish influence. They planted sugar-cane, tobacco, cacao and cotton. Meanwhile, the Spaniards were carrying on cattle ranching in the east, and the influx of Negro slaves was continuing. Soon the west—Haiti—was virtually all-black, with a handful of whites in control, and to this day the economic and cultural patterns of the eastern and western ends of the island are quite different.

The French Revolution provoked a revolt among the western Negroes in 1795, and they gained control of the Spanish east as well. As a result, the era of plantations and ranching in the east came to an end.

In 1804, the west proclaimed its independence. Between 1822 and 1844 it also held the east, which had broken away from Spain in 1821. Since 1844, however, the island has been divided into the western, French-speaking republic of Haiti and the eastern, Spanish-speaking Dominican Republic.

A new phase in the development of the Dominican Republic began when the U.S.A. became concerned about the security of its routes to the Panama Canal. Between 1916 and 1924, the republic was occupied by American marines, who laid roads, undertook sanitation projects and encouraged improved farming and the production of coffee, tobacco and cacao.

Hispaniola is mountainous, for it is in this island that the Antillean mountain system is best developed, and lacks any large lowland areas. When Columbus was asked, at the court of Spain, what Hispaniola was like he took a piece of paper, crumpled it up, threw it on the table and replied, 'That's Hispaniola; nothing but mountains and valleys.' In fact, two-thirds of the island are of this nature. There is a core of old mountains, the Cordillera Central, which runs across it from north-west to south-east reaching a maximum altitude of 10,000 feet. It is composed of granite, gneisses and diorite, and is flanked by Tertiary limestones and marls, which are also folded. Here and there volcanic materials are included in the Tertiary beds. There are a number of recent fault lines running parallel to the mountains; they make their presence felt in recurrent earth tremors.

Except during the winter, the island lies under the influence of the prevailing north-easterly winds all through the year, with frequent intrusions of cold air from the north. In the winter, south winds may also blow. In the autumn, as the trade winds slacken, the period of hurricane danger sets in.

The humid, low-lying areas of the island are covered with tropical rain-forest (forest covers a total of over 50%), which produces mahogany and ebony. The upland forests are rich in tree ferns and parasitic plants such as epiphytes and lianas. Where the upland soils are sandy, pine forest is found, while in the driest areas of the mountains the vegetation may deteriorate from savanna and thorn bush steppe to desert.

HAITI

'Republic of Haiti' is the proud title of the oldest independent Negro republic in the world, where 95% of the population is comprised of descendants of the half a million slaves who were brought here from the

Guinea coast of Africa. By contrast, the Dominican Republic is a predominantly mulatto state (68% of the population fall into this category; 19% are Negroes and 13% whites).

The following description of Haiti is taken from Herbert Lehmann:

Haiti means 'Land of Mountains'. Lofty ranges run across the island. They protrude westwards like two arms, encircling the Gulf of Gonave on which lies Port-au-Prince, the capital of the republic. The mountains rise steeply behind the city up to more than 5000 feet, so that one can leave the tropical heat of Port-au-Prince, and in half an hour be up in a zone of chill mist where one is glad to find a fire burning on the hearth. From up here one can look north and see—providing that the view is not obscured by tropical thunderstorms or curtains of damp mist—ridge upon ridge of the hills rising beyond the plain of Cul de Sac which lies, as it were, in the trough of a wave among the hillcrests. Far beyond these mountains in the foreground, one can imagine that he sees the main chain, which runs through the island like a backbone, and rises in places above 8000 feet. Generally by about mid-day the mountain tops become hidden by big cauliflower thunderclouds, and it is only in the early evenings that the veils of rain are lifted, to reveal the clear contours of the hills, lighted by the late afternoon sun. Nowhere in the West Indies do the tropics reveal their magic so richly and variously as in Haiti's mountains.

With her mountains as a refuge, Haiti has known more of freedom than her neighbour-island of Cuba. But this freedom has been purchased at the great price of grinding poverty. In relation to the size of the population, the amount of arable land is quite insufficient. The poor fields, with their maize, beans and cassava, climb the hillsides to the very tops, and cling precariously to the steepest slopes. And thus it is practically everywhere, except perhaps in a few fertile valley bottoms, where coffee and bananas can be grown. For a population density of more than 300 per square mile—a rural population at that—spells disaster for a hilly, forest-covered landscape like this. It means deforestation, and that leads to erosion, and so to the loss, in the short span of a few generations, of the fertility of lands which will now become desolate.[1]

After achieving independence in 1804, effective power devolved into the hands of a small number of mulatto families who were little concerned with the economic development of the island. The former extensive plantations on irrigated lowlands were largely abandoned and the freed slaves established subsistence agriculture throughout the country. Since then the only significant development has been in the size of the population—now over 3·5 million—and there is a grave and growing

1 Lehmann, H.

problem of pressure on the land. Even so, food production is inadequate for the country's needs and food imports have, in recent years, accounted for as much as 20% of total imports. The projected large-scale irrigation scheme for the Artibonite valley, though designed to remedy this situation, may do no more than enable food supplies to keep pace with the increasing population. Today, Haiti lacks all emigration opportunities (such as formerly existed in Cuba and in the Dominican Republic) and, moreover, does not offer the kind of political and economic climate which is needed to attract foreign investment for developing the country's mineral resources and tourist attractions. Thus Haiti seems likely to remain the poorest country in the whole of the western hemisphere.

THE DOMINICAN REPUBLIC

The Dominican Republic in eastern Hispaniola is not troubled by overpopulation as is Haiti, for with twice the land area it has fewer people (about 3 million). Moreover, 24% of the population live in the cities. The capital, originally known as Santo Domingo, called Ciudad Trujillo during the long dictatorship of Raphael Trujillo, and renamed Santo Domingo after Trujillo's assassination in 1961, was virtually wiped out by a hurricane in 1930, and has been rebuilt in North American style, with broad, clean streets and wide squares. It had a population of over 350,000 in 1960. Here and there an old church, a section of the old city wall or the ruin of a Spanish palace remains to serve as a reminder of the past. Columbus' house, where his son once lived, is still standing, and the remains of Columbus are buried in the cathedral.

Contrasting with the widespread distribution of population in Haiti, the rural population in the Dominican Republic is concentrated in the two lowland areas of the Cibao-Vega Real in the north and along the south-east coast. Sugar production is concentrated mainly in the latter area (sugar provides about 55% of the country's total exports), while in the north agriculture is much more diverse with tobacco and cacao, the main commercial crops, supplementing the output of food crops such as rice and maize. Attempts are being made to extend the areas of cultivation and to introduce new crops such as sisal and cotton but such developments are hindered by the system of land ownership which needs radical reform. At the moment much of the country is under-used—particularly in the western areas adjoining overcrowded Haiti—and this constitutes a potential source of conflict between the two countries.

Puerto Rico

With an area of 3435 square miles, Puerto Rico is the smallest island of the Greater Antilles. North of the island, the ocean floor falls to 30,000 feet below the surface, while to the south, similarly, there is a trough over 16,000 feet deep. The island thus rises as a horst between the two troughs, and at its highest is some 4000 feet above sea level. In structure, Puerto Rico resembles Haiti; the mountain backbone is made up of steeply-folded limestones, sandstones, slates, conglomerates and volcanic materials, as well as old igneous rocks. North of the main range lies, as in Jamaica, a limestone tableland on which the tropical karst formations are again in evidence (Fig. 53). In this case the cone-shaped hills tend to occur in lines, following the outcrops of certain limestone formations.

The climate of Puerto Rico resembles that of other West Indian islands. The annual range of temperature is small; the warmest month, August, has a mean of 79° F, and the coolest, January, one of 73° F. The wind pattern is so constant that the trees are permanently inclined. The trade winds drop their moisture over the mountains and there is, in consequence, the usual marked difference in the trade wind belt between windward and leeward sides of the island. The south coast receives an average of 45 inches of rain per year, while the north coast is much wetter. The flow of the rivers reflects the difference in these conditions. Those which flow northwards generally have a larger and more constant volume than those flowing to the south coast; in the dry season the latter often dry up altogether.

The original vegetation of the island has been so completely destroyed that it is impossible now to reconstruct a reliable impression of its character.

The agriculture practised by the original Indian inhabitants was a simple type using the digging-stick, a system which was completely altered by the European settlers with their wholly new complement of domesticated plants and animals, tools and attitudes. The Spaniards forced the natives to work in their goldfields. The Indians were left without the time necessary to till their own fields, and at the same time their boats were taken from them, officially in order to prevent their escape from the island, but with the result that they could no longer supplement their diet by fishing. Under these pressures, and those caused by new diseases, the Indian population could not long survive.

A new phase of economic development began during the seventeenth century. With the help of Negro slave labour, the Spaniards managed to support themselves on the island. Then, during the Wars of Independence within the Spanish Empire, Puerto Rico remained loyal to the Spanish crown, with the result that it became a gathering point for loyalist émigrés from the remainder of the empire as well as receiving Spanish settlers in the nineteenth century. Foreign trade, which in the old empire had been a jealously-guarded monopoly of Spain, was now free from monopolistic restriction, and this stimulated to some extent the production of sugar-cane, tobacco, coffee and cotton in the first half of the nineteenth century. The forest increasingly gave way to plantations. In particular, wide stretches of forested hill land were cleared for coffee and tobacco, which do well on upland locations. In general, however, the persistence of Spanish control until 1898 meant that the economic and social neglect of the island extended into the twentieth century, for Spain had little incentive or ability to improve its colonies at this period.

After the Spanish-American War of 1898, Puerto Rico was acquired by the U.S.A. Subsequent economic development was rapid, but led to virtual monoculture of sugar. The bulk of the population remained landless, while there were great plantations belonging to absentee owners. Wages were low and the social condition of the labourer bad. Families were large, and there was seasonal unemployment each year in the period between the sugar harvests. The initial impact of the U.S.A. was not, therefore, entirely favourable, although it has done a great deal for Puerto Rico, especially in the spheres of public health and education. These improvements, moreover, established conditions for a rapid rise in the population without providing the additional opportunities for employment.

Since 1948, however, when Puerto Rico was granted internal self-government, the situation has been radically changed. The problem of the increasing population pressure on the very limited amount of land physically and climatically suited for agriculture (a situation accentuated by the alienation of most of the better land for sugar production offering only limited employment opportunities except during the short cutting season) has been tackled by 'Operation Bootstrap'. Industries have been attracted to the island by means of tax incentives, the prospects of lower wage rates than on the U.S. mainland, and in the knowledge that their products could freely enter the U.S. market. Industry has now become the most important sector of the economy and manufactured goods the most important group of exports. Agriculture is now of secondary importance only and has been diversified to meet the growing demand for foodstuffs by a population whose living standards are advancing quickly, such that they are now well ahead of those anywhere else in the Caribbean. Pressure of population on the land has been reduced with the continued emigration of Puerto Ricans to New York, and the development of tourism with its associated employment opportunities also helps in this respect. Unemployment remains high—at some 13–15% of the employed population, but it is within manageable proportions compared with most of the rest of Latin America. Puerto Rico is often held up as an example to the rest of the under-developed world of the favourable impact of industrialisation, but success in Puerto Rico has depended very largely on its special relationship with the United States which is not likely to grant free entry to all goods made in all other industrialising countries.

The capital of Puerto Rico, San Juan (population 440,000), is the largest and most important city on the island and is growing very rapidly. Some sections of it are old (see Plate 1), but there are sharply-contrasting skyscrapers towering over fearful slums, which present one serious problem to the urban authorities. Other problems arise from difficulties over water supplies and traffic in this tropical city.

The Virgin Islands

It was in 1917 that the U.S.A. bought from Denmark for a sum of $25 million the islands now named the Virgin Islands. They are a group that lies on the submarine platform which extends eastwards from Puerto Rico for some 80 miles and has a breadth of 20–30 miles, and thus the islands form the easternmost extension of the Greater Antilles. They are essentially the summits of the submerged Antillean ridge which runs east-west through Cuba, Hispaniola, and Puerto Rico. To the north of this shelf lies the abyss of the Puerto Rico Deep.

The trade winds, which blow throughout the year, moderate the heat of the tropical climate. The annual rainfall averages 48 inches; most of it falls in summer. Since the hills of the islands run parallel to the wind direction, from east to west, orographic rainfall is not very important here.

Both evergreen and deciduous tropical rain-forests formed part of the original vegetation cover, but since the coming of man the forest area has markedly diminished. The early inhabitants were Arawaks, and they in turn were followed by the Caribs who fought against the Spaniards, but subsequently withdrew from the islands. In 1596, the island group was described as uninhabited.

At an early stage in their activities, Dutch, English and French pirates made the islands one of their bases. These buccaneers, as they were called (see p. 270), hunted livestock which had run wild when the islands were abandoned. Then in 1733 the Danes occupied three western members of the group, while the British took the eastern islands. Even although the Danes had claimed the islands, however, there was a continuing trickle of immigrants from Holland, France, and Britain. Negro slaves were brought in to work on the plantations; indeed, in the early eighteenth century the island of St Thomas in the Virgins group became the most important slave market in the West Indies. As time went on, the slaves came to form the largest element in the population, and the main language in use was English with a strong local accent.

In 1917, the U.S.A. bought the Danish West Indies. St Thomas has a fine harbour that has served as an excellent base from which to control the route to Panama. During the Second World War, the United States arrived at an agreement with Great Britain to build further naval bases on the British Virgin Islands (i.e. the easterly members of the group) as well.

Today, the population is 69% Negro, 32% mulatto and 9% white. Sugar-cane is grown on plantations, and the sugar is made into rum and molasses. Since unemployment is one of the island's problems, many of its inhabitants seek work in the U.S.A.

The main export commodity is rum.

The Lesser Antilles

This large group of islands lies along a 500-mile north-south orientated arc forming 'stepping stones' connecting the east-west-trending Greater Antilles to the north with the mainland of South America to the south. Traditionally, the group is divided into the Windward and Leeward Islands—the former to the north of Guadeloupe and the latter to the south. The division as far as structure is concerned, however, is rather into an outer and an inner line of islands. Both lines are based on a submarine ridge that separates the Atlantic Ocean from the Caribbean Sea: a ridge thought by some scholars to be a volcanic fissure. On the outer part of this ridge the volcanoes are dead and their peaks virtually eroded such that the islands are essentially low-lying coral islands whose limestone based soils are fertile but easily eroded. Karst forms are widespread and to ensure a water supply it is necessary to collect rain water very assiduously as there is little surface drainage.

The more westerly, inner line of islands is formed almost entirely of volcanic material as they consist of a series of fairly recent volcanic peaks reaching up to altitudes of almost 5000 feet. It is also certain that volcanic activity is by no means finished in this zone of instability and there have been eruptions in recent years. The most disastrous eruption was that of Mount Pelée on the island of Martinique in 1902.

The Mont Pelée Eruption of 1902

The eruption of Mont Pelée on 8th May 1902 is unique in history. There have been greater eruptions, and there have been times when more lives were lost, but nowhere else has a flourishing city of 30,000 inhabitants been wiped out in a matter of minutes.

St Pierre, the idyllically-situated capital of Martinique, spread over the lower slopes of Mont Pelée above the bay, up to a point where there opened out a valley which ran down from the peak, 5 miles distant. For half a century it had been assumed that the volcano was extinct; in its crater, a lake 200 yards wide had formed. From the beginning of April 1902 onwards, however, the mountain began to show signs of activity; first in the form of white clouds of steam, then there appeared a pillar of smoke which seemed to emit lightning, and ashes fell like rain. On May 5th, a hot mudflow poured down from the peak, 20 feet deep and half a mile wide, and travelling so fast that in three minutes it reached the sea, 4–5 miles away. On its way, it demolished a sugar factory with 200 people in it.

Although the ominous signs from the crater increased in frequency, a committee of experts announced on the evening of the 7th that the situation was not dangerous, and the governor and his wife returned to the city to restore public confidence. The next morning—it was Ascension Day—just before 8 a.m., with no breath of wind stirring, a small white cloud appeared on the peak. Two seconds later, this was followed by a much larger, dark cloud, which shot up into the air to a height of several thousand feet, and simultaneously began to spread down the valley that led towards the town and the sea. It was a monstrous dark-red cauliflower cloud, composed of superheated steam, poisonous gases, ashes and stones. The glowing, fiery cloud swept over the city like a hurricane, and blotted out every spark of life. Walls and trees were ripped up. The lighthouse disintegrated; the market hall, with its metal structure, was laid in ruins. No sooner had the hurricane passed than it began to rain red-hot ashes and stones, and everything inflammable caught fire. A few minutes later again, and the rain turned to mud, which continued to pour down for perhaps half an hour.

St Pierre was wiped out, partly by the force of the explosion, partly by poison gas and partly by heat. The temperature must have been between 500°C. and 1000°C. under the cloud.

During 1902 there followed other outbursts of the fiery cloud. It proved possible to observe them fairly precisely, and so to understand the fate of St Pierre. In August, there rose out of the crater a pillar of lava like a needle, which rose gradually to a height of almost 1000 feet. By August, 1903 the strange rock needle had sunk back into the crater.

The Lesser Antilles have a tropical maritime climate, and they lie beyond the reach of the intrusions of cold northerly air which we have noticed occurring from time to time in the Greater Antilles. Temperatures are held steady by the warmth of the seas which surround the islands. Average rainfall is in the order of 80–90 inches per annum, but is much lower on the low outer islands and higher on the islands with volcanic peaks. Such a combination of climate and soils is highly favourable to tree growth, but deforestation has been very thorough.

The population consisted originally of peaceful Arawaks, but they were overrun by the more warlike Caribs who were better armed and possessed more seaworthy boats. For their livelihood both Indian groups depended on primitive cultivation and fishing.

The Lesser Antilles were discovered by Columbus on his second voyage, but in the hundred years that followed, the Spaniards never really established themselves on the islands. Other Europeans gained a foothold, however, which served their purpose of breaking the Spanish grip on West Indian trade on which Spain claimed a monopoly such that English or Dutch products, for example, might only be handled by Spanish middlemen. It was a situation which invited smuggling. From this illicit trade, which Spain did its best to stamp out, it was an easy step to piracy. The so-called filibusters of the sixteenth and seventeenth centuries were not merely smugglers; they harried the Spanish merchant ships and, whenever they dared, plundered the shore settlements too. The Windward and Leeward Islands were a paradise of hiding places for such sea-going robbers. The filibusters belonged to many European nations, and over a century and a half did severe damage to Spanish interests in the New World.

On the Lesser, as on the Greater, Antilles there were cattle and pigs which had been brought in as domestic livestock but which had run wild. These animals were hunted by the 'buccaneers'. They dried, salted and cured the meat, and sold it to the pirate crews. They took their name from the wooden grid (*boucan*) on which they smoked the meat.

It was not until the end of the seventeenth century that this wild epoch in West Indian history drew to a close. For the first period of settlement in the islands, therefore, the economy—if it deserved that name—was based on smuggling, piracy and hunting. During this period, the native population was being swiftly annihilated (the last 5000 Caribs were banished by the British to the coast of Honduras), and there then began a new era of plantation agriculture based on African slave labour.

During this period, settlements were initially fortified, and were usually made at sheltered anchorages. The surrounding land was allocated to the white settlers. As time went on and the Indian population were gradually eliminated, smaller settlements would spring up in the vicinity of the original fort. These usually consisted of the house of the white landowner, the huts of his Negro slaves and the estate buildings—drying sheds for tobacco, sugar mills and sugar boilers. On the islands settled by the French, there was often also a monastery; the monks, moreover, were model farmers. Manioc, maize and beans were grown for local consumption, and tobacco, cotton, indigo, cacao and ginger for export. But from the beginning of the eighteenth century onwards, all other crops lost ground relative to sugar in most of the islands. The large sugar plantations became the basic economic units, with the secondary effect that the white element in the population diminished and the proportion of Negroes increased. Sugar, molasses and rum became the main exports.

The abolition of slavery in the first half of the nineteenth century undermined the economy, since the Negroes declined to work as hard when they were merely supplying their own immediate needs as they had done formerly under compulsion. They left the plantations and drifted away into the towns. The population began to increase rapidly and soon the coastal towns contained more Negroes than whites. To replace the Negroes on the plantations, Asiatic Indian labourers were brought in, while Chinese newcomers entered the retail trade.

Today, the white element in the population forms a small upper class. Overpopulation is serious in many of the islands and many Negroes have emigrated.

The main export commodities are sugar, together with arrowroot, cotton, nutmegs, fruits and various spices, with different islands specialising in one or other of these crops. Natural hazards such as volcanic eruptions and hurricanes hinder the development of these islands, but in addition they suffer serious economic difficulties as a result of fragmentation both in the physical sense—making inter-communication difficult—and from the point of view of administration which is divided between Britain, France and Holland. Fortunately, each of the colonial powers guarantees an export market at stabilised prices for the islands' sugar production, but this industry is not sufficient to provide employment for the rapidly growing population. For the British islands their membership of the short-lived West Indian Federation looked as though it might have eventually offered a solution through permitting economic diversification and migration of population from the more densely to the less densely populated islands. Following its dissolution, these small islands have now formed a federated group amongst themselves, but its success will depend, at least in the medium term, on the kind of help received from Britain. In the shorter term, the British islands, together with those of France and Holland, stand to gain in economic viability from the rapid growth of tourism in the Caribbean.

The Continental Off-Shore Islands

The final group of islands in the Caribbean consists of a very discontinuous line of islands running in an east-west direction off the coast of Venezuela and extending north-eastwards to include the British island of Barbados. They are essentially the few remaining parts of an outer coastal range of the northern part of the Andes and are thus structurally related to the mainland of South America rather than to the systems of Central America and the Caribbean.

The most important islands are Barbados, Trinidad and Tobago and the Dutch islands of Aruba and Curaçao. Apart from their basic structural similarities, they present contrasts in their geography.

BARBADOS

Barbados is composed mainly of sedimentary materials. There are raised beaches of coral limestone at heights of up to 1200 feet above the present sea-level and these limestones actually occupy six-sevenths of the area of the island. The present shoreline is flanked by coral reefs. Because of the surface limestone the drainage is almost entirely subsurface and water supplies have to be pumped up from underground. Barbados is one of the few islands in the Caribbean which never came under Spanish control and has been a colony of Britain for a continuous period of over 300 years. With a tropical climate tempered by its exposure to the moderating effects of sea and wind and without dense forest cover, it early developed a sugar plantation economy worked by British planters and large numbers of Negro slaves. Even following the end of slavery, the plantation economy persisted, for the former slaves had no other employment opportunities as land was not available for subsistence agriculture. Thus Barbados has remained primarily a sugar island—concentrating on this one crop to such an extent that imports of foodstuffs are necessary to meet the needs of the rapidly growing population. Pressure of population is the most serious problem that the island has to face, for the density now exceeds 1400 per square mile with few alternative occupations to employment in sugar-cane production and its processing into sugar, molasses and rum. As with other islands in the Caribbean, however, tourism is expanding and is providing both additional income to the island and employment opportunities for the largely Negro population.

TRINIDAD AND TOBAGO

Trinidad and Tobago lie within sight of the coast of Venezuela, only a few miles away across the Gulf of Paria. Trinidad is formed by a series of simple Tertiary folds striking east-west. The chalk and Tertiary formations involved are oil-bearing. Where clayey beds rich in hydro-carbons outcrop at the surface, mud springs and mud volcanoes occur. Fluid asphalt appears at the surface too, solidifying on evaporation into a plastic state. Such asphalt springs have created the famous pitch lake. The asphalt originally ran down to the sea, but as time went on the rate of exploitation increased and the rate of recharge diminished, so that the level of the lake fell and it is now without an outlet.

The two islands are so close to the equator that in autumn they experience light and variable winds. For the rest of the year, the trade winds blow persistently from the east or north-east. The eastern side of the mountains, in consequence, has as much as 150 inches of rain a year, while the west side has only 50 inches.

The vegetation cover is predominantly South American in character, but the effect of man upon it has been great even though effective settle-ment has been limited to the last 150 years.

In this period, however, there has been a succession of immigrants such that Trinidad is now more racially admixed than any other island of the Caribbean. The descendants of the original European settlers together with more recent arrivals from Britain form 3% of the popula-tion. The descendants of Negro slaves brought in the early nineteenth century now form 47% of the total population. Indentured labourers from India and other parts of the Far East who came in with the end of slavery have also given rise to an important part of the population—about 35%. 14% are of mixed parentage and the remaining 1% are mainly Chinese.

In addition to the diverse population, Trinidad also has a diversified economy. In the agricultural sector, sugar is still the most important crop being produced mainly on the alluvial lowlands—some of which have been reclaimed from the sea—bordering the Gulf of Paria. Coconuts also form an important plantation crop, particularly along the east coast, whilst cocoa is grown in the foothills of the upland areas. Citrus fruit, rice and horticultural products are also important. Agri-culture, however, is still in need of development in order to bring more land under cultivation and to make the island self-sufficient in food supplies. Agriculture is mainly in the hands of the Indians whilst the Negro side of the population is concentrated much more in the urban centres—particularly Port of Spain.

The oil industry of Trinidad is particularly significant for the export earnings which it achieves and because of the large payments that it makes to the government by way of royalties and taxes. Both the production and, more especially, the refining of petroleum have expanded rapidly since 1950. However, the uncertainties which face the industry in a period of world over-supply of oil and the possible dislocation of exports arising from the formation of the European Common Market emphasise the importance of further diversification of the economy into manufacturing industry for which, of course, there is an adequate supply of labour and a plentiful supply of cheap energy in the form of natural gas and locally refined petroleum products. Trinidad is edging in the direction of closer economic contacts with Latin America—ultimately perhaps to become a member of the Latin American Free Trade Area. If such contacts are achieved, then industry may be attracted to Trinidad as a secure and well-located base from which markets may be sought throughout the eastern side of the continent. In the meantime, however, Trinidad must rely on the continued expansion of the oil refining industry—on the prospects for which a United Nations Commission of Enquiry has reported favourably, given good relations between government and companies—and on a modest expansion in import-substitution industries.

The island of Tobago is a dependency of Trinidad and has a population of only 35,000. It lacks the natural resources of Trinidad itself and, moreover, suffers from its position in the path of autumnal hurricanes. It has, however, prospects for tourism given good air communications with the outside world.

ARUBA AND CURAÇAO

These are the two largest islands of a group lying off the north coast of Venezuela. They were originally brought under Dutch control so that a supply of salt for Dutch sailing vessels could be obtained from the lagoons surrounding the islands.

They are low-lying and have only a meagre rainfall such that the vegetation cover is sparse and agricultural activity severely limited. They have achieved modern economic significance largely as a result of the development of two of the world's largest oil refineries—one on Aruba and one on Curaçao. The refineries were built to process oil from Venezuela mainly because the companies concerned—Shell and Esso—preferred to locate their large investment in refining in stable, secure Dutch colonies rather than in Venezuela with a history of political instability. Since 1943, however, the refineries have ceased to expand because the companies were obliged to accept Venezuela's insistence that all new refining capacity which they required in the Caribbean area should be built in Venezuela.

With almost 200,000 people and faced with a situation in which employment in the refining industry is decreasing as a result of increasing automation, Aruba and Curaçao have been forced to look for alternative sources of income. The development of tourism has been the immediate answer to the problem, but in the longer term the island's economies will have to be diversified still further.

Further reading

GENERAL

Benham, F. & Holley, H. A., *A Short Introduction to the Economy of Latin America*, London, 1960.

Butland, G. J., *Latin America: a Regional Geography*, London, 1960.

Ellis, H. S. (Ed.), *Economic Development for Latin America*, London, 1961.

Hanson, S. G., *Economic Development in Latin America*, Washington, D.C., 1951.

Haring, C. H., *The Spanish Empire in America*, New York, 1947.

Hauser, P. (Ed), *Urbanisation in Latin America*, 1960.

Herring, H., *A History of Latin America*, New York, 1955.

Hirshman, A. O., *Latin American Issues; Essays and Comments*, New York, 1961.

Humphreys, R. A., *The Evolution of Modern Latin America*, Oxford, 1946.

Ireland, G., *Boundaries, Possessions and Conflicts in South America*, 1938.

—— *Boundaries, Possessions and Conflicts in Central America and the Caribbean*, 1941.

James, P. E., *Latin America*, New York, 1959.

Lavell, C. B., *Population Growth and Development in South America*, 1959.

Normano, J. F. & Gerbi, A., *The Japanese in South America*, New York, 1943.

Perkins, D., *Hands Off: A History of the Monroe Doctrine*, New York, 1943.

Platt, R. S., *Latin America: Countrysides and United Regions*, New York, 1943.

Steward, J. H. & Faron, L. C., *Native Peoples of South America*, New York, 1961.

United Nations, *The Economic Development of Latin America in the Post-War Period*, New York, 1964.

—— *Transport Problems in Latin America*, New York, 1953.

—— *Energy in Latin America*, New York, 1957.

—— *The Latin American Common Market*, New York, 1959.

UNESCO, *Sociological Aspects of Economic Development in Latin America*, Paris, 1963.

Urquidi, V., *Free Trade and Economic Development in Latin America*, Berkeley, 1962.

—— *The Challenge of Development in Latin America*, New York, 1964.

Wolf, E., *Sons of the Shaking Earth*, Chicago, 1959.

Wythe, G., *Industry in Latin America*, New York, 1949.

ARGENTINA

I.B.R.D. (World Bank), *Report on Argentine Transport*, Baltimore, Md., 1962.

Jefferson, M., *Peopling the Argentine Pampa*, New York, 1926.

Pendle, G., *Argentina*, London, 1963.

Rennie, Y. F., *The Argentine Republic*, New York, 1945.
Scobie, J. R., *Argentina. A City and a Nation*, New York, 1964.
Taylor, C. C., *Rural Life in Argentina*, Baton Rouge, La., 1964.
Whitaker, A. P., *Argentina*, Englewood Cliffs, N.J., 1964.

BOLIVIA

Alexander, R. J., *The Bolivian National Revolution*, Washington, D.C., 1958.
McBride, G. M., *The Agrarian Indian Communities of Highland Bolivia*, New York, 1921.
Osborne, H., *Bolivia, a Land Divided*, London, 1954.
United Nations, *Report of the U.N. Technical Mission to Bolivia*, New York, 1951.

BRAZIL

de Castro, J., 'The Brazilian Dilemma: Bread or Steel', in I. Sachs (Ed.), *Agriculture, Land Reforms and Economic Development*, Warsaw, 1964.
Freyre, G., *The Masters and the Slaves*, New York, 1946.
—— *New World in the Tropics*, New York, 1955.
—— *The Mansions and the Shanties*, New York, 1962.
Furtado, C., 'An Analysis of the Economic Development of Brazil', in I. Sachs (Ed.), *Planning and Economic Development*, Warsaw, 1964.
Harris, M., *Town and Country in Brazil*, New York, 1956.
Hutchinson, H. W., *Village and Plantation Life in North Eastern Brazil*, Seattle, 1957.
Robock, S. H., *Brazil's Developing North-East*, Washington, D.C., 1963.
Smith, T. L., *Brazil: People and Institutions*, Baton Rouge, La., 1963.
Wagley, C., *Amazon Town: a Study of Man in the Tropics*, New York, 1953.
—— *An Introduction to Brazil*, New York, 1963.
Webb, K. E., *Brazil*, Boston, 1964.
Wythe, G., *Brazil: an Expanding Economy*, New York, 1949.

CARIBBEAN

Augier, F. R., *et al.*, *The Making of the West Indies*, London, 1961.
Blanshard, P., *Democracy and Empire in the Caribbean*, New York, 1947.
Caribbean Commission, *The Sugar Industry of the Caribbean*, Gainesville, Fla., 1947.
Edwards, D., *An Economic Study of Small Farming in Jamaica*, 1961.
Geisert, H. L., *The Caribbean: Population and Resources*, 1960.
Guerra y Sanchez, R., *Sugar and Society in the Caribbean*, New Haven, Conn., 1964.
I.B.R.D., *The Economic Development of Cuba*, Baltimore, Md., 1964.
—— *The Economic Development of Jamaica*, Baltimore, Md., 1952.
Jones, C. F. & Pico, R., *Symposium on the Geography of Puerto Rico*, Rio Pedras, Puerto Rico, 1955.
Lowenthal, D. (Ed.), *The West Indies Federations*, New York, 1961.

Nelson, L., *Rural Cuba*, Minneapolis, Minn., 1950.

Parry, J. H. & Sherlock, P. M., *A Short History of the West Indies*, London, 1956.

Platt, R. R. *et al.*, *European Possessions in the Caribbean Area*, New York, 1941.

Proudfoot, M., *Britain and the United States in the Caribbean*, London, 1954.

Roberts, G. W., *The Population of Jamaica*, Cambridge, 1957.

Seers, D. (Ed.), *Cuba: The Economic and Social Revolution*, Chapel Hill, N.C., 1964.

Stead, W. H., *Fomento—The Economic Development of Puerto Rico*, New York, 1958.

Steward, J. H. *et al.*, *People of Puerto Rico*, Urbana, Ill., 1956.

de Young, M., *Man and Land in the Haitian Economy*, 1958.

CENTRAL AMERICAN REPUBLICS

Biesanz, J. M., *Costa Rican Life*, New York, 1944.

—— *The People of Panama*, New York, 1955.

Checchi, V., *Honduras, A Problem in Economic Development*, New York, 1959.

Geisert, H. L., *Population Problems in Mexico and Central America*, 1959.

Hoselitz, B. F., *Industrial Development of El Salvador*, 1954.

I.B.R.D., *The Economic Development of Guatemala*, Baltimore, Md., 1951.

—— *The Economic Development of Nicaragua*, Baltimore, Md., 1953.

Jones, C. L., *Costa Rica and Civilisation in the Caribbean*, 1935.

May, S., *Costa Rica, a Study in Economic Development*, New York, 1952.

May, S. & Plaza, G., *The United Fruit Company in Latin America*, Washington, D.C., 1958.

Parker, F. D., *The Central American Republics*, London, 1963.

Whetten, N. L., *Guatemala, the Land and the People*, New Haven, Conn., 1961.

United Nations, *Transport in the Isthmus of Central America*, New York, 1953.

—— *The Economic Integration of Central America*, New York, 1956.

—— *The Human Resources of Central America 1950–80*, New York, 1960.

CHILE

Bowman, I., *Desert Trails of Atacama*, New York, 1924.

Butland, G. J., *Chile: An Outline of Its Geography, Economics and Politics*, London, 1956.

—— *The Human Geography of Southern Chile*, London, 1957.

I.B.R.D., *The Agricultural Economy of Chile*, Baltimore, Md., 1952.

Jefferson, M., *Recent Colonisation in Chile*, New York, 1921.

McBride, G. M., *Chile; Land and Society*, New York, 1936.

Rudolph, W. E., *Vanishing Trails of Atacama*, New York, 1963.

United Nations, *Water Resources of Latin America: I. Chile*, New York, 1960.

COLOMBIA

Galbraith, W. O., *Colombia, A General Survey*, London, 1953.
Hunter, J. M., *Emerging Colombia*, Washington, D.C., 1962.
I.B.R.D., *The Basis of a Development Program for Colombia*, Baltimore, Md., 1950.
—— *Agricultural Development of Colombia*, Baltimore, Md., 1956.
—— *The Autonomous Regional Corporation of the Cauca*, Baltimore, Md., 1955.
Parsons, J. J., *Antioqueno Colonisation in Western Colombia*, Berkeley, Calif., 1949.

ECUADOR

Blomberg, R. (Ed.), *Ecuador: Andean Mosaic*, Stockholm, 1952.
Collier, J. & Buitron, A., *The Awakening Valley*, Chicago, 1949.
Linke, L., *Ecuador: Country of Contrasts*, London, 1960.
Rycroft, W. S., *Indians of the High Andes*, New York, 1946.
United Nations, *Integration of the Native Indian Populations of Ecuador*, New York, 1960.

GUIANAS

Adhin, J. H., *Development Planning in Surinam in Historical Perspective*, Leiden, 1961.
I.B.R.D., *Report on the Economic Development of British Guiana*, Baltimore, Md., 1953.
Smith, R. T., *British Guiana*, London, 1962.
Swan, M., *British Guiana: The Land of Six Peoples*, London, 1957.

MEXICO

Gonzalez Casanova, P., 'Mexico: A Semi-Capitalist Revolution', in I. Sachs (Ed.), *Planning and Economic Development*, Warsaw, 1964.
Gill, T., *Land Hunger in Mexico*, Washington, D.C., 1951.
Hayner, N. S., *Mexico City: Its Growth and Configurations*, New York, 1945
I.B.R.D., *The Economic Development of Mexico*, Baltimore, Md., 1953.
McBride, G. M., *The Land Systems of Mexico*, New York, 1923.
Mosk, S. A., *Industrial Revolution in Mexico*, Berkeley, Calif., 1950.
Parkes, H. B., *A History of Mexico*, London, 1962.
Tannenbaum, F., *The Mexican Agrarian Revolution*, New York, 1930.
Thompson, E. S., *Rise and Fall of Maya Civilisation*, London, 1956.
Vaillant, G. C., *The Aztecs of Mexico*, London, 1950.
Vernon, R., *The Dilemma of Mexico's Development*, Cambridge, Mass., 1964.
Whetten, N. L., *Rural Mexico*, Chicago, 1948.
Wolf, E., *Sons of the Shaking Earth*, Chicago, 1959.

PARAGUAY

Pendle, G., *Paraguay: A Riverside Nation*, London, 1956.
Raine, P., *Paraguay*, New Brunswick, N.J., 1956.
Service, E. R. & Tobati, H. S., *Paraguayan Town*, Chicago, 1954.

PERU

Bowman, I., *The Andes of Southern Peru*, New York, 1916.
Ford, T. R., *Man and Land in Peru*, Gainesville, Fla., 1955.
Mason, J. A., *The Ancient Civilisations of Peru*, London, 1957.
Osborne, H., *Indians of the Andes*, Cambridge, Mass., 1952.
Owens, R. J., *Peru*, London, 1963.
Stein, W. W., *Hualcan: Life in the Highlands of Peru*, Ithaca, N.Y., 1961.

URUGUAY

Farnworth, C. H., *The Agriculture of Uruguay*, Washington, D.C., 1952.
Fitzgibbon, R. H., *Uruguay: Portrait of a Democracy*, London, 1956.
Pendle, G., *Uruguay*, London, 1963.

VENEZUELA

CENDES (Centro de Estudios del Desarrollo), Papers of the First Latin American Conference on Regional Science, Caracas, Venezuela, 1963.
I.B.R.D., *The Economic Development of Venezuela*, Baltimore, Md., 1962.
Lieuwen, E., *Petroleum in Venezuela: a history*, Berkeley, Calif., 1954.
—— *Venezuela*, London, 1961.
Ward, E., *The New Eldorado: Venezuela*, London, 1957.

German sources quoted in the text

Boesch, H., *Zentralamerika heute*, Zürich, 1952.
Hauger, O., *Kreuz des Südens*, Braunschweig, 1950.
Hesse-Wartegg, Ernst von, *Die Wunder der Welt*, Stuttgart, n.d.
Hettner, A., 'Das Deutschtum in Südbrasilien und Südchile' (article), n.d.
Knoche, 'Chile' in the *Handbuch der Geographischen Wissenschaften*, Potsdam, 1930.
Kühn, Franz, 'Argentinien' in the *Handbuch der Geographischen Wissenschaften*, Potsdam, 1930.
Lauer, Schmidt, Schröder and Troll, *Studien zur Klima- und Vegetationskunde der Tropen*, Bonn, 1952.
Lehmann, Herbert, 'Der tropische Kegelkarst auf den Grossen Antillen' in *Zeitschrift für Erdkunde*, 1954.
Pahlen, K., *Südamerika, eine neue Welt*, Zürich, 1949.
Rohrbach, Paul, article in the *Deutsche Allgemeine Zeitung.*, n.d.
Schmid, Peter, *Nachbarn des Himmels*, Stuttgart, 1953.

Sick, Helmut, *Tucani. Unter Tieren und Indianern Zentralbrasiliens bei der ersten Durchquerung von SO nach NW*, Hamburg and Berlin, 1957.

Sievers, Wilhelm, *Sud- und Mittelamerika*, Leipzig, 1903.

Troll, C., 'Die Andenländer' in the *Handbuch der Geographischen Wissenschaften*, Potsdam, 1930.

Troll, C., 'Forschungen in Zentralmexiko' in *Tagungsbericht und Wissenschaftliche Abhandlungen des Deutschen Geographentages*, Hamburg and Wiesbaden, 1957.

Troll, C., article in *Wissenschaftliche Abhandlungen des Deutschen Geographentages*, Frankfurt/Main, 1951.

Wilda, Johannes, *Amerika—Wanderungen eines Deutschen* (Verlag Allgemeiner Verein für deutsche Literatur), Berlin, n.d.

Wilhelmy, H., *Südamerika im Spiegel seiner Städte*, Hamburg, 1952.

Zweig, Stefan, *Begegnungen*, Frankfurt/Main, 1956.

Statistical data

Brazil

LATITUDE 5° North-34° South   LONGITUDE 35°-74° West

AREA 3,288,000 square miles

POPULATION *Total:* 76,000,000 (1963 est.)

Average density: 21 per square mile

Chief urban areas:	
Brasilia (capital)	200,000
Rio de Janeiro	3,850,000
São Paulo	4,430,000
Recife	930,000
Belo Horizonte	800,000

ECONOMY *Unit of currency:* Cruzeiro

Agriculture. Land use (as percentage of total area):

Agricultural 14 (arable 2, grass 12)

Forest   61

Other   25

Chief crops: Maize, Rice, Coffee, Beans, Cotton

Mining. Chief products: Iron-ore, Manganese, Petroleum, Gold, Coal

Industry. Chief manufactures: Textiles, Steel, Metallurgical

Transport. Miles of railway   23,500

Miles of road—

Total 280,500

Improved   5,000

Vehicles in use—

Total 820,700

Commercial 331,800

FOREIGN TRADE *Imports:* Machinery, Fuels, Vehicles, Foodstuffs, Chemicals

Sources (as percentage):

North America 31   Western Europe 35

Latin America 21   Rest of World   13

Exports: Coffee, Cacao beans, Iron-ore, Meat products, Timber, Sugar, Cotton

Destination: North America 46   Western Europe 36

Latin America   8   Rest of World   10

Paraguay

LATITUDE   19°-27° 30′ South   LONGITUDE   54°-63° West

AREA   159,807 square miles

POPULATION   *Total:* 2,000,000 (1963 est.)
            Average density: 11 per square mile
            Chief urban areas: Asunción (capital) 310,000
                                 Villa Rica   32,000
                                 Concepción   33,000

ECONOMY   *Unit of currency:* Guarani
         Agriculture. Land use (as percentage of total area):
                        Agricultural   4 (only 1 % is cultivated)
                        Forest   50
                        Other   46
                   Chief crops: Maize, Manioc, Cotton, Beans, Rice,
                        Sugar-cane
         Mining. Chief products: Limestone
         Industry. Chief manufactures: Textiles, Sugar, Food processing,
                        Cement
         Transport. Miles of railway   910
                     Miles of road—
                             Total 4,600
                         Improved   400
                     Vehicles in use—
                             Total 6,400
                     Commercial 1,600

FOREIGN TRADE   *Imports.* Foodstuffs, Textiles, Transport equipment, Fuels
               Sources (as percentage):
                        North America 25   Western Europe 28
                        Latin America 25   Rest of World   22
               Exports: Meat, Timber, Quebracho extract, Yerba maté.
                        Hides, Cotton
               Destination: North America 27   Western Europe 28
                             Latin America 33   Rest of World 12

Uruguay

LATITUDE   30°-35° South   LONGITUDE   53°-68° West

AREA   72,172 square miles

POPULATION   *Total:* 3,000,000 (1963 est.)
            Average density: 40 per square mile

Chief urban areas: Montevideo (capital) 1,000,000
Paysandú 60,000
Salto 60,000
Mercedes 45,000

ECONOMY   *Unit of currency:* Peso

Agriculture. Land use (as percentage of total area):
Agricultural 77 (arable 11, grass 66)
Forest 5
Other 18

Chief crops: Wheat, Maize, Linseed, Flax, Oats, Barley

Mining. Chief products: Marble, Granite

Industry. Chief manufactures: Meat processing, Textiles

Transport. Miles of railway 1,874
Miles of road—
Total 28,000
Improved 5,300
Vehicles in use—
Total 100,000
Commercial 48,000

FOREIGN TRADE   *Imports:* Fuels, Foodstuffs, Machinery
Sources (as percentages):
North America 28   Western Europe 32
Latin America 29   Rest of World 11
Exports: Wool, Meat, Hides, Wheat and Flour
Destination: North America 16   Western Europe 69
Latin America 3   Rest of World 12

Argentina

LATITUDE   21° 30′-55° South   LONGITUDE   54°-74° West

AREA   1,072,746 square miles

POPULATION   *Total:* 22,000,000 (1963 est.)

Average density: 20 per square mile
Chief urban areas: Buenos Aires (capital) 6,765,000
Rosário 670,000
Córdoba 600,000

ECONOMY   *Unit of currency:* Peso

Agriculture. Land use (as percentage of total area):

    Agricultural 52 (cultivated 11, grass 41)
    Forest   36
    Other   12

Chief crops: Maize, Wheat, Oats, Barley, Potatoes

Mining. Chief products: Petroleum, Natural gas, Zinc, Lead

Industry. Chief manufactures: Food processing, Textiles, Steel, Cement, Chemicals

Transport. Miles of railway   30,000

Miles of road—
    Total   91,000
    Improved   32,000

Vehicles in use—
    Total   850,000
    Commercial 425,000

FOREIGN TRADE   *Imports:* Machinery, Vehicles, Iron and Steel, Fuels, Chemicals

Sources (as percentage):
| North America 27 | Western Europe 43 |
| Latin America 18 | Rest of World 12 |

Exports: Cereals, Meat, Wool, Hides

Destination:
| North America 9 | Western Europe 64 |
| Latin America 16 | Rest of World 11 |

Chile

LATITUDE   17° 30'-56° 30' South   LONGITUDE   65° 30'-75° 10' West

AREA   286,397 square miles

POPULATION   *Total:* 8,000,000 (1963 est.)

Average density: 28 per square mile

Chief urban areas: Santiago (capital) 1,700,000
                     Valparaiso   285,000
                     Concepción   170,000

ECONOMY   *Unit of currency:* Escudo

Agriculture. Land use (as percentage of total area):
    Agricultural 18
    Forest   21
    Other   61

Chief crops: Wheat, Potatoes, Maize, Oats

Mining. Chief products: Copper, Nitrate, Iron-ore

Industry. Chief products: Copper, Iron and Steel
Transport. Miles of railway   5,500
Miles of road—
Total   34,000
Improved   12,000
Vehicles in use—
Total   135,300
Commercial   73,900

FOREIGN TRADE   *Imports:* Machinery, Vehicles and equipment, Fuels, Chemicals, Foodstuffs

Sources (as percentage):

North America 49	Western Europe 30
Latin America 17	Rest of World 4

Exports: Copper, Nitrates, Iron-ore, Metallurgical products

Destination:

North America 37	Western Europe 52
Latin America 8	Rest of World 3

Bolivia

LATITUDE   9° 30′-23° South   LONGITUDE   57° 30′-69° 30′ West

AREA   424,162 square miles

POPULATION   *Total:* 3,600,000 (1963 est.)
Average density: 8·5 per square mile
Chief urban areas:

La Paz (capital city)	348,000
Sucre (legal capital)	60,000
Cochabamba	90,000
Oruro	82,000

ECONOMY   *Unit of currency:* Boliviano

Agriculture. Land use (as percentage of total area):

Agricultural	13 (arable 2, grass 11)
Forest	43
Other	44

Chief crops: Potatoes, Barley, Coffee

Mining. Chief products: Tin, Lead, Silver, Zinc, Tungsten

Industry. Chief products: Textiles, Foodstuffs

Transport. Miles of railway   1,500
Miles of road—
Total   13,000
Improved   2,500

Vehicles in use—
> Total 35,600
> Commercial 24,000

FOREIGN TRADE   *Imports:* Machinery, Foodstuffs, Textiles, Chemicals

Sources (as percentage):

North America	44	Western Europe	30
Latin America	17	Rest of World	9

Exports: Tin, Lead, Tungsten, Silver, Zinc

Destination:

North America	23	Western Europe	61
Latin America	12	Rest of World	4

Peru

LATITUDE   18° South-Equator   LONGITUDE   69°-81° West

AREA   496,000 square miles

POPULATION   *Total:* 12,000,000 (1963 est.)

Average density: 21 per square mile

Chief urban areas:

Lima (capital)	1,800,000
Callao	210,000
Arequipa	130,000
Trujillo	70,000

ECONOMY   *Unit of currency:* Sol

Agriculture. Land use (as percentage of total area):

Agricultural	10 (cultivated 3, grass 7)
Forest	56
Other	34

Chief crops: Potatoes, Maize, Rice, Barley, Cotton, Sugar

Mining. Chief products: Copper, Lead, Zinc, Iron-ore, Gold

Industry. Chief products: Textiles, Chemicals, Foodstuffs

Transport. Miles of railway   2,300

Miles of road—
> Total   24,000
> *Improved*   3,000

Vehicles in use—
> Total   172,000
> *Commercial*   70,000

FOREIGN TRADE   *Imports:* Wheat, Iron and Steel, Machinery

Sources (as percentage):

North America	47	Western Europe	36
Latin America	10	Rest of World	7

Exports: Copper, Cotton, Sugar, Iron-ore

Destination: North America 37   Western Europe 41

Latin America 16   Rest of World 6

Ecuador

LATITUDE 1° 30′ North - 5° South   LONGITUDE 75°-81° West

AREA 113,250 square miles (excludes Galapagos 3000 sq. mls.)

POPULATION   *Total:* 4,700,000 (1963 est.)

Average density: 40 per square mile

Chief urban areas: Quito (capital) 280,000

Guayaquil   410,000

Cuenca   67,000

Ambato   40,000

ECONOMY *Unit of currency:* Sucre

Agriculture. Land use (as percentage of total area):

Agricultural 10 (arable 3, grass 7)

Forest   61

Other   29

Chief crops: Potatoes, Rice, Maize

Mining. Chief products: Petroleum, Gold, Silver

Industry. Chief manufactures: Milling, Textiles, Cement

Transport. Miles of railway   700

Miles of road—

Total 18,000

Improved 7,000

Vehicles in use—

Total 23,000

Commercial 16,500

FOREIGN TRADE *Imports:* Machinery, Chemicals

Sources (as percentage):

North America 51   Western Europe 40

Latin America 5   Rest of World   4

Exports: Bananas, Coffee, Cacao, Rice

Destination: North America 63   Western Europe 26

Latin America 9   Rest of World   2

Colombia

LATITUDE 12° 30′ North-4° South   LONGITUDE 67°-79° West

AREA 439,519 square miles

POPULATION   *Total:* 15,000,000 (1963 est.)

Average density: 33 per square mile

Chief urban areas: Bogotá (capital)   1,300,000
Medellín   733,000
Cali   600,000
Barranquilla   500,000

ECONOMY   *Unit of currency:* Peso

Agriculture. Land use (as percentage of total area):
Agricultural 13 (arable 3, grass 10)
Forest   60
Other   27

Chief crops: Maize, Potatoes, Coffee, Rice

Mining. Chief products: Gold, Silver, Platinum

Industry. Chief manufactures: Foodstuffs, Textiles, Brewing

Transport. Miles of railway   2,000

Miles of road—
Total   12,500
Improved   4,000

Vehicles in use—
Total   158,300
Commercial   74,500

FOREIGN TRADE   *Imports:* Machinery, Iron and Steel

Sources (as percentage):
North America 60   Western Europe 32
Latin America   5   Rest of World   3

Exports: Coffee, Petroleum, Bananas

Destination: North America 66   Western Europe 29
Latin America   4   Rest of World   1

Venezuela

LATITUDE   1°-12° North   LONGITUDE   60°-73° West

AREA   352,150 square miles

POPULATION   *Total:* 8,000,000 (1963 est.)

Average density: 21 per square mile

Chief urban areas: Caracas (capital)   1,336,000
Maracaibo   455,000
Barquisimeto   205,000
Valencia   161,000
Maracay   125,000

ECONOMY *Unit of currency:* Bolivar

Agriculture. Land use (as percentage of total area):

          Agricultural 21 (arable 2, grass 19)
          Forest 20
          Other 59

        Chief crops: Maize, Potatoes, Rice, Coffee

Mining. Chief products: Petroleum, Iron-ore, Asbestos, Gold

Industry. Chief manufactures: Sugar, Meat products, Brewing

Transport. Miles of railway 698

        Miles of road—
            Total 11,000
          Improved 8,000

        Vehicles in use—
            Total 274,000
          Commercial 88,000

FOREIGN TRADE *Imports:* Machinery, Steel, Chemicals

        Sources (as percentage):

          North America 55   Western Europe 36
          Latin America 2   Rest of World 7

        Exports: Petroleum, Iron-ore, Coffee

        Destination: North America 47   Western Europe 16
                   Latin America 36   Rest of World 1

The Guianas

LATITUDE 1° 30′-8° North   LONGITUDE 52°-62° West

AREA 173,275 square miles

POPULATION *Total:* 950,000 (1963 est.)

        Average density: 4·4 per square mile

        Chief urban areas: Georgetown (capital, Brit. Guiana) 148,500
                         Paramaribo (capital, Surinam)   120,000
                         Cayenne (capital, Fr. Guiana)   15,300

ECONOMY *Unit of currency.* British Guiana: Dollar
                      French Guiana: Franc
                      Surinam: Florin

Agriculture. Land use (as percentage of total area):

          Agricultural 2
          Forest 76
          Other 22

        Chief crops: Sugar-cane, Rice, Coconuts, Coffee

Mining. Chief products: Bauxite, Gold

Industry. Chief manufactures: Sugar and Timber processing

Transport. Miles of railway *circa* 120
Miles of road   *circa* 900
Vehicles in use—
Total 17,100
Commercial 5,000

FOREIGN TRADE   *Imports:* Foodstuffs, Machinery, Manufactured goods
Sources: Western Europe, North America
Exports: Raw sugar, Bauxite, Timber, Rice, Rum
Destination: North America, Western Europe

Guatemala

LATITUDE   14°-23° North   LONGITUDE   88°-92° 30′ West

AREA   42,042 square miles

POPULATION   *Total:* 4,100,000 (1962 est.)
Average density: 93 per square mile
Chief urban areas: Guatemala City (capital) 385,000
Quezaltenango   37,000

ECONOMY   *Unity of currency:* Quetzal
Agriculture. Land use (as percentage of total area):
Agricultural 15 (arable 10, grass 5)
Forest   43
Other   42
Chief crops: Maize, Coffee, Bananas, Tobacco, Sugar-cane
Mining. Chief products: Zinc, Lead, Antimony
Industry. Chief manufactures: Mineral and Fruit processing
Transport. Miles of railway   719
Miles of road—
Improved 2,500
Vehicles in use—
Total 34,100
Commercial 11,900

FOREIGN TRADE   *Imports:* Machinery, Fuels, Textiles, Foodstuffs
Sources (as percentages):
North America 51   Western Europe 29
Latin America 16   Rest of World   4

Exports: Coffee, Bananas, Cotton

Destination: North America 56   Western Europe 33
             Latin America 6   Rest of World   5

British Honduras

LATITUDE 16°-18° North   LONGITUDE 88°-89° West

AREA 8,866 square miles

POPULATION *Total:* 94,000 (1963 est.)

        Average density: 10 per square mile

        Chief urban areas: Belize (capital) 40,000
                      Corozal   7,350

ECONOMY *Unit of currency:* B.H. Dollar

        Agriculture. Land use (as percentage of total area):
                Agricultural 27
                Forest   50
                Other   23

                Chief crops: Citrus fruits, Coconuts, Maize, Beans

        Mining: Negligible

        Industry. Chief manufactures: Sugar milling, Fruit processing

        Transport. Miles of railway —

                Miles of road—
                    Total 250

                Vehicles in use—
                    Total 1,500
                    Commercial 800

FOREIGN TRADE *Imports:* Foodstuffs, Machinery, Textiles

        Sources (as percentage):
                North America 47   Western Europe 40
                Latin America 3   Rest of World 10

        Exports: Mahogany, Chicle, Pine

        Destination: North America 22   Western Europe 40
                      Latin America 18   Rest of World 20

El Salvador

LATITUDE 13°-14° North   LONGITUDE 87° 30'-90° West

AREA 8,260 square miles

POPULATION *Total:* 2,900,000 (1963 est.)

        Average density: 327 per square miles

Chief urban areas: San Salvador (capital) 255,000

Santa Tecla   40,000

San Miguel   80,000

Sonsonate   84,000

ECONOMY   *Unit of currency:* Colon

Agriculture. Land use (as percentage of total area):

Agricultural 60 (arable 25, grass 35)

Forest   15

Other   25

Chief crops: Maize, Coffee, Rice, Beans

Mining. Chief products: Gold, Silver

Industry. Chief manufactures: Textiles, Brewing, Cement

Transport. Miles of railway   388

Miles of road—

Improved   764

Vechicles in use—

Total 25,700

Commercial 6,900

FOREIGN TRADE   *Imports:* Chemicals, Foodstuffs, Machinery, Fuels

Sources (as percentage):

North America 45   Western Europe 32

Latin America 15   Rest of World   8

Exports: Coffee, Cotton

Destination: North America 35   Western Europe 42

Latin America 11   Rest of World   12

Honduras

LATITUDE   13°-16° North   LONGITUDE   83°-89° West

AREA   43,277 square miles

POPULATION   *Total:* 2,000,000 (1963 est.)

Average density: 46 per square mile

Chief urban areas: Tegucigalpa (capital) 125,000

San Pedro Sula   60,000

ECONOMY   *Unit of currency:* Lempira

Agriculture. Land use (as percentage of total area):

Agricultural 27 (arable 9, grass 18)

Forest   37

Other   36

Chief crops: Maize, Coffee, Bananas, Tobacco

Mining. Chief products: Gold, Silver

Industry. Chief manufactures: Brewing, Foodstuffs

Transport. Miles of railway   800

          Miles of road—

               Improved   337

          Vehicles in use—

               Total 11,200

               Commercial 5,800

FOREIGN TRADE   *Imports:* Machinery, Vehicles, Chemicals, Textiles, Steel

          Sources (as percentage):

               North America 57   Western Europe 19

               Latin America 16   Rest of World   8

         Exports: Bananas, Coffee, Timber, Silver, Cattle

         Destination: North America 59   Western Europe 17

                   Latin America 23   Rest of World   1

Nicaragua

LATITUDE   11°-15° North   LONGITUDE   83°-88° West

AREA   57,145 square miles

POPULATION   *Total:* 1,597,000 (1964 est.)

          Average density: 28 per square mile

          Chief urban areas: Managua (capital) 233,000

                       León   46,000

                       Granada   31,000

ECONOMY   *Unit of currency:* Cordoba

          Agriculture.   Land use (as percentage of total area):

                       Agricultural 15

                       Forest   40

                       Other   45

               Chief crops: Cotton, Coffee, Rice, Maize, Sugar-
cane

          Mining. Chief products: Gold, Silver, Copper

          Industry: Cement, Shoes, Textiles, Soap, Brewing

          Transport: Miles of railway   216

                 Miles of road—

                       Total   6,200

                     Improved   835

                 Vehicles in use—

                       Total 14,400

                   Commercial 6,300

FOREIGN TRADE   *Imports*: Machinery, Chemicals, Pharmaceuticals, Iron and Steel, Foodstuffs

Sources (as percentage):

North America 50	Western Europe 23	
Latin America 15	Rest of World 12	

Exports: Coffee, Gold, Meat, Wood, Sugar, Copper

Destination: North America 40   Western Europe 28
Latin America   4   Rest of World 28

Costa Rica

LATITUDE   8°-11° North   LONGITUDE   83°-86° West

AREA   19,695 square miles

POPULATION   *Total:* 1,300,000 (1963 est.)

Average density: 61 per square mile

Chief urban areas: San José (capital)   110,000
Alajuela   20,000
Puntarenas   19,000

ECONOMY   *Unit of currency:* Colon

Agriculture. Land use (as percentage of total area):

Agricultural 19 (arable 5, grass 14)
Forest   21
Other   60

Chief crops: Coffee, Maize, Rice, Potatoes, Sugar-cane

Mining. Negligible

Industry. Chief manufactures: Furniture, Textiles, Foodstuffs

Transport. Miles of railway   816

Miles of road—
Improved 1,707

Vehicles in use—
Total 29,600
Commercial 10,400

FOREIGN TRADE   *Imports:* Iron and Steel, Machinery, Foodstuffs, Chemicals

Sources (as percentage):

North America 50   Western Europe 31
Latin America 10   Rest of World   9

Exports: Coffee, Bananas, Cacao, Abaca, Cattle

Destination: North America 56   Western Europe 36
Latin America   7   Rest of World   1

Panama

LATITUDE   7°-9° 30′ North   LONGITUDE   77° 30′-83° West

AREA   28,753 square miles (excluding area of Canal Zone, 648 sq. miles)

POPULATION   *Total:* 1,200,000 (1963 est.)

Average density: 38 per square mile

Chief urban areas: Panama City (capital) 270,000
Colón   62,000

ECONOMY   *Unit of currency:* Balboa

Agriculture. Land use (as percentage of total area):

Agricultural 14 (arable 6, grass 8)
Forest   71
Other   15

Chief crops: Rice, Bananas, Maize

Mining. Chief products: Gold, Mercury

Industry. Chief manufactures: Brewing, Clothing, Cement

Transport. Miles of railway   240

Miles of road—
Improved   711

Vehicles in use—
Total 22,800
Commercial 7,900

FOREIGN TRADE   *Imports:* Iron and Steel, Machinery, Foodstuffs, Chemicals

Sources (as percentage):

North America 53   Western Europe 18
Latin America 13   Rest of World   16

Exports: Bananas, Cacao, Re-exports, Shrimps

Destination: North America 97   Western Europe 2
Latin America   1   Rest of Europe 0

Mexico

LATITUDE   14° 30′-32° 30′ North   LONGITUDE   87°-117° West

AREA   760,373 square miles

POPULATION   *Total:* 38,000,000 (1963 est.)

Average density: 46 per square mile

Chief urban areas: Mexico City (capital) 4,500,000
Guadalajara   750,000
Monterrey   600,000

ECONOMY   *Unit of currency:* Peso

Agriculture. Land use (as percentage of total area):

Agricultural	44 (arable 9, grass 35)
Forest	19
Other	37

Chief crops: Maize, Cotton, Wheat

Mining. Chief products: Lead, Copper, Zinc, Silver, Petroleum

Industry. Chief manufactures: Steel, Cement, Textiles, Foodstuffs

Transport. Miles of railway   14,547

Miles of road—

Total	83,000
Improved	17,774

Vehicles in use—

Total	756,700
Commercial	321,600

FOREIGN TRADE   *Imports:* Machinery, Chemicals, Fuels, Foodstuffs

Sources (as percentages):

North America 75	Western Europe 21
Latin America 1	Rest of World 3

Exports: Cotton, Coffee, Lead, Copper

Destination:

North America 73	Western Europe 13
Latin America 4	Rest of World 10

Index

The most important references under a particular subject are in italics